THE SCOTS HERBAL

For Ian, with all my love

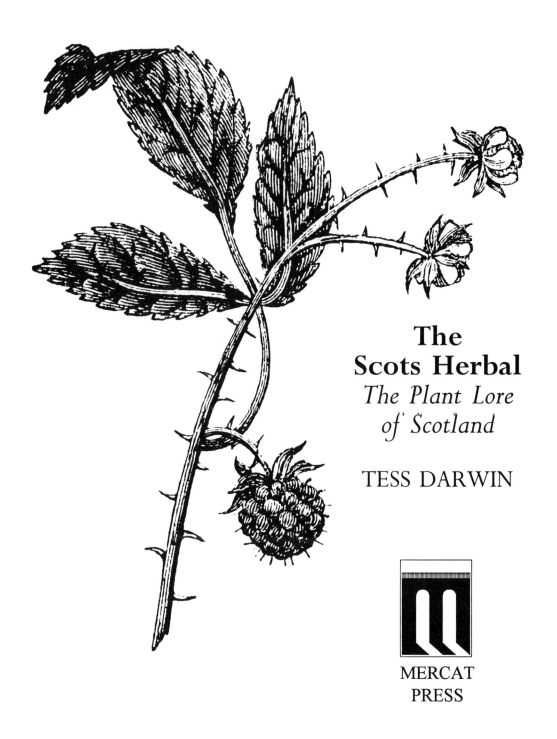

The
Scots Herbal
*The Plant Lore
of Scotland*

TESS DARWIN

MERCAT
PRESS

First published in 1996 by Mercat Press
James Thin, 53 South Bridge, Edinburgh EH1 1YS
Reprinted 1997, 2000

ISBN: 1873644 604

The illustrations used to decorate the text are taken from
A Family Herbal: Familiar Account of the Medical Properties
of British and Foreign Plants *(London, 1814) by Robert John Thornton*
and are engraved by Thomas Bewick

Typeset in Ehrhardt at Mercat Press
Printed and bound in Great Britain by
Redwood Books, Trowbridge, Wiltshire

CONTENTS

Introduction: the Role of Wild Plants in Scotland   ix
Author's note   xi
Acknowledgements   xii
Some notes on the text   xiii
List of place-name abbreviations   xiv

PART ONE: THE ROLE OF WILD PLANTS

Food for Foragers   1
Medicine, Magic and Myth   10
The Domestic Economy   24
Textiles   37

PART TWO: THE PLANT FAMILIES

FUNGI: Mushrooms and Toadstools   43
LICHENS   45
ALGAE: Seaweeds   48
MUSCI: Moss family   55
LYCOPODIACEAE: Clubmoss family   56
EQUISETACEAE: Horsetail family   58
FILICOPSIDA: Ferns   58
CUPRESSACEAE: Cypress family   62
PINACEAE: Pine family   63
TAXACEAE: Yew family   65

APIACEAE: Carrot family   67
AQUIFOLIACEAE: Holly family   71
ARACEAE: Arum family   72
ARALIACEAE: Ivy family   72
ASTERACEAE: Daisy family   73
BERBERIDACEAE: Barberry family   84
BETULACEAE: Birch family   84
BORAGINACEAE: Borage family   86
BRASSICACEAE: Cabbage family   86
CAMPANULACEAE: Bellflower family   89
CAPRIFOLIACEAE: Honeysuckle family   89
CAROPHYLLACEAE: Pink family   91
CHENOPODIACEAE: Goosefoot family   94

CLUSIACEAE: St John's wort family 95
CONVOLVULACEAE: Bindweed family 97
CORNACEAE: Dogwood family 97
CORYLACEAE: Hazel family 98
CRASSULARIACEAE: Stonecrop family 99
CYPERACEAE: Sedge family 101
DIPSACACEAE: Teasel family 102
DROSERACEAE: Sundew family 103
EMPETRACEAE: Crowberry family 104
ERICACEAE: Heath family 104
EUPHORBIACEAE: Spurge family 111
FABACEAE: Pea family 111
FAGACEAE: Beech family 115
FUMARIACEAE: Fumitory family 117
GENTIANACEAE: Gentian family 117
GERANIACEAE: Geranium family 118
GRAMINAE: Grass family 119
GROSSULARIACEAE: Currant family 122
IRIDACEAE: Iris family 123
JUNCACEAE: Rush family 124
LABIATAE: Labiate family 125
LENTIBULARIACEAE: Butterwort family 128
LILIACEAE: Lily family 128
LINACEAE: Flax family 129
LYTHRACEAE: Loosestrife family 130
MALVACEAE: Mallow family 131
MENYANTHACEAE: Bogbean family 131
MYRICACEAE: Bog-myrtle family 132
NYMPHAEACEAE: Water lily family 133
OLEACEAE: Olive family 133
ORCHIDACEAE: Orchid family 135
OXALIDACEAE: Wood sorrel family 136
PAPAVERACEAE: Poppy family 137
PLANTAGINACEAE: Plantain family 137
POLYGALACEAE: Milkwort family 138
POLYGONACEAE: Dock family 139
PRIMULACEAE: Primrose family 141
RANUNCULACEAE: Buttercup family 143
RESEDACEAE: Mignonette family 147
ROSACEAE: Rose family 147
RUBIACEAE: Bedstraw family 159

SALICACEAE: Willow family   161
SCROPHULARIACEAE: Figwort family   164
SOLANACEAE: Nightshade family   170
ULMACEAE: Elm family   171
URTICACEAE: Nettle family   171
VALERIANACEAE: Valerian family   174
VIOLACEAE: Violet family   174
VISCACEAE: Mistletoe family   175
ZOSTERACEAE: Sea grass family   176

Bibliography   177
Index of plants   183
General index   192

'In these present, evil, strenuous, materialistic days, a little honest belief in something—even if the belief is obviously wrong—is worth chronicling. If you believe a thing you often save yourself a lot of bother, and you at least possess the grace of acknowledging that someone else may know more than you do. And it sweetens ordinary conversation a good deal.'

David Rorie (1867-1946)
Folk Tradition and Folk Medicine in Scotland (ed. Buchan, 1994)

INTRODUCTION
The role of wild plants in the Scottish domestic economy

As we approach the new millennium, there are children in Scotland, brought up with supermarkets, who are incapable of making the connection between their bowl of breakfast cereal and the living plant from which it was produced. Far less do they realise that we are still dependent on plants for a wide variety of our daily needs. They do not see the crops growing or the tree being shaped by the woodworker; even their carrots and potatoes are washed clean of the earth in which they grew. If they have any familiarity with plants, they are likely to divide them into garden plants, crops and weeds.

Yet it is these 'weeds' that have been the basis of survival for most of human history, and separation from awareness of their usefulness is a very recent thing, even in Scotland. Elsewhere in the world rapid change threatens to wipe out in one generation knowledge and skills that have taken thousands of years to develop. In Scotland, where traditions of using wild plants survived the longest in Britain, we are fortunate that much information was recorded. This book is an attempt to collect and celebrate what is known, in the hope that present and future generations will value and preserve these traditions.

Most of the material on which this book is based has been published before, in diverse books and articles spanning several hundred years, and is here collected together for the first time. The book should be viewed as a starting point. There is a great deal more work to be done on the subject. This century has seen many advances in the research and collection of folklore, of the oral tradition, recorded on countless hours of tapes held by institutions such as the School of Scottish Studies of Edinburgh University and largely inaccessible to the general public, awaiting the heroic act of transcribing.

From material which has been published, it can be seen that wild plants were still in regular use at least in the remoter parts of Scotland until around the time of the Second World War. The social and economic changes of the 1940s onwards, however, were the beginning of a period in which lifestyles and traditions recognisable through many centuries rapidly disappeared.

Many of the modern changes were essential and beneficial; the old lifestyles are rightly now the stuff of folk museums and nostalgia. Sadly, what has been lost along with the old traditions is some of the strength of community co-operation and interdependence, when people worked together on tasks as diverse as waulking the tweed, harvesting the corn or bringing a baby safely into the world.

It was often the hardest work and most stressful occasions that brought communities together, and while no one would want to return to those hardships and dangers, they are remembered with both joy and sadness by some of the older inhabitants I have spoken with in the Highlands and Islands, who have seen in their lifetimes the kitchen ceilidh replaced by the television, the produce of the croft replaced by the supermarket, reliance on the gentle healing powers of wild plants replaced by dependence on antibiotics and 'wonder' drugs.

Now, as it is increasingly realised that sophisticated technology has its shortcomings and that modern medicine, with its almost total concentration on healing the body without considering the mind and spirit of the patient, does not have all the answers to the illnesses arising from our modern lifestyles, there is a great revival of interest in traditional crafts and skills, herbal remedies and their potential for healing.

AUTHOR'S NOTE

This book has been a long time growing.

The idea first came to me in 1980, when I was employed as a seasonal Countryside Ranger/Naturalist in Grampian Region. Having lived in Scotland less than two years, I had a great deal to learn about local wildlife, and the challenge of leading guided walks as the 'expert' naturalist was an excellent incentive to improve my knowledge.

To my surprise, I found there was at that time very little published information specifically on Scottish plants and the aspects people on my walks asked most questions about—what is it called? How did it get that name? Was it really used for that? I began collecting all the stories and snippets I could find, but that glorious summer of 1980 ended all too soon, and, newly married, I moved to an even greater challenge when I took the post of forest ecologist at a research institute in Central Africa.

During the next two years, however, my interest in ethnobotany—the ways that people use plants—continued to develop. We lived in one of the poorest countries in the world where there was no concept of waste. Everything had a use: empty Vaseline jars were the standard measure of beans and rice in the market; old plastic bags and empty bottles could be sold to be refilled and reused.

Similarly, it seemed every plant had a use: for food, drink, medicine, magic, house building, thatch, utensils and many other purposes. Baskets and mats were made to the highest standards and sold for pennies; some that I bought have now been in daily use for 14 years and are still perfect. I learned to respect the skills and resourcefulness of people living simply but richly, without modern technology and completely dependent on their immediate environment to meet all their needs. Living, in fact, in much the same way as most people in Scotland did until the twentieth century.

On my return to Scotland in 1983, I began to investigate the subject more systematically. I discovered that in fact a great deal had been written on the uses of Scottish plants but most of it was inaccessible, scattered references in old, out of print books. Thus began what was to become a decade of research (in the time I could spare from caring for two young children and working in community education) collecting information for what I hoped would become this book.

Over the years, I have seen interest in the subject of ethnobotany increasing rapidly, both in Scotland and elsewhere in the world, with the realisation that traditional knowledge was being lost in the space from one generation to the next in this time of rapid change that is now affecting every culture on earth. The search for new drugs and cosmetics from plant sources has been the most significant driving force.

In 1993, my family had the opportunity to spend a year travelling in Malaysia and Australia, where once again I was able to meet and learn from people—the Dayak and Iban of Sarawak and Aborigines of Queensland—who used wild plants to meet many of their needs. Sitting on grass mats in a longhouse made entirely from locally grown materials, being taught to make plaited baskets by three delightful crones whose only English words were 'one, two, three' (all you need for a plaited basket, really), is one of my warmest memories of that wonderful year.

'The Book' went on hold again—but the urge to complete it on my return was strengthened. Here, at last, it is.

ACKNOWLEDGEMENTS

Although every reference I have used is listed in the bibliography, several sources have been particularly helpful and I wish to acknowledge them here. In chronological order, they are Martin Martin (seventeenth century), John Lightfoot (eighteenth century), Alexander Carmichael (nineteenth century), Mary Beith, Geoffrey Grigson, Isobel Grant and F. Marian McNeill (twentieth century).

James Sutherland, a seventeenth century botanist, left an invaluable record of plants grown in the Edinburgh Physic Garden for medicinal purposes, and these are indicated throughout the text by the symbol ❀.

Of the several books published on plant dyes, I have used the work of Jean Fraser and Su Grierson as the definitive ones.

I am grateful to Little Brown and Company (UK) for permission to quote from *Crowdie and Cream* by Finlay J Macdonald.

Jackie Muscott of the Botanical Society of Scotland and Henry Noltie of the Royal Botanic Garden, Edinburgh were kind enough to check and update the scientific names and other botanical information, for which I am very grateful. The responsibility for remaining errors is entirely mine.

Without the constant support of my husband Ian Edwards, this book would not have been completed. I would also like to thank my long-suffering children, Hazel and Robin, who over the years have perhaps seen less of me, and more of folk museums, than they would have chosen. Many friends and colleagues have helped by sending information and commenting on the text; in particular I would like to mention Alastair MacIntosh and Tess Campbell. I also wish to thank my editor at Mercat Press, Tom Johnstone.

SOME NOTES ON THE TEXT

The book is divided into two sections. The first part consists of four introductory chapters giving an overview of the subject matter. The main part of the book contains information on around 300 individual plant species. This is arranged in plant families because often members of the same family have similar properties and uses.

The emphasis throughout is on indigenous species that grow wild in Scotland and on information that applies specifically, though not necessarily exclusively, to Scotland. Where a plant is recorded as having been used medicinally in Scotland but little or no other information on the ways it was used has been found, supplementary information has been added from Mrs Grieve's *A Modern Herbal.*[61]

In general, information has been left out if the plant referred to is not native to Scotland, or if the use described was not definitely known to have been applicable to this country. A few exceptions have been made where the use is particularly interesting or important, or the plant has been naturalised for hundreds of years, or its status is uncertain. Botanical research is constantly coming up with information that illuminates our understanding of the history and family relationships of plants. It should also be noted that plants used for medicinal purposes (often indicated by *officinalis* in the scientific name) were frequently cultivated in physic and domestic gardens, so that it cannot be presumed that because they are native plants, they were being collected from the wild.

Where information on plant use comes from a specific published source, or a quotation about it appears in the text, this is keyed to the bibliography by a superscript italic number, e.g.[23]

Every plant has a common and a scientific name; the latter has often changed, perhaps several times, since the information used in this book was first published. I have tried to trace species accurately and use the most up-to-date taxonomical nomenclature available, but inevitably there will be errors and misnomers. The standard reference used throughout for plant names is the *New Flora of the British Isles* by Clive Stace (Cambridge University Press, 1995).

Where Scots, Gaelic or local names are known they are included; for these I owe a great debt to Geoffrey Grigson and John Cameron, who did an excellent job of collecting vernacular names while they were still in daily use. It will be noticed that there are many variations of spelling, for example from one island to the next. The area where a local name originates is indicated by an abbreviation; for the list of abbreviations used see p. xiv.

As if the difficulties of taxonomy, plant status and language were not enough, I have found the realms of plant folklore to be a labyrinth for the humble ethnobotanist, with very few guides to show the way. This seems to be an under-explored and under-resourced area, and I can only hope the publication of this collection may stimulate more interest.

PLACE-NAME ABBREVIATIONS

Note: many of these regional names are no longer in official use, but all are still clearly recognisable areas—more so than the new names that have replaced them!

Aber	Aberdeenshire
Ayr	Ayrshire
Banff	Banffshire
Berw	Berwickshire
Caith	Caithness
Clack	Clackmannanshire
Dumf	Dumfriesshire
Inv	Invernessshire
Kinrs	Kinross-shire
Kirk	Kirkudbrightshire
Lan	Lanarkshire
Loth	Lothian
Mor	Morayshire
nS	north Scotland
Ork	Orkney
Peeb	Peeblesshire
Perth	Perthshire
Renf	Renfrewshire
Rox	Roxburghshire
Selk	Selkirkshire
Shet	Shetland
sS	south Scotland
Stir	Stirlingshire
swS	south west Scotland
Wigt	Wigtownshire

PART ONE: THE ROLE OF WILD PLANTS

Food for Foragers

Stone Age Diet

Britain's first known settlers arrived from Europe over 300,000 years ago in the time we call the Palaeolithic, or old Stone Age, the glacial period when great ice sheets waxed and waned across northern Europe. They were nomadic hunters who appear to have visited this land whenever the ice and Arctic weather retreated sufficiently to make it habitable. They left only a few tantalising traces of their existence in England and Wales—fragments of stone and bone, nearly all found at coastal and riverside occupation sites. Although no sites have yet been identified for certain in Scotland, it seems highly likely that such rich hunting grounds would have been utilised during the 300,000 year Palaeolithic period.

As the ice began its final retreat from the British Isles around 10,000 years ago, people gradually reoccupied the land, arriving by sea or overland from the south. The earliest people of Scotland, arriving in areas recently scoured and blasted by the Ice Age, would have faced a hostile and challenging environment. However, pollen analysis indicates that mixed woodland, heather moorland and other plant communities were beginning to be established by 9,500 years ago, providing the trees, shrubs and herbs people needed for survival. The oldest evidence of human settlement yet found in Scotland is on the island of Rum, dated to 8,590 years ago, the Mesolithic (middle Stone Age) period, but it is likely occupation was far more widespread by then than archaeological remains suggest.

These hunter-gatherers were totally dependent on their detailed knowledge of local plants and animals for survival. They had an immediate impact on the environment as they cut and burned wood for fuel and building, perhaps even beginning to manage woodland for hazel, alder and willow coppice products. Evidence for vegetation changes due to human activity has been found by archaeologists examining charcoal deposits and pollen changes in ancient soil.[1]

Stone Age people are still often portrayed as rampant carnivores, savage hunters of the great beasts that roamed the wilderness; modern archaeologists recognise that this misconception has arisen because bones survive well to become archaeological evidence whereas plant foods rarely leave any trace. In reality, it is far more likely that men hunting big game

1. Pollen grains have distinctive shapes and surfaces so that they can be identified to plant family and sometimes to species. They are tough and survive for millennia in soil, especially peat. Palaeobotanists are therefore able to examine changes in the type and amount of pollen present in soil layers at different depths, indicating how the surrounding vegetation changed as the soil gradually formed.

1

only supplied a small proportion of each group's dietary requirements. The bulk, in the form of plant products and small animals, would have been collected or caught by women and children, using detailed information and understanding of their environment which was passed on from one generation to the next.

Useful information on the likely diet of the hunter-gatherers of prehistoric Scotland comes from extensive anthropological studies of societies in which this way of life has survived into modern times, such as Australian Aborigines and the African !Kung .[8, 99] These people have an extraordinary relationship with their environment, and skills which enable them to survive in the deserts to which they have been driven by agriculturalists, who require the better land to grow crops (which are, of course, derived from the wild plants all our ancestors collected).

What plants did people eat in Scotland before farming began around 5,500 years ago? Archaeological evidence is sparse because, as has been said, plant material rarely survives and is easily missed in excavations, leaving only clues in the form of the occasional seed husk, nut shell, charred remains or impression in a clay pot. Skeletal evidence such as the way teeth are worn down can be a good indication of diet. Something can be deduced from the tools used to prepare food—implements for cutting, grinding, pounding and cooking, although many Stone Age tools were multi-purpose.

For example, tiny sharpened flakes of flint (called microliths) found with grinding stones suggest people were cutting grasses and making flour from the crushed seeds. Larger straight-edged knives may have been used to cut roots, while microliths set in rows on a flat board appear to have been for grating. Pitted grinding stones found in the excavation of a Neolithic (new Stone Age) farmstead on Papa Westray, in Orkney, are thought to have been used:

> *as grinders for wild seeds, hammers for flaking other stones, as anvils, and as targets for teaching children to throw spears. Overall it would appear that the most common primary use of these stones was to grind wild seeds...the gathering and processing of wild plant food in early Neolithic Orkney should not be underestimated.*[114]

Indeed, these people survived on wild food for hundreds of years and must have had extensive knowledge of which plants were edible. Therefore examination of palaeobotanical information, to see which edible plants grew then, in conjunction with archaeological and anthropological evidence, enables us to establish a reasonably accurate idea of what pre-agricultural people of Scotland were eating.

The diet of Stone Age people was probably 50-90% plant based, with

10-20 staple species but perhaps over 60 different kinds of plant being used at some time each year. They would have eaten leaves, roots, seeds, stalks, fruit, nuts, flowers, gums, seaweed and fungi. Most wild plants contain more protein and calcium than their cultivated relatives and unprocessed plant foods are high in fibre. What they had, therefore, was a varied and wholesome diet, which combined with lean meat and plenty of exercise actually means the average Stone Age person may well have been healthier than many Scots are today. However, they would always have had to contend with seasonal variations and shortages.

Most of the earliest people of Scotland lived on or near the coast, where they had first arrived or found areas attractive to settle, with drift-wood for fuel and building shelters and plenty of food available including fish, seals, sea birds and their eggs, shellfish and crustaceans, even occasional beached whales. It is highly likely they also sampled seaweed and found none poisonous, some delicious and most kinds easy to prepare and cook and highly nutritious (see **Algae**). They were probably nomadic, however, moving along the coast and inland according to the seasonal availability of both animal and plant foods. Animals available to hunt included deer, elk, wild ox, wolf, pine marten, horse, hedgehog, boar, bear, badger and beaver, as well as wildfowl. It is possible they also ate the stomach contents, thus taking extra plant food in a partially digested form.

Dandelion

That aside, detailed research on prehistoric foods by Jane Renfrew and other archaeologists suggests a diet that a modern gourmet would not find unappetising, using plants that were certainly commonly eaten by the people of Scotland in later times. Seeds of land plants found in excavations include a variety of 'greens', such as fat hen (*Chenopodium album*), nettles (*Urtica dioica*), wild cabbage (*Brassica oleracea*), great bistort (*Polygonum bistorta*), cleavers (*Galium aparine*), white deadnettle (*Lamium album*), charlock (*Sinapsis arvensis*) and orache (*Atriplex patula*).

Roots that were available and may have been boiled, roasted and ground into meal were silverweed (*Potentilla anserina*), pignut (*Conopodium majus*), dandelion (*Taraxacum* species), wild parsnip (*Pastinaca sativa*), wild carrot (*Daucus carota*), sow thistle (*Sonchus arvensis*) and yellow goatsbeard (*Tragopogon pratensis*).

For salads and flavouring they could have used the tangy leaves of sorrel (*Rumex acetosa*), wood sorrel (*Oxalis acetosella*), dandelion (*Taraxacum* species), hairy bittercress (*Cardamine hirsuta*), or ramsons (*Allium ursinum*, garlic flavour), tansy (*Tanacetum vulgare*, ginger flavour), mint (*Mentha* species), lady's smock (*Cardamine pratensis*, peppery), salad burnet (*Poterium sanguisorba minor*, cucumber flavoured), the clove-flavoured roots of herb bennet (*Geum urbanum*) or spicy juniper berries (*Juniperus communis*).

Some of these plants would have been used to flavour drinks, in addition to elder (*Sambucus nigra*) flowers and berries, gorse (*Ulex europaea*) and heather (*Calluna vulgaris*) flowers, sweet woodruff (*Galium odoratum*) and wild thyme (*Thymus polytrichus* ssp. *britannicus*). Archaeologists excavating three Bronze Age cist burials in Fife discovered what appear to be remains of a mead-like drink which had been in a bark container.[39] The thin deposit of blackened, crumbly matter was found to contain various plant remains, including large quantities of lime (*Tilia cordata*) and meadowsweet (*Filipendula ulmaria*) pollen. It seems likely the drink consisted of fermented lime honey flavoured with meadowsweet (the name meadowsweet derives from mead, not meadow). Interestingly, lime trees were rare in Scotland at that time and it seems likely that the honey or mead itself had been imported from England or even further afield.

Seasonally available fruit and nuts included hazelnuts (*Corylus avellana*), acorns (*Quercus* species), sloes (*Prunus spinosa*), rosehips (*Rosa* species), haws (*Crataegus monogyna*), rowan berries (*Sorbus aucuparia*), crab apples (*Malus sylvestris*), wild strawberries (*Fragaria vesca*), brambles (*Rubus fruticosus*), raspberries (*R. idaeus*), cranberries (*Vaccinium microcarpon*) and blaeberries (*V. myrtillus*). Mushrooms rarely survive to be found by archaeologists, and there may have been reluctance to eat them even in prehistoric times (see p. 43) but being seasonally abundant, delicious, nutritious, easy to dry, store and prepare, one wonders how prehistoric cooks could have resisted them. Of more than 3,000 British species, only 20 are poisonous (including four that are deadly); many of the rest are unpalatable but people would have quickly learnt from experience!

It has been shown by numerous anthropological studies that contemporary hunter-gatherers spend far less time producing and processing food than agriculturalists, therefore having more time for crafts and creativity, socialising and spiritual pursuits. They are no more vulnerable to fluctuations in food supply due to the natural vagaries of climate, pests and diseases than farmers; perhaps less so, since they have a far wider range of foods to draw on. What, therefore, was the driving force that propelled the momentous change from foraging to farming?

The First Farmers

Around 4,000 years ago, cereal pollen begins to appear in the palaeoenvironmental record on Rhum—the first evidence of plant cultivation. About the same time, grass pollen became far more common, suggesting these early farmers relied more on rearing livestock than growing crops. There is evidence of forest clearance, possibly for pasture, in other parts of Scotland in the same era but cereal pollen appears later, e.g. in Aberdeenshire in the Bronze Age, around 1,000 BC, and in Galloway about 600 BC, during the transitional time between the Bronze and Iron Ages.

It is likely that foragers and farmers co-existed in Scotland for a long period, and certainly people continued to gather wild plants for food until the twentieth century—and of course some still do so. The change to dependence on cultivated crops for the bulk of dietary requirements was a very gradual one. Over many generations, people would have acquired detailed knowledge of plant biology while gathering plants and plant products; they saw seeds fall and germinate, seedlings grow healthy in deep, moist soil and wither on stony ground, fruits become abundant in warm wet years and scarce in cold dry ones.

Two related factors may have been most significant in the transition from foraging to farming. Firstly, greater effort was required to move around continually according to where food was available compared to the ease experienced when there was a seasonal abundance of something that could be stored for leaner times. Secondly, there was a gradual increase in population. Once food began to be stored, someone had to guard it from human or animal thieves. Stored or spilled grain may even have germinated around the dwelling place, giving people a further incentive to stay and harvest it, before they developed the idea of deliberately planting. Once nomads became sedentary, they could begin to accumulate material possessions that previously would have been an unnecessary encumbrance, such as agricultural tools, grinding stones and food containers. Such goods then in themselves became a further reason to stay put in one place.

These early farmers grew primitive forms of wheat (*Triticum boeoticum*) and barley (*Hordeum* species) and kept cattle, sheep, goats and pigs. There was still plenty of seafood, wildfowl and game to hunt, although elk had been wiped out and wild ox were becoming scarce. Added nutrition and flavour came from weeds harvested accidentally with arable crops. Soft curd cheese was made and flavoured with herbs; the leaves of butterwort (*Pinguicula vulgaris*) or lady's bedstraw (*Galium verum*) or the juice of nettles (*Urtica dioica*) were added to curdle milk when rennet was not available. Butter, perhaps flavoured with ramsons (*Allium ursinum*), was stored in bogs, in baskets or wooden containers, or wrapped in cloth, bark or leather.

By the time the Romans came to Scotland in the first century AD, agriculture was well established. Evidence from Roman writings and from extensive excavation of settlements such as those along the Antonine and Hadrian's Wall indicates that the soldiers' diet was mainly vegetarian. Pit latrines at Bearsden, the western end of the Antonine Wall, contained identifiable remains of wild foods such as raspberries (*Rubus idaeus*), wild strawberries (*Fragaria vesca*), wild celery (*Apium graveolens*) and hazelnuts (*Corylus avellana*).[71]

5

Frugal, feast or famine?

For hundreds of years thereafter, the Scottish diet varied little, either from century to century or from day to day. The arrival of oats (*Avena fatua*), which gradually spread northwards having been introduced to Britain by the Romans, was a rare improvement, being both more productive and more nutritious than other cereals in the cool, damp Scottish climate. Potatoes were not widespread until the late eighteenth century, initially being viewed with some mistrust, suspected of being poisonous or causing incontinence and uncontrollable passions. The typical diet for most of the last two millennia was a frugal but healthy one: oatmeal porridge, brose made from barley, oats, beans and pease, broth with kail, vegetable stew, milk, butter, cheese, eggs, fish and blood from cattle. This was a diet high in fibre, calcium and iron but seasonally deficient in several essential vitamins and minerals.

A handful of hazelnuts (*Corylus avellana*), a dish of blaeberries (*Vaccinium myrtillus*), a few roasted silverweed roots (*Potentilla anserina*) would have been welcomed with relish for the flavour, but also served as a vital source of extra nutrients. At Clunie in Perthshire, people in the late eighteenth century were recorded eating 'watercresses, sloes, hawthorns, hipthorns, wild rasps, earthnuts, seaweed, silverweed, nettles, wild spinach, wild garlic and wild carrots'.[123] Time spent with livestock at the summer shielings was used both to enjoy and gather for storing a great variety of wild foods, as well as plants for medicines and dyeing. Households living far from the sea obtained seaware from travelling vendors and it appeared on the menu as a delicacy at elegant dinners in many wealthy houses; the Ochertyre House Booke of Accomps kept by the Murray family in Perthshire 1737-9, records the occasional purchase of 'a pennyworth of dulse and tangle'.[127]

Wild food continued to be appreciated along with cultivated crops. Carmichael describes a wonderful west coast and islands harvest festival held in the nineteenth century, and perhaps for centuries before that, to honour St Michael, patron saint of the sea, on 29 September.[23] The preparations involved the collection by women and girls, on the previous Sunday afternoon, of wild carrots (*Daucus carota*), a symbol of fertility (see p. 69). If the carrots did not come up easily, they were dug out in a special way, by cutting an equal sided triangle using a three-pronged mattock. Carmichael interprets the symbolism of this as representing St Michael's trident and possibly the Trinity, but it must be significant that three is the sacred number of the triple goddess (maiden, mother, crone), symbolised since ancient times and in many cultures by a triangle.

The women sang individual 'runes' as they worked and there was much rivalry as to who would get the most and finest carrots; a forked specimen caused great excitement! They were tied in bunches with three-ply thread, usually red, the colour of blood, therefore of life itself. The roots were stored until the feast day, when they were distributed by women to men as tokens of affection and good wishes during the celebration and the evening dance. This was surely the Christianised descendant of a pagan fertility ritual, celebrating earth's natural harvest.

A special bannock, the *strubhan Micheil*, was baked for the feast by a woman in each household. It usually had three corners, but sometimes five, seven or nine, or it was made circular to symbolise eternity. The basic ingredients included equal portions of each kind of grain grown on the family holding, mixed to a dough with ewe's milk (sheep being considered the most sacred animal and ewes kept in milk until Michaelmas for the purpose, though goat's milk could also be used). Wild fruits such as cranberries, blaeberries or brambles were sometimes added.

From *The blessing of the struan*:

> *Each meal beneath my roof,*
> *They will all be mixed together,*
> *In the name of God the Son,*
> *Who gave them growth.*

> *Milk, eggs and butter,*
> *The good produce of our own flock,*
> *There shall be no dearth in our land,*
> *Or in our dwelling...*

> *Consecrate the produce of our land,*
> *Bestow prosperity and peace...*

> *Dandelion, smooth garlic,*
> *Foxglove, woad and butterwort,*
> *The three carle-doddies,*[1]
> *And marigold.*
> (from *Carmina Gadelica* by Alexander Carmichael)

The *struan* was blessed and baked on St Michael's eve over a fire of sacred woods such as oak, rowan and bramble; blackthorn and aspen, associated with evil, were to be avoided. While it was cooking, the struan was battered on each side with layers of eggs, cream and butter, usually applied with feathers from the family cockerel, but in Uist a bunch of bent-grass (*Agrostis* species) was used. A large communal *struan* was baked,

---

1. Carl- or curl-doddy is a common Scots name meaning 'curly-head', used for several different plants including daisy, ribwort plantain, melancholy thistle, devil's bit scabious and orchids.

plus smaller individual ones for each family member, including those absent or dead. These latter ones were shared in the person's memory, or given to the poor. The *struain* were blessed in church on the feast day, divided at a ritual meal and one quarter of the communal one was given to the poor.

Dependence on cultivated foods made people vulnerable to famine due to bad weather or disease. Few generations were unaffected; for example, a period of climatic deterioration led to famines in 1563, 1577 and 1595. There were several years in the late 1600s when it is estimated one third of the population died in some places; further famines occurred in 1709, 1740 and 1760. In the 1790s, potatoes made up one third of the diet; by the 1840s, this peaked at three-quarters. When blight decimated the crop, the consequences were· horrendous. At such times, knowledge of edible wild foods made the difference between life and death.

> *During these hungry years, as starvation stared the people in the face, the instinct of self-preservation overpowered all other feelings, and even natural affection became extinct in crowds of men and women forced to prowl and fight for their food like beasts. Old and young struggled together for nettles, docks, and grass in spring, while they gathered the loathed snails in summer and stored them for the winter's use.[56]*

However, wild plant foods were as often relished as despised: although the lowlands of Scotland were called 'the Land of Kail' by Meg Dods in the eighteenth century,

> *The Highlander preferred the common nettle in his broth, and appears to have regarded the use of kail as a symptom of effeminacy.[94]*

In most parts of Scotland, nutrition improved somewhat with agricultural developments in the 1700s, only to deteriorate again for many when the drift to factories and cities began with industrialisation in the middle of the eighteenth century. Those with fields or cottage gardens had an increasingly varied and healthy choice of food available, while the landless poor and city slum dwellers were malnourished and diseased. When medical records began to be kept in more detail in the late nineteenth century, there was a great contrast observed in the Scottish lowlands between well grown, robust country children and under-sized, sickly town dwellers.

Meanwhile, in the Highlands and Islands, massive social and economic disruption continued with the clearances, when people were brutally evicted from the land they had farmed for generations to make way for sheep and sporting interests. Forced onto marginal areas, often rocky coastal strips, many survived only by gathering wild food (plants, shellfish and sea fish) and by heaving heavy loads of seaweed onto the thin soil as mulch, enabling

them to grow potatoes and other crops (see also **green manure, p. 35,
seaweed,** p. 49 and **medicine, pp. 22-3).**

Even in the twentieth century, wartime shortages sent people back to
the hedgerows gathering fruit, such as rosehips for vitamin C, and wild
plants for non-food purposes. Seaweed has continued to be vital in the
crofting economy for fodder and fertiliser. Gathering mushrooms for personal use and commercial sale takes place in some areas (see p. 43). Dick
Peebles, an enterprising individual based in Glasgow, has recently set up
a company called Caledonian Wildfoods to supply restaurants with over
fifty species of mushrooms and many varieties of wild fruit, herbs and
vegetables. While wishing to encourage increasing interest in wild foods,
Peebles keeps detailed records of where his team of foragers collects in
order to monitor their impact. For conservation reasons, it would not be
wise or even legal to advocate a large scale return to uprooting plants from
the wild. However, collecting fruit, picking mushrooms, taking a few leaves
here and there from very common plants for salad or seasoning does
nothing harmful to the species concerned and encourages us to value and
respect, as well as to enjoy, natural resources, which hopefully leads to
taking responsibility for and protecting our local environment.

Medicine, Magic and Myth:
Health and Healing with Plants

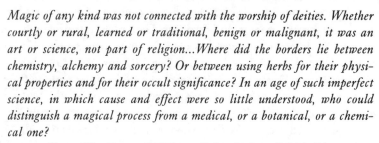

Magic of any kind was not connected with the worship of deities. Whether courtly or rural, learned or traditional, benign or malignant, it was an art or science, not part of religion...Where did the borders lie between chemistry, alchemy and sorcery? Or between using herbs for their physical properties and for their occult significance? In an age of such imperfect science, in which cause and effect were so little understood, who could distinguish a magical process from a medical, or a botanical, or a chemical one?

(from *The Pagan Religions of the Ancient British Isles*
by Ronald Hutton)

Valerian

When I began researching this book, I tried to exclude information on the medicinal uses of plants that appeared to relate to magic powers, not scientifically possible to prove. As time went on I gradually came to understand that it is not actually possible to separate the healing properties of plants into two categories—'real' and 'magic'—because both illness and healing are highly complex processes that require treatment of the whole person, body, mind and spirit. Many folk remedies address this in ways that seem strange, even ridiculous to us now; but such beliefs would not have persisted over so many generations if they had no basis in experience. It is also important to note how many of the healing powers attributed to plants have proved to be valid after chemical analysis.

Prehistoric Possibilities

Our understanding of the ways in which plants were used for healing in prehistoric times is based on inference from archaeological evidence, on legend and on contemporary writings, often anecdotal. The people who may have been the earliest Stone Age visitors to Scotland, nomadic Neanderthal hunters of the Palaeolithic period from about 300,000 years ago, left no recognisable trace of their activities (see p. 1). It is likely, however, that they shared some of the beliefs and practices of other European tribes of that time.

Neanderthals, hominids closely related to modern humans, have long been considered by archaeologists to have been of low intelligence and therefore presumed devoid of spiritual life. But in 1960 a cave excavated in northern Iraq was found to contain the grave of a young Neanderthal man who had been buried 60,000 years ago with a variety of plants that have medicinal properties.[72] The body, curled up with his head resting on his hands as if asleep, was laid on a bed of horsetails (*Equisetum* species) and flowers strewn around him included ragwort (*Senecio jacobaea*), groundsel (*Senecio vulgaris*), yarrow (*Achillea millefolium*) and other species used to treat wounds and fever.

This strongly suggests these 'primitive' people had some belief in an afterlife, leading them to equip the body with healing herbs for his journey into the next world. Neanderthals visited England, Wales and perhaps Scotland throughout the Palaeolithic period whenever climatic conditions of the Ice Ages permitted. Whether they shared these beliefs and this knowledge of the healing properties of plants we can only guess. What we do know for certain is that they survived for hundreds of thousands of years in an environment that people of today would find challenging, to say the least.

By 5,300 years ago, there were people settled in many parts of Scotland, and we have considerably more information on their lifestyle and beliefs. We know they were building monuments apparently with ritual purposes (see p. 28) and burying at least some of their dead with care and with grave goods which must have had some significance. Unfortunately organic material rarely survives, so plants with medicinal or magic properties have left no trace. However, a fascinating insight into the extensive use of plants being made by contemporary people elsewhere in Europe is offered by studies of the Stone Age man found frozen in the Alps in 1991.[126]

Among the many plants he had made use of in dressing and equipping himself for what was to be his last journey (see p. 24), the Iceman carried the birch fungus *Piptoporus betulinus*, which has antibiotic properties characteristic of several species of tree fungus, recognised in the first century AD by the Greek physician Dioscorides and prescribed into the twentieth century by herbalists for treating wounds and infections. He also had a sloe or blackthorn berry (*Prunus spinosa*), which might be classified as food rather than medicine, but has a bitter, acid taste (perhaps more familiar to us nowadays in sloe gin than in the fruit) and was eaten from prehistoric times for its vitamin and mineral content rather than for its flavour. It has also been found occasionally in graves.

Other evidence of prehistoric knowledge of the healing properties of plants comes from the excavation of a grave in Perthshire, where a Bronze Age warrior was found with a chest wound packed with sphagnum moss. Although in this case clearly it did not save his life, the antibiotic and absorbent properties of sphagnum were used right up to the Second World War to prepare effective wound dressings.

Druids, Romans and Country Folk

Over many generations extensive knowledge of the healing and protective properties of plants, both medicinal and magic, undoubtedly accumulated; what we cannot know is how widespread this knowledge was, or to what extent it was in the hands of a powerful, educated elite such as the *druidhean* (Gaelic for magicians, philosophers), as described by Pliny (see **clubmoss**, p. 56, and **mistletoe**, p. 175).

For example, it is curious that there are very few references to the use of hallucinogenic fungi in Scotland, although they are widespread and well used in some other European cultures. It has been suggested that in fact the druids were very well aware of their properties, but kept the knowledge secret so that during ceremonies the unsuspecting audience could be given mushrooms and would attribute the resulting hallucinations to the power of the *druidhean* (see p. 43). It seems likely that healing plants in general could have been employed similarly to enhance the reputation of those with the knowledge of how to use them, and that would partly explain why it is so difficult to separate medicine from magic in traditional healing.

Further insight into the state of medicine in prehistoric Scotland can be gleaned from Irish records; it is known that there were very close links with Ireland, where early physicians were a subordinate class of druids skilled in medical botany. Legend has it that Josina, ninth king of Scotland (reputed to have lived in the second century BC) was educated in Ireland by the native physicians and composed a treatise on the virtues and powers of herbs.

Although Romans only penetrated the south of Scotland, they brought with them a relatively highly developed knowledge of medicine and hygiene that cannot have failed to impress local people who encountered them. Their extensive pharmacopoeia included the native Scottish plants gentian (*Gentianella* species), iris (*Iris pseudacorus*), juniper (*Juniperus communis*), male fern (*Dryopteris*), mistletoe (*Viscum album*), rose (*Rosa* spp.), valerian (*Valeriana officinalis*) and resin, possibly from Scots pine (*Pinus sylvestris*), all of which they may well have collected locally.

The Arrival of Christianity

The gradual ascendancy of Christianity over Paganism took place over many centuries with marked regional differences, leaving us with a confused and confusing picture. In some parts of England, Christianity became the dominant religion in just one generation, while in remoter parts of northern Scotland the old religions appear to have survived until the end of the seventh century AD.

Along with the new religion,

The missionaries also brought with them a code of non-violence and they had a confident approach to disease and healing. These tough and re-sourceful men thus could engage successfully in contests of healing skills with the folk healers and medical men they encountered.[64]

The earliest hospitals, which the missionaries established, were prima-rily refuges for old and disabled people and for travelling pilgrims, rather than places to treat the sick. However, each monastery had an infirmary where treatment was available with herbal remedies made from plants cultivated in the physic garden.

The healing properties of plants were henceforth frequently attributed to their association with particular saints, especially Bridget, John, Columba and Patrick, beliefs that survived to the end of the nineteenth century, at least. Herbal remedies were only one of the resources available—healing wells, stones, charms and incantations all played their part, often in com-bination. What is most significant and remarkable in considering traditional medicine is the fact that belief in magic survived despite increasingly ruthless suppression. In his thorough and fascinating study of *The Pagan Religions of the Ancient British Isles*, Ronald Hutton explains it thus:

church-going was an activity designed to ensure that the worshipper secured a better life after death and that the whole community, whether conceived of as the village, the district or the state, was protected from harm. The same person would often employ a magical remedy for mat-ters apparently too trivial for the concern of Almighty God...magic did a lot of the work later taken over by pharmaceutical medicine, fertilisers, insurance schemes and advertisement columns. Those practising it were generally devout Christians and saw charms and rituals in the same functional sense as these modern commodities and services. Such magic had in the eyes of its practitioners or purchasers, nothing to do with the great contest between God and Satan: it was concerned with the morally neutral forces of nature, which could be turned to good or bad effect just like those of the natural world.

The picture that emerges from the shadowy centuries of the Dark Ages is of two parallel traditions developing. On one side, there were the monastic and university trained physicians (all men), mainly town and city based and serving the wealthy. On the other, there was self-treatment and folk healers (usually women) in the rural areas. They were often using the same plant remedies, but operated in different and rarely overlapping circles, with great distrust of each other. The situation was later distorted by centuries of religious persecution and witch hunting which involved the execution of many thousands of folk healers (see pp. 18-20). Herbal medicine survived, but never regained the status it had and still has in many parts of the world.

Medieval Monastic Medicine

The earliest known herbal of British origin is the Saxon *Leech Book of Bald*, written early in the tenth century, and making reference to remedies of Scottish origin. By the twelfth century, learning in Scotland was undergoing a period of great progress under Queen (later Saint) Margaret and then David I. Records exist for at least 150 medieval hospitals attached to religious houses in Scotland. The monastery at Soutra in south east Scotland was founded in 1164, and has over recent years been the subject of extensive archaeological excavation by a team led by Brian Moffat. Examination of the hospital waste at Soutra has revealed the use of many medicinal plants both native and imported (see pp. 67, 71, 170).[103]

Recent excavation of Jedburgh Abbey produced clear evidence of the medicinal use of one plant: great quantities of pollen from tormentil (*Potentilla erecta*) were found with the eggs of whipworm, an unpleasant parasite which causes severe diarrhoea. Tormentil has other uses, mainly in tanning and dyeing, but it can be safely assumed that in this case it was being used for its astringent properties to treat the diarrhoea caused by whipworm infestation.

The National Library of Scotland has in its collection a Gaelic medical manuscript, attributed to the fifteenth or sixteenth century and believed to have been in the possession of John Beaton, a member of the famous hereditary medical family that served generations of the MacLeods and the Lords of the Isles. The *Regimen Sanitas* (Rule of Health) includes many anecdotes and folk beliefs, and quotes numerous ancient medical authorities. It emphasises the importance of a healthy lifestyle, moderation in eating and drinking, and taking plenty of exercise.[54]

Among the native Scottish plants prescribed in simple herbal remedies are violet (*Viola* species) for headache and catarrh, shepherd's purse (*Capsella bursa-pastoris*) for bleeding wounds and iris root (*Iris pseudacorus*) as a laxative and diuretic, and to remove obstructions of the spleen, kidneys and bladder. After bloodletting, vitamin-rich plants such as mallow (*Malva* species), bugloss (*Echium vulgare*) and violets were recommended to be eaten. Whisky was to be used medicinally in moderation, much of the benefit probably deriving from the aromatic herbs then used to flavour it such as thyme (*Thymus polytrichus* ssp. *britannicus*), mint (*Mentha* species), juniper (*Juniperus communis*) and cranberries (*Vaccinium microcarpon*).

Royal Progress in the Fifteenth Century

Under James IV (1473-1513), a period of peace and stability led to the establishment of three Scottish Universities, but none of these taught medicine properly until the seventeenth century. Scottish students continued to travel to the continent for medical expertise. With the King's encouragement, medical advances were made and this period saw the emergence of the the first secular surgeons. However, in the rules of the Edinburgh College of Surgeons and Barbers laid down in 1505, the main emphasis was still on bloodletting and studying the influence of the stars.

This was a time of growth in towns and cities that further widened the divide between traditional folk healers and university-trained professionals. Only the wealthiest city dwellers could afford medical treatment, and since poorer people frequently lost not only their access to folk healers, but also their sources of healing plants, fresh food and clean water, it is hardly surprising that city life brought with it epidemics largely unknown to Scotland's earlier widely dispersed, low density population. These included typhus and plague, and later (from 1497) syphilis.

The Sixteenth Century

An insight into medical knowledge in the sixteenth century is gained from the story Comrie relates in his *History of Scottish Medicine*. Scottish physicians in 1552 were unable to alleviate the chronic severe asthma of the Archbishop of St Andrews, John Hamilton, who had access to the very best medical treatment available at the time. On the recommendation of a friend the Archbishop consulted Geronimo Cardano, a famous Italian physician who, after observing his health for seventy days, prescribed herbal remedies including soup made with coltsfoot (*Tussilago farfara*) leaves, and using a pillow stuffed with seaweed instead of feathers.

This, combined with rest, showers, fasting during attacks and a sparing nutritious diet at other times (not to mention banning his custom of having sexual intercourse every night before and after supper), led to a rapid improvement in the Archbishop's health. He felt better within a month, and two years later was still well, having occasional but far less severe attacks. It might be thought that the Archbishop's Scottish physicians would have learned from the success of this method of treatment, but in fact their response was to accuse Cardano of witchcraft and black magic.

Information on the medical advice available to humbler folk at that time can be found in an old manuscript copied in the late sixteenth century and now kept in Edinburgh University Library. It does not inspire confidence in the modern reader. For example, 'To know if a wounded man shall live or die', the first test was whether the patient could hold down a drink of either grass or pimpernel (*Anagallis* species) leaves. If he vomited, he was not curable, whereupon presumably all attempts to save him were abandoned. However, if he managed not to be sick, he was then to be given a potion of pimpernel, bugle (*Ajuga reptans*) and sanicle (*Sanicula europaea*) for three days 'to purge the wound'. The next good sign to look for was whether a drink of pimpernel and water came out at the wound, in which case survival was guaranteed; if on the other hand lettuce in water made him vomit, there was no hope. Alternatively, he could be given the plant mouse-ear (*Cerastium* species) with ale, and if he held on to it until the same time next day, he would live—'or else not'. Fears of litigation even then?[54]

The Seventeenth Century:
Frogspawn and Physic Gardens

There had been very little improvement in the training of medical students a century later, when Scottish medical practice was considered far inferior to that on the continent of Europe. The Edinburgh College of Physicians was founded in 1681, yet the 1737 edition of the Edinburgh *Pharmacopoeia* still made much use of remedies such as frogspawn, spiders' webs, hens' gizzards and woodlice.

> *In attempting to establish themselves as a superior caste, the physicians had to distance themselves from the other healers...they took the widely known medical recipes and made them even more complex...[using] substances ranging from the exotic to the disgusting...remedies could contain 30 to 40 constituents prepared with extensive boiling, extraction, mixing and decanting.*[64]

During the seventeenth century, the health of ordinary people appears to have actually deteriorated, especially relative to England, where agricultural reforms were bringing about increased food productivity and prosperity for many. Famine exacerbated the depredations of typhus, plague, dysentery, whooping cough, smallpox and the 'ague' (probably malaria).

However, changes had begun that were to make Edinburgh-trained doctors some of the most skilled in the world and Scottish plants had an important place in the improvements. Two Edinburgh medical doctors played a significant role in these developments. Andrew Balfour was born in Fife in 1630 and his studies took him from St Andrews University to Paris, and from philosophy to medicine, with a special interest in the uses of plants for healing. By 1668, he was practising in Edinburgh where he met Robert Sibbald, born (in 1641) and educated in that city but who had finished his medical training at some of Europe's finest universities, including Paris and Leiden.

Physicians were the university-educated elite of medical practice. They diagnosed, advised and prescribed but left actual treatment to surgeons, who served apprenticeships and were skilled craftsmen, and to apothecaries, who made up medicines. The latter had no craft guild but could, by charging high prices for medicines or even by seeing patients directly and undercutting fees, become as wealthy as physicians, and there were constant power struggles between them. Sibbald was appalled at the state of medicine in Edinburgh, where the ignorance of the surgeons and apothecaries was greater than anything he had seen elsewhere in Europe.

In response to this, he began studying and growing the indigenous healing plants of Scotland, and in 1670 Sibbald and Balfour established, near Holyrood Abbey, a Physic Garden containing between eight and nine hundred plants from all over the world, including many Scottish species. At first the Surgeon Apothecaries were totally opposed to the garden, seeing the two doctors as their rivals, but Balfour handled them so skilfully that they in fact assisted in the acquisition in 1675 of a larger piece of land, on a site now covered by Waverley Station (where a plaque commemorates it); this Physic Garden contained over two thousand plants. Here was the beginning of what eventually evolved into the Royal Botanic Garden Edinburgh, used by generations of Scottish medical students to learn botany and herbal medicine until well into the twentieth century.

In 1683 James Sutherland, the Head Gardener, published his *Hortus Medicus Edinburgensis—A Catalogue of the Plants in the Physical Garden at Edinburgh*. This provides a useful record of native Scottish plants being cultivated for medicinal use at that time (indicated by ❀ in the text). Although no information has been found on the medicinal use of some of the species being grown, it is clear that Scottish plants were used extensively as herbal remedies.

The main source for information on herbal remedies used by country folk of the late seventeenth century is Martin Martin, a Gaelic speaking medical doctor trained in Montpellier, France. He travelled extensively in the Highlands and Islands (possibly at the suggestion of Sibbald) collecting a wealth of fascinating details on the lives of people he met, published in 1697 and 1703.[100] Although he has been accused of including 'hearsay and disputable information',[33] his work had considerable influence on subsequent generations of both medics and botanists and has frequently been quoted (and misquoted).

Martin appears to have been a remarkable person, adventurous and uncomplaining of the hardships he encountered at a time when travel was difficult in those remote regions. His excitement at the discoveries he made can be felt reading his words three hundred years later. He was clearly skilled at getting people to talk about sensitive issues and although one often wonders at his uncritical reporting of extraordinary information, he supplies an invaluable insight into the lives of humble people living marginal existences in the most isolated parts of Scotland.

The picture built up from his writings is of working folk, mostly illiterate but with a detailed knowledge of the properties, both medicinal and magic, of the plants that grew in their area; people who were relatively healthy (indeed who boasted numerous cases of remarkable longevity including someone who claimed to have reached 180 years of age) and had simple herbal remedies for all the afflictions of body and mind that they were prone to suffer.

In 1697 Martin visited St Kilda and was amazed at the contrasting situation there, where he noticed several healing plants growing wild, yet,

> *The inhabitants are ignorant of the virtue of these herbs...they never had a potion of physick given them in their lives, nor know anything of phlebotomy* [bloodletting]*; a phisician* [sic] *could not expect his bread in this commonwealth.*

Examining the variety of herbal remedies recorded by Martin gives an indication of the health problems that concerned Highlanders and Islanders of the late seventeenth century. There were several remedies for consumption and coughs, suggesting that tuberculosis and chest infections were widespread. Intestinal problems also figure large, with nine remedies for constipation and diarrhoea, worms, wind and 'stitch'. Seven plants were used to treat broken bones, wounds and swellings and to raise blisters, a favoured way to deal with localised infections. Three sedatives were known, plus two general painkillers and two remedies for sciatica. There were also remedies for stones, scurvy and fever.

Martin describes an old method Skye islanders used to induce sweating:

> *To cause any particular part of the body to sweat, they dig an hole in an earthen floor, and fill it with hazle sticks, and dry rushes; above these they put a Hectick-Stone* [quartz] *red hot, and pouring some water into the hole, the patient holds the part affected over it, and this produces a speedy sweat.*

The seventeenth century was, however, a precarious time to be a folk healer. While most relied mainly on herbal remedies and commonsense advice, some dabbled in love potions and foretelling the future, and one spectacular cure might be enough to earn a local reputation for supernatural powers, that could as easily be turned to evil as good. Witchcraft—defined by religious authorities as the misuse of supernatural powers derived from the Devil to cause harm—was largely an invention of the church and served the dual purpose of explaining all the evil in the world that could not be attributed to an all-powerful but benevolent God, and of keeping women in their place: of more than 1,000 people executed for witchcraft in Scotland, 80% were women. The church thereby endeavoured to ensure that local authority over bodies as well as souls lay in the hands of the village minister.

Martin described the work of Neil Beaton, an illiterate but clearly skilled and knowledgeable folk healer on Skye who was accused of witchcraft:

> *He pretends to judge of the various qualities of Plants, and Roots, by their different Tastes; he has likewise a nice Observation of the Colours of their Flowers, from which he learns their astringent and loosening qualities; he extracts the Juice of Plants and Roots, after a Chymical way, peculiar to himself, and with little or no charge...The Success attending to this man's cures was so extraordinary, that several People thought his performances to have proceeded rather from a Compact with the devil, than from the Virtue of Simples.*[1]

Unfortunately Martin was unable to determine the man's fate. Occasionally, those accused were acquitted. For example, in 1661, when Janet Campbell of Rothesay in Bute was found guilty by the Kirk Session of attempting to heal 'desperate' diseases with herbs, she was banned from giving any further remedies on pain of being proved a witch if she did so.

The Highlands and Islands were little affected by witch hunts for several reasons. The Kirk Session had less influence; all cases had to go to Edinburgh, which was too much bother for the Highland authorities; they then had to be translated from the Gaelic. This was an important factor in the survival of traditions of herbal healing in remoter areas of Scotland: it meant that knowledge survived 'not as the province of the outcast but within the natural context of a preindustrial society'.[6] This was particularly the case in predominantly Catholic areas, such as the Hebridean islands of Barra and South Uist, where many ancient customs survived to be recorded by folklorists of the late nineteenth and twentieth centuries. Presbyterian clergy were more inclined to disapprove of and suppress what they feared to be pagan practices.

Aside from the hysteria of 'confessions' extracted under torture, there is actually very little evidence that pagan religious practices continued into the seventeenth century, or that devil-worship existed at all. Those who

1. 'Simples' were herbal remedies made from one or two plants—simple as opposed to the complex concoctions described on p. 16.

were persecuted were for the most part entirely innocent victims who had somehow upset a neighbour or became the scapegoat/sacrifice on whom all local problems were blamed. It was certainly not the case that most were wise old women healers. Some were attractive young women who had perhaps drawn wrath upon themselves by being indiscreet in their relationships with men. Others were the innocent children of those accused of witchcraft. It is as difficult for the rational mind to understand the mass slaughter of the 'burning years' that across Europe are estimated to have accounted for nine million deaths through the centuries, as it is to explain the more recent persecution of Jews or the civil war in Yugoslavia. For many of the victims, it seems their only 'crime' was to have been different from their neighbours.

Eighteenth Century Enlightenment

The last Scottish execution of a suspected witch was in 1727. Herbal medicine survived—of necessity, there being so few medical practitioners outside towns and cities. Two eighteenth century herbalists are described by David Rorie, who collected information on *Folk Tradition and Folk Medicine* during his work as a country doctor in the nineteenth century. George Buchan was a leech (bloodletter) but also treated people with ale brewed using herbs from his garden behind Inverugie Castle in Aberdeenshire until he died in 1738. Adam Donald

> *conducted an extensive business, not only as a doctor and herbalist, but as an exponent of the powers of divination. His ointments and medicines were prepared by himself from herbs gathered in the country, and it was firmly believed by the credulous that he could give an infallible remedy for every ailment under the sun...His usual consultation fee was sixpence.*[115]

Detailed information on plant uses was included in *Flora Scotica*, the work of an outstanding English botanist, John Lightfoot, published in 1777. Lightfoot was the travelling companion of his zoologist friend Thomas Pennant, whose work *A Tour in Scotland* is equally well known, and who paid for the publication of Lightfoot's book. Pennant insisted it should be in English, not Latin, to Lightfoot's disgust, because he feared this would appear unscientific. They were accompanied for a large part of the Scottish tour, made in the spring and summer of 1772, by John Stuart of Luss, Dumbartonshire, who supplied much of the information on Gaelic names and uses of plants that appeared in *Flora Scotica*.

Lightfoot was primarily interested in the plants themselves—their identification and distribution—and his work was a major contribution to Scottish botany. Since both he and Stuart would have been familiar with Martin's writings, it is difficult to ascertain to what extent the information on plant remedies in *Flora Scotica* was original, but the book certainly implies that traditions of plant use were thriving in Scotland towards the end of the eighteenth century. In that century, the first simple health—or rather disease—records began to be kept, showing that the major killer was 'consumption' (including other wasting diseases beside tuberculosis), 'fever' (mostly typhus), and smallpox.

The late eighteenth century also saw the beginning of the great expansion in tourism and travelling in Scotland, the time when Captain Cook was sailing the world with the naturalist Sir Joseph Banks, yet

> *To the southern inhabitants of Scotland, the state of the mountains and the islands is equally known with that of Borneo and Sumatra: of both they have only heard a little, and guess the rest.*
> (Samuel Johnson, *A Journey to the Western Islands of Scotland*)

Unfortunately the travellers, mostly wealthy gentlemen, recorded frustratingly little information on the use being made of wild plants; much of what they wrote was superficial impressions, often heavily laden with prejudice, intolerant and lacking any real understanding of the lives of the 'natives' they viewed as an exotic life form.

An exception was Patrick Neill, who made *A Tour Through Some of the Islands of Orkney and Shetland*, published in 1806. In Kirkwall, he examined the old garden of the late Dr Sutherland, who had studied under Boerhaave, a professor at the University of Leiden who taught practical rather than theoretical medicine to hundreds of Scottish students between 1709 and 1738. Sutherland had kept a physic garden, supplying the herbs he needed for his patients, and also collected from a glen known as the Guills of Scalpa, where Neill found the medicinal plants valerian (*Valeriana officinalis*), wild angelica (*Angelica sylvestris*), kidney vetch (*Anthyllis vulneraria*), purging flax (*Linum catharticum*), lady's smock (*Cardamine pratensis*), orchids (*Dactylorhiza* species), bogbean (*Menyanthes trifoliata*) and Scots lovage (*Ligusticum scoticum*).

Lady's Smock

In Dr Sutherland's time, it was possible to train as a physician in Scotland but still normal practice to go to the continent for further study; however, after Boerhaave died in 1738, Leiden became less attractive. By the end of the eighteenth century Edinburgh and Glasgow were the dominant medical schools in Britain: 87% of university-trained British medical practitioners between 1751 and 1800 were trained in Scotland, and Edinburgh was one of the foremost in Europe during that period. This great progress was part of the Scottish Enlightenment, a period of rapid intellectual and philosophical development that gave medicine high priority. However, as late as 1791, it was still possible to buy medical diplomas from Marischal College of the University of Aberdeen without any examination or interview, and these diplomas were accepted by the Royal College of Physicians in London.

Botany was important in the syllabus and physic gardens continued to be used to teach medical students about herbalism. The 1783 edition of the Edinburgh *Pharmacopoeia* included information on plant remedies based on scientific observation rather than the archaic recipes of the first edition in 1699. The Royal Infirmary, established in Edinburgh in 1741 with 228 beds, was considered enormous at the time and was designed to take patients from all over Scotland for teaching purposes. Other hospitals followed, giving seriously ill people who were not wealthy access to the best medical care of the time—but only if they were able to travel to hospital and be recommended for treatment by a subscriber who would pay their expenses, and also were not paupers (who had to go to the workhouse), servants or apprentices (who had to be treated at their master's home), infectious, incurable or pregnant.

Nineteenth Century Nemesis

It was a hundred years after Lightfoot when the next major contributor to plant lore visited the Gaelic speaking areas of Scotland. Alexander Carmichael, in his beautiful, six volume, bilingual (Gaelic and English) work *Carmina Gadelica* (Gaelic songs, hymns and incantations, published between 1900 and 1971), recorded a fascinating testimony to the survival not only of belief in the protective and healing powers of plants, but also of a deep reverence for and strong relationship with the natural world as part of daily life. He collected evidence of an unbroken tradition that can be traced back to the earliest Celtic church in Scotland, and the unique blend of Pagan and Christian belief that characterised the gradual, peaceful integration and assimilation of the new religion.

However in general the nineteenth century saw a regionalised decline in health and hygiene that left many people open to the ravages of disease and chronic illness. In cities, workers were crammed together in appalling living and working conditions to make the Industrial Revolution possible. Desperate conditions required desperate remedies; Rorie describes the 'earth cure', which can by a stretch be considered a herbal remedy, used by Fife miners suffering from the effects of poison gases in the nineteenth century:

> *a hole was dug out for the sufferer's face to lie over, and when sufficiently recovered to be put to bed, the divot of turf was laid on his pillow, so that, in his slumbers, the gentle breath of Mother Earth might still play around him.*[115]

22

In rural areas, whole communities were forcibly cleared from their ancestral lands and forced either to emigrate (where, if they survived the journey, further suffering as often as not awaited them) or to live in marginal areas where food could only be grown or gleaned with enormous, exhausting effort. Often the only work to be obtained was the heavy, damp collection and processing of seaweed for kelp (see pp. 49-51). Belated awareness of the inhuman conditions under which a large proportion of the population was living eventually led to improved medical care, hygiene and public health measures in the second half of the nineteenth century.

The Twentieth Century: Progress?

The twentieth century brought all the wonders of modern medicine and synthetic drugs, but it is of interest to note that around one third of medicines in the current pharmacopoeia contain plant extracts, and a further third is derived from compounds using synthesised versions of plant chemicals, so our dependence on herbal remedies continues. Increasingly, it is to wild plants that researchers are turning in desperate searches for remedies to treat the main ailments of our time, heart disease, cancer and AIDS.

Traditional remedies, still in daily use in many parts of Scotland earlier this century, have become the stuff of folklore: but fortunately, as this book shows, a great deal of information has been recorded. The current revival of interest in holistic health treatment, that seeks natural healing rather than wonder drugs wherever possible (without denying the immense value of life-saving modern medical intervention) will hopefully lead to recognition of the value of herbal remedies, used correctly under the supervision of a trained medical herbalist. Perhaps the next generation will not share the lament of Kate Ann Maclellan, born in Tigharry, North Uist, in 1933, who remembers her grandmother making herbal remedies:

I'm very sad that I don't know the names of any of these plants or anything about them. I'm sure they are there yet and the same things could be done with them. They were made into ointments and liquids...It's one thing I regret very much: that I didn't take more interest in those things I saw her doing.[90]

The Domestic Economy

When using archaeological evidence to attempt to reconstruct the everyday lives of ancient people, we are faced with two major problems. Firstly, most of our insights come from excavations of graves—useful information but unlikely to reflect accurately what was important to the living rather than the dead. Secondly, although it has always seemed highly likely that extensive use was made of plant materials, very few artefacts have survived.

However, a recent discovery is causing great excitement among archaeologists for the information it reveals about Stone Age life. In 1991, a 5,300 year-old corpse was found frozen into a glacier in the Alps between Italy and Austria. Research into this unique find will continue for many years and may provide some of the best evidence we can hope to have on the lives of prehistoric people living in Scotland. The great value of the Iceman is that he became deep-frozen and perfectly preserved accidentally, in the prime of life, and with all the equipment he carried on what was to be his last journey. It appears that he was overcome by a late autumn snowstorm while seeking refuge in the mountains above his village after an attack had taken place. An enthralling and informative account of the discovery and initial research, *The Man in the Ice*, has been written by Konrad Spindler.

The Iceman gives us a unique and fascinating insight into the resourcefulness of prehistoric people in making use of natural materials for all their needs. Although this man lived and died far from Scotland, we know from tracing trade routes that people of that time travelled widely throughout Europe; some of the sparse archaeological information we have from the same period in Scotland shows similarities with the culture to which the Iceman appears to have belonged. The Iceman was carrying items made from no less than sixteen species of tree, as shown in Table 1. Several of these species, or closely related ones, grew in Scotland at that time.

The Iceman's yew (*Taxus baccata*) axe handle is unique; similar ones found previously have been made of ash, oak or beech. His yew wood bow-stave was unfinished, but is typical of others found not only dating from prehistoric times, but for as long as bows continued to be made. In fact, many artefacts devised in ancient times changed very little until the Industrial Age. Yew is strong and elastic, therefore ideal for the purpose. Most of the arrows he carried had shafts made from shoots of the wayfaring tree, *Viburnum*, like one found in Aberdeenshire. A cord made from tree bast (fine strips of bark) which had been carefully stored in the quiver may have been destined for use as the bow string.

The wooden-framed backpack, made from larch and hazel, is in design remarkably similar to modern metal-framed ones. The beautiful birch bark containers were so fragile one was crushed in the clumsily managed rescue of this priceless find, but it must have been robust when made because one appears to have been used to carry live embers, wrapped in fresh leaves of Norway maple (*Acer platanoides*). The charcoal itself came from at least six different species of tree.

Bast (probably from lime, *Tilia* sp.) had been used to sew together the birch containers and other items, and to plait the fine scabbard, formed from a small mat which was folded and sewn with grass thread. A leather thong, threaded longitudinally through the scabbard, allowed it to be attached to the belt. This item is a unique find.

In his leather belt pouch (just like a modern 'bumbag') the Iceman carried various flint tools, including one that appears to have been used for cutting grass (see p. 26), and a black lump of the tree fungus *Fomes fomentarius*, known as the tinder fungus, parasitic on birch or, less commonly,

Tree	Scientific name	Part used by Iceman	Use
Alder	*Alnus viridis*	wood	fuel
Ash	*Fraxinus excelsior*	wood	dagger handle
Birch	*Betula* sp.	bark, sap	container, tar (glue)
Blackthorn	*Prunus spinosa*	fruit	food
Dogwood	*Cornus* sp.	wood (shoot)	arrow-shaft
Elm	*Ulmus* sp.	wood	fuel
Hazel	*Coryllus avellana*	wood (stem)	backpack frame, quiver bracing
Juniper	*Juniperus* sp.	needles	unknown
Larch	*Larix decidua*	wood	boards of backpack, fuel
Lime	*Tilia* sp.	wood (branch) bast	retouching tool, cord, binding material
Norway maple	*Acer platanoides*	leaves	insulating material
Norway spruce	*Picea abies*	wood, needles	fuel
Pine	*Pinus* sp.	wood	fuel
Wayfaring tree	*Viburnum lantana*	wood (shoot)	arrow-shaft
Willow	*Salix reticulata*	wood	fuel
Yew	*Taxus baccata*	wood	bow, axe-helve

Table 1: Trees used by Stone Age man found frozen in Alps [after Spindler, 1993]

beech. Until modern times, the fruiting part between the outer crust and the lower layer was commonly sliced, steeped in potassium or sodium nitrate, dried and then stored in this cotton-wool like state for use as tinder. Once the spark from pyrites or flint ignited the fungus, dried plant material (bog cotton, rushes, thistledown, willow bast, mosses, grass, twigs) or feathers were carefully added until the fire was established. Being able to make fire in any conditions was a skill on which life depended. Indeed, in the rain forests of central Africa and the highlands of New Guinea, twentieth century hunter-gatherers still carry embers wrapped in leaves so that fires for cooking food and warming themselves can quickly be started, even when, as is often the case, it is raining heavily.

The Iceman's equipment incorporated numerous pieces of string made from twisted grasses, used to tie or sew things together. He also wore or carried several items made of grass, including a net (perhaps for catching birds), shoes made from grass cord knotted into a net then stuffed with grass and covered with leather, and a grass cloak very similar to ones still being worn by shepherds in that area into the twentieth century. Very long grasses had been plaited then knotted in the top half of the knee-length garment and allowed to hang free below, producing a warm, water-resistant and camouflaging garment suitable for shepherds or hunters to wear by day and sleep in at night.

Finally, at least thirty species of moss have been found with the Iceman. Some of these were growing locally at the time but others came from lower altitudes. They may simply have been sticking to his clothing but it seems likely that some had been carried by the Iceman for a purpose. Pieces of the weft-forming mosses *Hylocomium splendens*, *Neckera complanata* and *N. crispa*, for example, may well have been used for packing and wiping purposes (like modern toilet paper and cotton wool), as they were throughout Europe, forming an important part of the economy in Swiss, German and Italian lakeside villages.

Five thousand years on, ethnobotanical studies of the Nitinaht people of Vancouver Island in Canada provide information on the plant use of a modern people living in a way which the Iceman might have found familiar. Many of the plants that grow there are closely related to Scottish species and the diversity of Nitinaht plant uses recorded in the 1970s and 80s reflects that which existed in Scotland until the twentieth century. As well as for food, medicine and magical purposes, plants were being used for:

- cord, binding twine, fishing lines, nets, sewing thread and needles
- masks, ceremonial outfits, face paints and dyes
- sling shots, fish and bird traps, barbecue sticks, digging sticks

- fuel, fire-drill and tinder
- baskets, bowls, plates, cups, containers and serving platters
- blankets, bedding, clothing, hats and mats
- glue, pitch, protective coating
- toys, balls, rattles, whistles, ornaments
- scent (to disguise the human smell of hunters), hairwash and soap
- ointment for softening hands
- wiping, wound dressings, towels, nappies and sanitary pads.[134]

We can compare this with a glimpse of late nineteenth century domestic life in Scotland that shows people meeting their needs with equal resourcefulness using local materials and wild plants. Alexander Carmichael in *Carmina Gadelica* described a winter's night around the fire in the house of a storyteller somewhere—anywhere—in the Highlands:

The houseman is twisting twigs of heather into ropes to hold down thatch, a neighbour crofter is twining quicken [rowan] rods into cords to tie cows, while another is plaiting bent grass into baskets to hold meal.

Wild plants, in fact, had a role to play in almost every aspect of daily life for countless generations of Scottish history.

Building

The first dwellings built in Scotland, by prehistoric nomads, would have been temporary shelters, perhaps circular tipi-like structures or maybe resembling the tents used by travelling folk within living memory, as described by storyteller Duncan Williamson. Their long, low tents were shaped like upturned boats so that wind could not lift the canvas off. Instead of canvas, Stone Age people used animal skins, branches, bark and turf, with clods of earth and stones to block holes, but the frame of bent saplings might have been the same. An experienced eye was needed to choose young trees of the right size and suppleness; birch or rowan saplings about 5 metres long were considered by Williamson's people to make the best tent poles, stuck about 20 cm into the ground, bent over and tied at the top in pairs.[140]

Other simple shelters may have resembled the tipi-like shieling huts on Jura described by Pennant in 1772:

[We landed] on a bank covered with sheelins, the inhabitations of some peasants who attend the herds of milch cows. These formed a grotesque group, many conic, and so low that entrance is forbidden, without creeping through the little opening, which has no other door than a faggot of

*birch twigs, placed there occasionally: they are constructed of branches
of trees covered with sods: the furniture a bed of heath, placed on a bank
of sod...above, certain pendant shelves, made of basket work, to hold the
cheese.[111]*

When people settled in an area, they built more permanent homes,
using whatever local materials were available. Wooden houses leave few
remains for the archaeologist but the arrangement, diameter and depth of
post holes give useful clues for the detective work on which so much of
our understanding about prehistoric times depends. Building styles varied
in different areas and at different times. The earliest houses, perhaps built
around 9,000 years ago, were probably circular, like those of the same
period excavated in Ireland from where some of Scotland's first settlers
almost certainly came. Circular houses were characteristic of the whole
Mesolithic (middle Stone Age) period and indeed the appearance of rectangular dwellings is one of the indicators of the gradual change to the
Neolithic period, although later people of the Iron Age built circular
homes once again.

Where wood was scarce, houses and even furniture were built of stone.
The Neolithic village of Skara Brae in Orkney has survived almost intact
to give us another extraordinary glimpse of life 5,000 to 4,500 years ago—
the site appears to have been occupied for about 500 years. The settlement
was apparently abandoned hurriedly, perhaps because of a storm that blew
in tons of sand and buried the seashore site, preserving it until 1850 when
another great storm blew the sand away and exposed some of the buildings, now excavated to reveal an entire village. The houses there were,
apart from the roof, entirely built and furnished in stone, with stone beds,
shelves and store cupboards. There is evidence that large timber may have
been available in that area from driftwood that had crossed the Atlantic;
fragments of spruce, a North American species, have been found at Skara
Brae, and it is estimated that 700 metres of dressed foreign timber was
used in the construction of later prehistoric buildings at Stanydale in
Shetland.[40] This suggests stone was used from choice.

Neolithic people were great builders of monuments; stone circles and
cairns have survived, but they also built massive wooden structures apparently for ceremonial or defensive use, such as the timber palisade across a
peninsula between two streams discovered at Meldon Bridge near Peebles.
Timber henges preceded stone circles in some areas; indeed the techniques used to construct some stone circles were clearly those of a
woodworker, such as the use of mortice and tenon joints. Unfortunately
this sequence is difficult to detect in excavations because the same holes
may have been used again or post holes been overlooked by archaeologists

concentrating on the impressive stone structures. Wooden chambers were also built inside burial mounds and may well have been carved as the stones often were, but nothing now remains.

In the Iron Age, defensive structures called crannogs were built in lochs in many areas of Scotland. These consisted of a raft of logs and branches, floated out across the marshy loch edge then anchored with a circular fence of wooden posts. Within this a round, thatched house about 15 metres diameter with light, woven wattle walls was built with a walkway around the outside. A narrow causeway gave access from the land, but could easily be defended from attack, while people and animals sheltered safely inside. Information from ten years of archaeological excavation of a crannog in Loch Tay in Perthshire has been used to build a replica in the loch near Kenmore, using authentic materials and techniques as far as is known. The main structure is built from alder logs cut from woods along the loch shore and held together with oak dowels. Hazel wattle forms the walls and the roof is thatched with reeds from the River Tay below the loch.

Houses on the Hebridean islands were built to withstand the elements and to economise on scarce timber, with low (less than two metres high) drystone walls two to three metres thick consisting of inner and outer faces of stone filled between with moss and turf. The roof timbers, undressed tree trunks, were supported by the inner walls, leaving a rampart around the tops of the walls where children played and cattle even grazed. This style of building continued into the twentieth century, and it is a common sight to find new 'kit' houses built beside the rapidly crumbling remains of old 'black houses'. Fortunately some are being restored as folk museums or simple hostels—and some, of course, are still lived in.

Where sufficient wood was available, the rafters were placed before the walls were built and sunk into the ground. Where they met and crossed at the apex, a long tree trunk was placed longitudinally, the roof-tree on which the whole structure and thatch depended. When a crofting family moved house, they took the precious roof timbers with them; when ruthless landlords cleared people from the land for sheep in the nineteenth century, they made sure to burn the roof, so the family was truly homeless.

In 1995, the five hundred year old roof of the Great Hall in Stirling Castle needed to be replaced. Around 350 oak trees, each 200 years old, were extracted from Bailefuil Wood near Strathyre using traditional 'snigging' methods with Clydesdale horses. The trees were trimmed into 10 metre logs to make roof beams using the peg and dowelling method developed by craftsmen in the fifteenth century. Although the source of the original roof timbers is not recorded, oak trees were growing and being coppiced in Bailefuil Wood when the Great Hall was built between 1488 and 1513.[35]

For many centuries, the very poorest dwellings were simply built from stacked turf and in all areas turf sods were cut to cover the roof like tiles, often pinned together with willow. This was usually then thatched with bundles of heather, broom or grass, but a great variety of plants were used according to local availability and individual preference. Other thatching materials included bracken, straw, marram grass, rushes and yellow iris. A song collected by Willie Mitchell, *The Thatchers of Glenrea*, was written by an Irish labourer working in Argyll and passed around the Mull of Kintyre; in a mixture of Scots and Irish dialect, it ran:

> *I can theek wi' ould rashes, wi' heather or ling,*
> *Bent, bracken, or dockens or any wan thing.*[65]

Bent grass (*Agrostis* species), commonly used for thatch on more exposed parts of the West coast, had to be replaced annually and therefore was simply raked into place. Before the innovation of fireplaces and chimneys, smoke from the central hearth—in a firepit or on a stone slab—simply drifted up through the roof (hence the name 'black house'—the interior became coated in soot, as did the older inhabitants!). It was usual to remove the thatch once a year to spread on the fields as rich fertiliser, neighbours working together so each roof could be removed and replaced in a day. The thatch was tied down with ropes, often made from heather, and weighted with stones. In the more prosperous lowlands, where it was common to plaster houses with clay, some cottars and farm labourers could afford to buy dressed timber for rafters and wooden slabs from the nearest sawmill to support the turf and thatch roof.

House Interiors

In most areas it was unusual to lock houses at any time, a tradition that survives in many remoter parts of Scotland to this day. If the family was away for any length of time, the house door might be locked and the key left hanging from a nail in the wall. Nevertheless, Highland locksmiths used to make ingenious wooden locks, with wooden keys.

For centuries most rural houses had only one room, the family living space being separated from the animals' end by a wooden partition or a wattle screen woven from hazel. Furniture was usually home-made and basic: box beds filled with ferns, straw, feathers or bundles of heather crammed in upright to make a springy but scratchy mattress (see p. 107); stools or benches to sit on, chests to store clothes and food, perhaps a dresser with shelves, cupboards and drawers in more wealthy houses. The floor was beaten earth, sometimes covered with clay, more usually just strewn with rushes that could be swept out occasionally with all the debris, using brushes or besoms made from broom or heather. Examples of these homes have been restored as folk museums throughout the Highlands and Islands.

Summer shielings or bothies remained simple structures but graduated from the rough tents described by Pennant to more solid, turf-covered, stone built bothies, that nevertheless still required restoration work at the start of each season of occupation, in particular to repair the thatch and clean out the debris that always accumulated over the winter.[1] Often half the hut would be the sleeping area, separated from the living area by a row of kerb stones or a wooden board, making a bed space to be filled with turf, then heather. In the other half, there might also be a seating area of piled up peats near the fire.

Later, in the nineteenth and twentieth centuries, wooden floors were laid down. In his autobiography Finlay J. MacDonald recalls the laborious business of keeping them clean. As a boy it was his job to collect *mealtrach*,

> *the very fine roots of the marram grass[2] which mat loosely together and fringe the under edges of the wind-blown sand cliffs of the sea shore like pubic hair peeping out from an incautious bathing costume. Every Saturday in life, till blessed linoleum came along, I had to forage along the sea cliffs and collect a sackful of* mealtrach *and carry it home, and then, from the same source, ferry innumerable pails of fine white sand. Then, on the Saturday evening, my mother would scrub the wooden floor with carbolic soap, using the* mealtrach *as a scourer, and before the floor was dry she would cover it liberally with sand. Just before bedtime she would brush off the sand, leaving the wooden floor pristine white for the Sabbath. Woe betide the person who left nature's last call to 'the pee-tub' unanswered till after the sand had been swept![78]*

Inside the windowless house it was dark, the fire providing the sole or main source of light. Simple lights were made from wicks of stripped rushes dipped in fish oil or animal fat (see p. 125). Resinous pine roots, usually collected from bogs that had encroached the sites of ancient forests, were valued as torch lights (see p. 64).

Fuel

Firelighting methods have already been described with reference to the Iceman (pp. 25-26). Once the tinder was alight, fuel was added: peat, turf, heather, gorse and whatever wood could be found. When peat banks became exhausted in certain areas, such as Angus in the late seventeenth century, stripping turf denuded the land of precious topsoil. At that time

1. See, for example, descriptions in *Island Going* by Robert Atkinson of how quickly shielings deteriorated when left for just a year.
2. *Ammophila arenaria*

common land was being enclosed, depriving villagers of access to areas where they had collected turf, whin, heather and twigs. People then had to buy peat and wood by the cartload, and bundles of 'white cows'—weather-bleached stalks of heather, whin or broom gathered after the annual muir burning.

The fire was never willingly allowed to go out; a skilled housewife carefully banked the peats before going to bed so that next morning she just had to blow to get flames to heat the morning meal. Many prayers and invocations to be said when smooring the fire at night have been recorded from Gaelic speaking areas; the well-being of the family centred around hearth, not just for warmth and cooking, but as a symbol of survival and continuity.

> *I will smoor the hearth*
> *As Brigit the Foster-mother would smoor.*
> *The Foster-mother's holy name*
> *Be on the hearth, be on the herd,*
> *Be on the household all.*[23]

Peat was also used to make charcoal. The technique recorded on Jura was to drop red hot peats into a chamber about 70 cm diameter; when full it was covered with turf sods to exclude air. This produced charcoal for blacksmiths which was nearly as good as coal.

Household Goods

> *Choose the willow of the streams,*
> *Choose the hazel of the rocks,*
> *Choose the alder of the marshes,*
> *Choose the birch of the waterfalls.*
>
> *Choose the ash of the shade,*
> *Choose the yew of resilience,*
> *Choose the elm of the brae,*
> *Choose the oak of the sun.*
> (from *Carmina Gadelica* by Alexander Carmichael)

Furniture, dishes, containers, brushes, tools, spinning wheels—many household goods were of necessity home-made from locally available materials. Where wood did not grow, as on the Outer Isles, driftwood was used. Where there was no willow, other materials were used for basket making (see p. 33). Great resourcefulness was displayed; most items were made to last several generations and did so.

The shortwood in the glens is worked into various useful articles, and disposed of in the low country. In the month of August there is a timber market held in Aberdeen for several days, which is of ancient origin, and to which the Highlanders bring ladders, harrows, tubs, pails, and many other articles; those who have nothing else, bring rods of hazel and other young wood, with sackfuls of aitnach or juniper and other mountain berries.[76]

Alexander Ross also described nineteenth century Highlanders from the glens taking long trains of carts, sometimes as many as forty tied in a row, to markets in Dundee, Inverness and Aberdeen. There they sold wooden utensils such as bowls, cups, ladles, buckets, tubs, walking sticks and bread platters. Occasionally finely carved walking sticks, shepherds' crooks or dirk handles were for sale. All this was the produce of long winter months and they returned home carrying luxuries from the lowlands.[116]

There were superstitions governing the use of wood, perhaps based on experience. In the Western Isles, Carmichael was told by Mr Robertson of Eigg,

Neither would they cut withes of hazel or willow for creels or baskets, nor would they cut tree of pine to make a boat, in the black wane of the moon. The sap of the wood goes down into the root, and the wood becomes brittle and crumbly, without pith, without good. The old people did all these things at the waxing or at the full of the moon.[23]

Basket Making

From ancient times, baskets of many shapes, sizes and materials were made for every conceivable domestic use. They varied from crude baskets quickly woven for temporary use to finely-made durable creations that, with care, lasted centuries. Remains of a heavy-duty basket found in a Shetland bog have been estimated by specialists at the Royal Museum of Scotland to be around 1,500 years old, and it appears to have been made from willow using the same stake-and-strand method Scottish basket makers use today.

Most people probably knew the basics of basket-making, but specialists in the craft supplied local needs and traded, even to the continent. Some of these were travelling folk, who gathered hedgerow materials as they went; others planted and grew their own willows. A long-established basket making business was carried on in Skye until the 1960s and attempts are now being made to revive it.

Most baskets are worked from the base up the sides to the rim; some styles require another approach.

The plan adopted in making the fish creel and peat basket in Jura was to stick a row of hazel or willow the size of the intended basket into the turf, and then plait the withies round them, gradually reducing the diameter of the basket, as required, until the crown was closed in.[116]

In nineteenth century Inverness, wickerwork carts or sleighs called lupins, pulled by Shetland ponies, were a common sight on the streets.

The lupin, or basket, was in the form of an inverted cone, dropped into a frame with shafts to yoke the horse in; in rough hill ground the shafts were extended to form sliders behind, but on the roads solid wheels were fixed on axles, and took the place of sliders.[116]

Where other materials suitable for basket making were unavailable, ingenious inhabitants tried anything, including ragwort (*Senecio jacobaea*) stems and grass. Various containers were made of bent grass (*Agrostis* species) using skilful coiling techniques found throughout the world (and currently being revived by members of the Scottish Basketmakers Circle). The use of straw was widespread, especially where few woody plants grew, e.g. in the Orkneys and Hebridean islands. Although a cultivated rather than a wild plant, therefore strictly speaking outwith the scope of this book, it is interesting to consider this use of a natural resource as a substitute for wild plants, rather than the reverse.

I have seen seventeen basketsful of eggs taken at one time from Stachbiarrach, and at another time the same season fourteen. These baskets hold each about four hundred of these eggs. As no wood of any kind grows on the island, these so-called baskets are made entirely of straw. They resemble large flat-bottomed bee-hives, but they are not constructed in the same way. No string or fibre is used. The straw is twisted into ropes and woven into shape. They are used for a variety of purposes, and are wonderfully strong and durable. Sacks for storing grain and feathers are also made in this way. For them the straw is twisted into much thinner ropes, and they are put together so that they are quite flexible. The making of straw ropes for these purposes, and for binding down the thatch on their houses, occupies much of the time of the men during the winter evenings.

(from *Episodes in the Life of the Reverend Neil MacKenzie at St. Kilda* by J.B. MacKenzie)

There has recently been a significant revival of interest in basket making in Scotland. The Scottish Basketmakers Circle has an increasing membership, some of whom are growing their own willow as well as experimenting with other materials, e.g. rushes, oak strips and stuff from hedgerows. Basket designs are being copied from old examples, photos and sketches, and the traditions look set to survive.

Rope

Rope was made from a variety of plant materials, including heather (see p. 105) and seaweed (see p. 49). Patrick Neill visited Orkney in 1806 and noted several kinds of rope:

> *At Deerness we saw very strong ropes, calculated for different purposes in husbandry, made of the shoots of the crowberry heath (*Empetrum nigrum*). The ropes for hanging the caseys or baskets over the horses' backs, were made of the fibrous roots of sea-reed (*Arundo arenaria[1]*). Tethers and bridle-reins were wrought of long meadow grasses, such as* Holcus lanatus, *which grasses here receive the name of* pounce, *or* puns.[106]

The Game of Shinty

The game of shinty made ingenious use of natural materials, as described by Hugh MacKinnon from the isle of Eigg.[86] The ball was made from a lump of hazel root, whittled with a knife then smoothed with a rasp or file. It was boiled in a pot of water over a fire to toughen it so it would not split when hit. The caman (shinty stick) was cut in the woods from hazel, oak, willow, birch or anything suitable. Birch was light but easily broken; oak was hard, strong and long-lasting but gave a 'sting' to the batsman's hands when the ball was hit.

The caman was whittled into shape; elm often had a natural bend in the wood already but other kinds had to be artificially bent. The bend was placed about a quarter of the way along the 130 cm long stick. The heavy lower end was put in a peat fire, care being taken not to burn the wood or it would split while it was in the clamp. It was left in a clamp for three days, after which the caman would keep its shape. Oak and elm bent nicely but hazel was difficult to work.

Green Manure

Of vital importance in the domestic economy was the use of green manure of various kinds, including thistles, ferns, ragwort and many other plants, collected fresh and left in heaps covered with earth until well-rotted. Seaweed was most commonly used in coastal areas, even carted several miles inland where possible, valued for its high nutrient content and the fine structure it imparted to the soil. In many marginal areas, especially those onto which people were forced during the Clearances, it was only

1. *Ammophila arenaria*

possible to cultivate at all by using seaweed with the thin soil to build up ridges, creating the characteristic ridge and furrow patterns still visible in many areas of the Highlands and Islands, testimony to the desperation, tenacity and capacity for hard work of those people.

Animal husbandry

Rearing livestock was, of course, until modern times, based almost totally on the use of wild plants and seaweed as fodder; growing fodder crops and 'improved' pastures never accounted for a high proportion of animal feed in Scotland. In addition, magical plants were employed to protect the animals from harm. Milk production, before refrigeration and pasteurisation, was particularly vulnerable and malevolent people occasionally fed their neighbours' cows on plants known to prevent the milk from turning into butter, such as mint, or to reduce yield, such as horsetail or sorrel.

Many different plants are mentioned as being good fodder in pre-twentieth century writing quoted elsewhere in this account. Neill, writing about Orkney early in the nineteenth century, will be allowed the last word on the subject here.

> *Any thing is thought good enough for the staigs and the stirks* [year old horses and young oxen respectively]...*The Loch of Aikerness has been nearly drained with the view of getting at the luxuriant but coarse aquatic grasses with which it abounds. I shall perhaps scarcely gain credit when I say, that great quantities of* Carex ampullacea,[1] *and of* Typha latifolia, *with a small proportion of* Holcus lanatus, *were here carefully gathered and dried, and denominated meadow hay. None but the half-starved beasts of Orkney would eat such fodder. It is to be mentioned with regret, that though several of the sweetest and best pasture-grasses are natives of all the islands (for example,* Festuca duriuscula,[2] *F. rubra, F. eliator,[3] Poa trivialis, P. pratensis; and* Alopecurus pratensis), *yet no attempt has hitherto been made to cultivate any of them.*[106]

1. *Carex rostrata*
2. *F. lemanii*
3. *F. pratensis*

Textiles

Every colour imaginable could be obtained from a common vegetable source, and the tweeds from particular districts could be fairly accurately identified from the proliferation of plants native to these parts. In our area, which had been the heartland of the Harris Tweed industry when it became formally established as a craft, there was a wealth of colour to be distilled from nature because of the lush growth on machair and on moor. And every girl, up to my mother's generation at least, had to know exactly which colour each plant provided when it was boiled with a fleece.

(From *Crowdie and Cream* by Finlay J. MacDonald)

Sadly, in travelling the length of the Outer Isles and Inner Hebrides, I have not been able to find any evidence of continuous routine use of dyes from wild plants, only vibrant memories and a few hanks of wool, a few knitted garments for sale to tourists. However, the many different plants and recipes used in dyeing are increasingly well documented and there is now considerable interest in preserving and reviving these traditions, producing wool and fabric in subtle, attractive, long-lasting hues that have great appeal in these days of mass-production and standardisation.

For important conservation reasons, it is not now possible to collect most species of plants in the quantites required for dyeing, and it is totally unacceptable to uproot plants or pick rare flowers. However, many can be grown in the garden, or care can be taken only to use small amounts of common species that are abundant. Lichens, which are extremely slow growing and increasingly endangered by air pollution, should never be picked.

There is of course far more to the use of plants in textile manufacture than dyeing: many fabrics are woven from plant fibres, using tools made from plants. For example, fine, durable linen was woven from nettle fibres (see pp. 172, 173), possibly from prehistoric times, and certainly until the use of flax and later cotton became widespread in the eighteenth century. In general, there is not a great deal of archaeological or documentary evidence to provide a detailed picture of the manufacture or appearance of Scottish textiles before the eighteenth century, but the important role of plants is undisputed.

Virtually every home had simple equipment made from local trees and plants for spinning and weaving. The best shuttles were made from birch or yew, bobbins were sometimes made from cow parsley stalks, and reeds or marram grass were used to make combs to space the warp and beat the weft into place. It is perhaps the very ordinary nature of such women's work, using local materials to produce useful, everyday fabrics and garments that were worn or used until they fell to pieces, that accounts for the lack of information on the subject. There also appears to have been some secrecy arising from competitiveness surrounding the 'recipes' for dyeing; some methods were never written down, or the information was deliberately destroyed.

Scotland is of course virtually synonymous with tartan—finely woven woollen cloth with checked patterns in many combinations of colours; the myths and misapprehensions around the subject require and have books of their own. The Romans referred to British Celts wearing mantles with small squares in many colours; the earliest known tartan was found with Roman coins dating from AD 250. There is evidence of early Scots' love of strong, bright colours, although the Scottish flora mainly produces pale greys, tans and yellows. Some of the earliest trade routes carried significant quantities of dye substances unavailable in Scotland such as indigo, cochineal and madder, to enable dyers to obtain brighter blues and reds. Adding rowan (*Sorbus aucuparius*) berries to madder or cochineal gave even brighter colours. Fields of madder *(Rubia tinctorum)* were grown around Aberlady to supply commercial dyers in Haddington with the quantities they required.

Little is known about the dyeing process before the seventeenth century, when woollen fabric became more common than linen woven from flax. Some of the most significant archaeological information comes from excavations of a twelfth century site in Perth, where a concentration of possible dye plants has been identified suggesting that it may have been a dyer's workshop. They include shoots of alpine clubmoss (*Diaphasiastrum alpinum*) and stag's-horn clubmoss (*Lycopodium clavatum*), heather (*Calluna vulgaris*) shoot tips and flowers, weld (*Reseda luteola*), slivers of bark from birch (*Betula* species), seeds of tormentil (*Potentilla erecta*) and fragments of bracken (*Pteridium aquilinum*).[109]

Long summer days were the time for collecting dye plants; the colours obtained depended on many variables including where the plant grew (location, soil type, availability of light and water), the season, time of day and maturity of the plant when collected. Then there had to be taken into account the material being dyed, the kind of dye pot and amount of dye available, the type of water and length of time for which it was boiled, and the mordant (fixing agent) used.

Many women had extensive and detailed knowledge of all these factors, accumulated over the generations. However, with so many variables, predictable and reproducible results were difficult to achieve, so it made sense to use the limited amounts of each colour available to weave intricate checked patterns that would usually be unique to that length of cloth.

Each weaver may well have had her particular favourite combinations of colours and patterns and have prided herself on producing distinctive cloth. It would only have been possible to manufacture identifiable family tartans much later, when quantities of dyestuff and mordants to fix the exact shade required were available for purchase by professional weavers—i.e. not until the eighteenth century in some areas, and much later in others. Imported dyes were being widely used in the Islands by the 1890s, when certain philanthropists tried to re-establish home industries such as weaving that had virtually disappeared after new technology, introduced from the mid-eighteenth century, made domestic production uneconomic.

In the domestic setting of the seventeenth to nineteenth centuries, dyeing was also usually a summer occupation, using the freshly gathered dye plants at the time when fleeces were available from the newly sheared sheep. It is still possible to find old cauldrons on the banks of streams beside abandoned croft houses in remoter areas such as the Outer Hebrides; dyeing was best done outdoors and it was easiest to carry the pot and wool to the water and build up a peat fire beside the stream.

In 1895, Alexander Ross made 'as complete a list of native plants used for dyes as I have been able to procure' (see Table 2, p. 41), observing that 'the dyeing was a matter which gave scope for much ingenuity...Many of the colours were extremely bright and pretty'. He made detailed notes on the process:

I saw a dye being made as follows in the island of Jura. A large pot was filled with alder leaves and twigs from which a black dye was prepared by a simple infusion like tea, and the colour was made fast by the addition of logwood and copperas.[1] The process of dyeing with vegetable home dyes was to wash the thread thoroughly in lye[2] (Gaelic, maighstir*), to rinse and wash it in pure water, and then put it into the pot of dye, which was kept hard boiling on the fire. The thread was occasionally lifted out of the pot on the point of a stick, and plunged back again till thoroughly dyed. If blue, the thread was washed in salt water; any other colour in fresh. The yarn was then hung out to air, and when dry gathered into balls or clews, when it was ready for the weaver's loom. A mode of introducing intermittent colours, which enabled the weaver to produce a pattern without difficulty, was carried out by tying the hank of yarn tightly, at intervals, with a piece of thread or twine. (Some said the inner bark of the Elm was more efficacious; others that any string would prevent the dye reaching the wool).[116]*

1. Copperas is iron (ferrous sulphate); the same mordant effect was often obtained simply by using an iron pot for the dyeing.
2. Lye is an alkaline washing solution made by adding vegetable ashes to water.

In summer, wool was usually dyed in the fleece. Although this meant extra work, because the lanolin had to be removed for dyeing then replaced by fish oil for spinning, it had several advantages over the alternative of dyeing spun yarn: it resulted in deeper, brighter, more even colours, that could also be blended into other shades during carding; and the work could be completed before the fleece was stored, leaving the time-consuming processes of carding, spinning and weaving to occupy winter days when outdoor work was impossible. Also, fleece-dyed wool undergoes most shrinkage after it is woven, in the waulking process, so that weaving is easier and the finished product is tighter, more hard-wearing cloth.

Finlay MacDonald evocatively describes the dyeing process, remembered from his childhood.

> *Crotal was the grey lichen which, over hundreds of years, had grown over the moorland rocks...In the summer it ripened and, at the same time as the wool began to rise from the sheep ready for shearing, the grey crotal eased itself off the mother rock. That was when the women went for it, equipped only with an old soup spoon off which one corner had been filed to leave it with a scraping edge and a sharp point to get into the crevices...Each croft wife had a huge three legged pot, capable of taking two or three fleeces...First a layer of washed fleece, then a good thick sprinkling of crotal, another layer of fleece and another layer of crotal and so on, tier upon tier, till the pot was almost full, leaving just room for water. The whole cauldron was then boiled for several hours with the addition of only extra water to keep it from boiling dry and one handful of common sorrel to fasten the dye. At the end of the day the fleeces were a rich dark red and they were tipped into the river for the flowing water to take away waste red liquid and the lichen, which was now bleached white, having surrendered its colour.*[78]

Most dye plants went straight into the pot in layers with the wool but tougher roots and bark were crushed or chopped. The most common mordant was urine; the 'pee-tub' was a common sight outside every house and it was considered courteous after taking refreshment with a household to use the tub before departure. Dock leaves were also used to brighten and deepen colours, sometimes wrapped around a paste of the dye stuff mixed with urine. The boiling time varied from only ten minutes with some flowers to three hours with gorse bark and six when using oak bark. After boiling, the mix might be left to stew for days or even weeks. The characteristic smell of true Harris tweed is a combination of wool, dye stuff (mostly crotal lichen) and urine!

The current revival of interest in traditional dyeing techniques has led to increasing experimentation with wild plants, especially to develop dyes

Colour	Common name	Botanical name	Gaelic name[1]
Black	flag iris root	*Iris pseudacorus*	*seilisdear*
	alder (with copperas)	*Alnus glutinosa*	*fearna*
	dock root	*Rumex* species	*copaig*
	oak bark and acorns	*Quercus* species	*darach*
Brown	crottle	*Parmelia saxatilis*	*crotal*
	yellow wall lichen	*Parmelia parietina*	*crotal buidh*
	dark crottle	*Parmelia ceratophylla*	*crotal dubg*
	dulse	*Rhodymenia edulis*	*duiliasg*
Dark brown	blaeberry (with nut galls)	*Vaccinium myrtillus*	*lus nan dearc*
	redcurrant (with alum)	*Ribes rubrum*	*raosar dearc*
	water-lily root	*Nymphaea alba*	*cairt-an-loch*
Fawn	birch bark	*Betula* species	*beatha*
Blue	blaeberry (with copperas)	*Vaccinium myrtillus*	*lus nan dearc*
	elder (with alum)	*Sambucus nigra*	*druman*
Blue-black	sloe	*Prunus spinosa*	*preas nan airnaig*
	red bearberry	*Arctostaphylos uva-ursi*	*grainnseag*
Dark green	heath (pulled just before flowering from a dark, shady place)	*Erica cinerea*	*fraoch-bhadain*
	whin/furze bark	*Ulex europaeus*	*ruisg conasg*
Green	flag iris leaf	*Iris pseudacorus*	*seilisdear*
Lively green	weld (with indigo)	*Reseda luteola*	*lus buidhe mor*
Purple	blaeberry (with alum)	*Vaccinium myrtillus*	*lus nan dearc*
	sundew	*Drosera rotundifolia*	*lus na fearnaich*
Violet	water cress	*Rorippa nasturtium-aquaticum*	*biolair*
	vetch	*Vicia orobus*[2]	*cairmeal*
Red	rock lichen	*Ramalina scopulorum*	*crotal*
	white crottle	*Lecanora pallescens*	*crotal geal*
	blaeberry (with verdigris and sal ammonia)	*Vaccinium myrtillus*	*lus nan dearc*
Bright red	lady's bedstraw	*Galium verum*	*bun-an-ruadh*
	tormentil	*Potentilla erecta*	*leanartach*
Scarlet	crottle corkir (white; ground and mixed with urine)	*Lecanora tartarea*	*crotal*
	limestone lichen	*Urceolaria calcarea*	*crotal clachaoil*
Yellow	crab apple	*Malus sylvestris*	
	ash	*Fraxinus excelsior*	
	aspen	*Populus tremula*	
	elm	*Ulmus glabra*	
	bog myrtle	*Myrica gale*	*rideag*
	ash root	*Fraxinus excelsior*	*craob-uinnseann*
	bracken root	*Pterdium aquilinum*	*an raineach mhor*
Bright yellow	St John's wort	*Hypericum perforatum*	*caod aslachan colum chille*
	sundew (with ammonia)	*Drosera rotundifolia*	*lus na fearnaich*
Orange	ragwort (stinking willie)	*Senecio jacobaea*	*buadhlan*
	barberry root	*Berberis vulgaris*	*barbrag*
Dark orange	bramble	*Rubus fruticosus*	*dreas-smeur*
Magenta	dandelion	*Taraxacum* species	*bearnan bride*

Table 2: based on Ross 1895,[3] *'as complete a list of native plants used for dyes as I have been able to procure'*

1. Some of the Gaelic names given by Ross vary from those used by others for the same plants. 2. This species is rare in Scotland. The name *cairmeal* also applies to *Lathyrus linifolius*. Su Grierson found that closely related *L. pratensis* (Gaelic *peasair bhuidhe*) dyed yellow. 3. Note: some non-native plants have been excluded and botanical names have been updated.

for wool that will withstand machine washing with modern soap powders. For example, Lynn Ross on the island of Arran has experimented with numerous local plants. Her list includes heath and heather (*Erica cinerea* and *Calluna vulgaris*), nettle *(Urtica dioica)*, birch (*Betula* species) leaves, flag iris (*Iris pseudacorus*), elder berries (*Sambucus nigra*), dandelions (*Taraxacum* species), St John's wort (*Hypericum perforatum*), ragwort (*Senecio jacobaea*), broom (*Cytisus scoparius*), wood sorrel (*Oxalis acetosella*) and the mushrooms *Hydrophorus coccineus* and *Paxillus involutus*.

Members of the Spinners, Weavers and Dyers Guild throughout Scotland are also experimenting with a wide range of plants (see, for example, p. 44) and the Royal Highland Show held near Edinburgh each year encourages this with a competition category for natural plant dyes. Much of the information on dyes recorded in *The Scots Herbal* is of historical rather than practical interest; Su Grierson has pioneered extensive testing and improving of the old recipes, and one can do no better than refer readers to her book, *The Colour Cauldron*.[60]

PART TWO: THE PLANT FAMILIES

Fungi
MUSHROOMS AND TOADSTOOLS

There is a noticeable contrast in the attitude towards fungi in the southern, eastern and French parts of Europe compared with the northern, Germanic and Celtic areas. Despite the number of delicious edible species that grow in Scotland, we are curiously reluctant to use mushrooms for any purpose. It has been suggested that this antipathy may date back to the shamanic use of hallucinogenic species in prehistoric times, when they were a powerful tool reserved for the initiated, strictly taboo for the rest of the tribe except under special circumstances. Perhaps this taboo then gradually extended to all fungal species, and despite (or perhaps because of?) the decline in use of hallucinogenic mushrooms under Christianity, fear of mushrooms has persisted to the present day.[58,108]

This appears to be changing, however, with more varieties available in supermarkets, television series extolling the virtues of wild fungi and gourmet mushroom dishes on the menu in many restaurants. Chanterelles (*Cantharellus cibarius*) are picked commercially from parts of Aberdeenshire, and magic mushrooms (*Psilocybe semilanceata*) are collected for their hallucinogenic properties in many parts of Scotland (also, see p. 9).

Very few historical records exist, though it is likely various species were used for at least some of the purposes to which they have been put elsewhere, including food, medicines, dyeing, tinder, dried strips for sharpening arrow heads and razors, even teased out and beaten to form a shammy leather-like material made into caps, aprons or small purses.[34]

One clue to possible uses in Scotland is the discovery of a few dried puffballs (*Bovista nigrescens*) in the Neolithic settlement of Skara Brae in Orkney. They may simply have been stored for plugging holes in leaking thatch, or dried for tinder; or they may have been kept to treat wounds. The spores contained in the cotton-wool-like inside of puffballs have styptic (blood-clotting) properties, making them useful as a wound dressing; or smouldering puff-balls could have been used to cauterise a wound. Indigenous Vancouver Islanders still use puffballs medicinally, to heal leg sores and check bleeding. The spores have also been used as a diuretic.[6,30,34,134]

In Gaelic, according to Mary Beith, puffballs are known as *balg smuid*, smoke bag,

> balg peitach bocan, *the goblin's music bag and* bochdan-bearrach,
> *perhaps the shaven or crop-headed goblin? There's more than a hint*

there of old associations with the magical and the mysterious.[6]

Giant puffballs (*Langermania gigantea*) arrived in Scotland later, after farming had created the well-manured ploughed fields that are their preferred habitat. Mary Beith believes the Gaelic name *beac* or *beacan*, derived from *beach*, a bee, suggests that in Scotland as elsewhere, smoke from burning these fungi was used to stupefy bees so that honey could be collected.

Chris Simpson makes paper from mushrooms, by soaking and liquidising the fungi then pressing the pulp into thin layers using a paper-making mould and deckle. The most suitable species are woody bracket fungi that grow on trees. Each species produces paper of a particular colour and texture, but they can be combined. Common Scottish species that she uses are listed in Table 3.

Members of the Spinners, Weavers and Dyers Guild in Scotland have been experimenting with the use of fungi for dyeing, with some very promising results (Table 4).

Species	common name	paper colour	texture of paper
Coriolus versicolor	many-zoned polypore	buff	smooth
Ganoderma adspersum		brown	textured
Laetiporus sulphureus	sulphur polypore	yellow	fine
Piptoporus betulinus	birch polypore	white	fine
Polyporus squamosus	dryad's saddle	creamy	textured

Table 3: Fungi species suitable for paper-making.[121]

Species	Colour obtained
Boletus species	lemon, olive
Cortinarius subgenus *Dermocybe*	red, yellow
Inonotus hispidus	yellow, gold
Paxillus atrotomentosus	blue, purple, green
P. involutus	brown, gold
Phaeolus schweinitzii	yellow, green

Table 4: Fungi species used for dyeing yarn.[121]

Lichens

Few records have been found for uses of lichens apart from dyeing, for which they were well known in Scotland (see **Crotal** below). Lichens are edible; in other north European countries they have been used as animal fodder (reindeer in Scandinavia being the most obvious example) and even food for humans in lean years. Boiling lichens in an alkaline solution, easily made by adding wood-ash to the water, removed the bitter taste; the boiled lichens were then dried and ground into flour to add to grain flour, soup or stews. Iceland moss (*Cetraria islandica*) was commonly eaten in this way in Scandinavia and Iceland. The nineteenth century Arctic explorer John Franklin survived eleven days on boiled lichens alone.[34, 55]

Medicinally, various species have been used in Britain and almost certainly in Scotland, according to the 'Doctrine of Signatures', in which the appearance of the plant was used to indicate the disorder which it would heal. Thus hair-like old man's beard (*Usnea* species) was recommended for problems with the hair and scalp; tree lungwort or oak lung (*Lobaria pulmonaria*) for chest complaints, and the orange-yellow coloured lichen *Xanthoria parietina* for jaundice (see p. 47). Other species were used for their purgative and astringent properties in tonics and to treat rabies, fever, diarrhoea and skin complaints.[34]

Crotal and corcur

Crotal (or crottle) is used as a general Scottish name for more than forty kinds of lichen used in dyeing, especially of wool for tweed. Strictly speaking the word refers to the red/brown dyes obtained, rather than the lichen itself. Corcur (or Korkir), on the other hand, is the name for purple dyes obtained from lichen. Lichens growing on stones were said to yield better dye than those on trees. Lichen dyes require no mordant; some are simply boiled with the yarn, others are soaked first in ammoniacal liquid—traditionally putrid urine. The characteristic smell of Harris tweed, as noted on p. 40, was a rich combination produced by wool, lichen and urine together, and the use of lichen dyes was said to leave the wool moth-proof. The traditional dyeing process is described on pp. 37-42. A detailed account of dyeing with lichens is given by Su Grierson in *The Colour Cauldron*.[52,60]

Fishermen wearing crotal-dyed clothes had also to wear blue for protection;[1] there was a widely held belief that something plucked from the rocks must return to the rocks. Powdered crotal worn in the soles of stockings was said to protect the feet from inflammation on long journeys.[52]

---

1. In general, red was the colour of protection, but it is obvious why fishermen would choose blue.

Corcur, cudbear
*Ochrolechia tartarea (*syn. *Lecanora tartarea),*
O. androgyna

LOCAL NAMES: Korkir, korkalett (Shet)

Martin reported that on Skye,

> *The stones on which the scurf called corkir grows are to be had in many places on the coast, and in the hills. This scurf dyes a pretty crimson colour; first well dried, and then ground to a powder, after which it is steeped in urine, the vessel being well secured from air; and in three weeks it is ready to boil with the yarn that is to be dyed. The natives observe the decrease of the moon for scraping this scurf from the stone, and say it is ripest in August.*[100]

This is a common lichen in the Western Isles, used since ancient times to dye wool shades of red to purple. The name *cudbear* is said to be derived from the name of Dr Cuthbert Gordon, who with his brother George pioneered commercial use of the lichen, starting at a dye-works in Leith in 1758, but moving to Glasgow in 1777.[34,125]

With the commerical production of cudbear, which required fourteen days soaking in 'spirit of urine', the latter became a valuable source of income for people living near the works. Unfortunately, while urine is a renewable resource, lichen is not. In the late 1700s and early 1800s, collectors of this very slow growing species were being paid to gather 20-30 lbs a day in parts of the Highlands; this was clearly unsustainable.[34]

Dog lichen
Peltigera canina

✿Used medicinally as a gentle purgative, for liver complaints and to treat rabies (though presumably not in Scotland, where the disease does not occur). It is from this use that the name dog lichen is derived, although according to Lightfoot it was not always successful![34,61,75]

Ramalina scopulorum

SCOTS NAMES: Sea ivory, beard of the rock
GAELIC NAME: *fiasag nan creag*

Used in Shetland and South Uist for dyeing orange and brown.[52]

Xanthoria parientina

This bright yellow lichen, often found growing on gravestones, was used to treat jaundice. It was used in the Highlands and Islands to produce pink, blue and purple dye. This may be the lichen described by Rorie as 'stane-raw', which, in the early years of the nineteenth century when the Napoleonic Wars prevented the import of dyes, was collected where it grew profusely on rocks and drystane dykes in Strathdon. It was valued at £100 a ton, and women and children could make half a crown (12.5p) a day gathering it.[52, 55, 115]

Species	common name	colour obtained
Bryoria fuscescens		golden yellow
Cladonia portentosa		leaf green
C. rangiferina	reindeer moss	light brown, dark red brown, dark brown
Evernia prunastri	oak moss	pink, green, yellow
Haematomma ventosum	blood spot	dark purple
Hypogymnia physoides	puffed shield lichen	brownish/orange
H. tubulosa	tubular lichen	honey yellow
Lobaria pulmonaria	lungwort lichen	chestnut brown
Parmelia species		brown, orange, yellow
Platismatia glauca	glaucous leafy lichen	orange, yellow
Pseudevernia furfuracea		orange
Usnea subfloridana	lesser old man's beard	yellow, olive green
Xanthoria parientina		rosy pink, blue, purple

Table 5: Other Scottish lichens used for dyes. *Based on several sources*

Algae
SEAWEEDS

Come and come is seaweed,
Come and come is red sea-ware,
Come is yellow weed, come is tangle,
Come is food which the wave enwraps.[23]

Seaweed has been an essential resource for people living near the coast in Scotland since prehistoric times; indeed it was so highly valued that it was traded far inland and in cities right into this century. The importance of seaweed was so great, magic rituals evolved to ensure it was available in sufficient quantities. These involved chanting and pouring libations of ale or even porridge into the sea:

> *In the Hebrides, Maundy Thursday was 'the day of the Big Porridge'*
> *when if the supply of seaweed was not sufficient for the farmers' needs,*
> *a large pot of specially rich porridge was made and then poured from*
> *selected headlands into parts of the sea known to be fertile seaweed*
> *grounds, accompanied by chants and rhymes. This should only be done in*
> *stormy weather, and the result was, the people hoped, a good crop of*
> *seaware.*[21]

The words of one chant have been recorded:

> *O God of the Sea*
> *Put weed in the drawing wave*
> *To enrich the ground*
> *To shower us with food.*[122]

On Lewis in the seventeenth century, the rite carried out on All Hallows (traditionally the first day of the old Celtic year) was a curious mixture of Pagan and Christian belief. It began and ended at the church of St Mulvay, but involved someone wading into the sea and chanting to invoke the sea-god Shony, offering a cup of ale in return for a good crop of seaweed to fertilise the fields for the following year. Back at the church, the altar candle was extinguished and the festival continued into the night with drinking, singing and dancing. Even after the ceremony was repressed, people continued to gather on the shore and invoke the Pagan god Briannuil, praying for a strong north wind to blow the seaweed ashore.[13]

In a fertility ritual enacted in Aberdeenshire until the last century, farmers gathered the year's first seaweed crop on New Year's morning and placed a small heap at the door of each farm building, then shared the rest between the fields.[59]

Several nutritious kinds were eaten raw or in soups, stews and puddings:

My grandmother used to go down to the seashore and take a lot of dulses and seaweeds and things home and make different dishes with them. Nobody does that now...She used to take home dulse, which was very sweet tasting. We'd eat it raw, or she would boil it in milk. And in February and March, there was another kind of weed[1] which you just twirled around your finger to take it off the rock. I just can't remember very well the recipe for that, but I know it was washed several times to remove any sand and it was put into a three-legged cast iron pot, and she kept beating it with a wooden spoon until at last it was in liquid form when it was cooked. And then it was drained and bottled and it had a lot of iron in it. So if you were rundown or listless, it was used for that.

(Kate MacLellan, speaking to Fiona McDonald in *Island Voices*)

Many tons of seaweed are still collected annually as fodder and 'green' manure for potatoes and other crops. On North Ronaldsay, in Orkney, even today sheep subsist almost entirely on a seaweed diet. In the Outer Hebrides, it was the extensive use of seaweed manure that made potato cultivation possible on the thin, wet, exposed soil: layers of seaweed were covered in earth to make lazy-beds (traces of which can still seen in many places), ridges about 30 cm high and 1 metre across, with a shallow trough between each bed.[98, 136]

Dried seaweeds were smoked or chewed as tobacco substitutes, while medicinal uses included relieving fever, scurvy, burns, headaches, sleeplessness and constipation and as a tonic.[18, 100]

Filamentous seaweeds were made into rope, fishing lines and nets. Some species were used in scouring flax. Ash from burnt seaweed was a valuable source of salt to preserve food and the basis of the kelp industry (see below). Until recently, some crofters still supplemented their income by collecting for factories in the Hebrides and Orkneys, that processed seaweeds into brown granules of alginic acid to be used in desserts, drinks and other foodstuffs, in paint, pharmaceuticals and textile manufacture. In the Orkneys alone over one thousand tons were harvested each year during the 1970s.[98]

Kelp

Kelp making was the commercial production of ash from burnt seaweed (mainly *Fucus* species and *Laminaria digitata*) for use in the manufacture of soda, glass and soap. It was first recorded on Stronsay in 1722. Twenty four tons of seaweed were required to produce one ton of ash. By the early

1. Possibly carrageen, *Chondrus crispus*, see p. 52.

1800s, when the Napoleonic Wars made kelp the only source of soda and pushed prices up to £22 a ton, the industry was valued at £80,000 a year—equivalent to the rent from 150,000 acres of Hebridean arable land—with annual yields of fifteen to twenty thousand tons.[89, 116, 125]

One objective of the Highland Clearances was to provide landowners with large supplies of cheap labour for the heavy and unpleasant work of kelp making. The average family of working men, women and children earned £6 to £10 a season for this back-breaking labour. In some areas, they worked in conditions tantamount to slave labour. However, when the kelp industry failed in the 1820s[1] the workers were once again ruthlessly cleared from the estates.[63, 89]

Patrick Neill described the impact of the kelp industry on the economy of the Orkneys and Shetland in 1806:

> *The greater part of the Shetland tenants appeared to be sunk into a state of the most abject poverty and misery. I found them even without bread; without any kind of food, in short, but fish and cabbage; living, in many cases, under the same roof with their cattle, and scarcely in cleaner appartments; their little agricultural concerns entirely neglected, owing to the men being obliged to be absent during summer at the ling [fishing]...Since the introduction of the kelp-manufacture in Orkney, a great change has taken place in the state of society in Kirkwall. Country gentlemen have thus acquired from their bleak estates, sums of money, great beyond all former experience...throughout Orkney, the state of agriculture is very low...the landholders pay attention to nothing but the manufacture of kelp...kelp will be the ruin of Orkney.[106]*

Attempts were made to revive the industry in North Uist from 1862. The British Seaweed Company built a chemical works at Dalmuir in Glasgow and leased the rights to all kelp from the shore of North Uist for £1,000 a year.

> *The weed is cut once in three years...The crofters and cottars remove from their homes to the shores of these bays and islands, and live in shielings during the kelp making, generally from 15th June to 15th August. The first thing to be done is to roof the old shieling, and make it as comfortable as possible for from four to six people to live in for two months. When the tide is out, the weed is cut from the rock and stones with a common reaping hook; a heather rope is taken and stretched round where the seaweed is being cut. When the tide comes in the rope*

---

1. When barilla, a cheaper raw material, could again be imported and a cheap method of making soda from salt had been discovered, as well as vast deposits of sulphate of potash in Germany, the price for kelp fell to £2 a ton.[33]

and seaweed float, and at high water the kelpers drag at both ends of the
rope and pull it ashore, with the seaweed enclosed.

(From *Scottish Home Industries* by Alexander Ross)

Creels full of weed were then carried ashore and spread out to dry, being turned occasionally to prevent fermentation. When enough weed was dried to make about a ton of kelp, it was forked into a trench—the kiln—4 to 8 metres long by 70 to 100 cm wide, and 70 cm deep, with stone walls and a turf bottom.

Provost Ross romanticised what was in fact a scene of heavy drudgery in North Uist:

It is very interesting on a fine summer day to see the little groups of busy
men and women along the shore, collecting and keeping alight the dried
seaweed; and the smoke rising high in the air, or drifting in picturesque
clouds across the hillocks, forming a sight to be long remembered, whilst
the odour of iodene strongly taints the air, and the pungent flavour is not
unpleasing.

The weed was kept burning with straw or heather fuel for four to eight hours. It was a skilled job (often done by women) keeping the flames steady without letting in air; the heat was intense. Once all the weed was alight, two or three men would rake and pound the mass together using long-handled iron clubs. The kiln was then covered with seaweed and stones to keep the contents dry. Next day it was cool enough to be broken into lumps and loaded onto ships for export, to be used as the raw material of a variety of chemical processes, especially in the manufacture of soap and glass.

The seaweed industry was once again briefly revived in North Uist earlier this century, as described in a display at Taigh-Chearsabhagh Museum, Lochmaddy. In 1946, the Scottish Seaweed Research Association reported 'The rockweed growth of Lochmaddy is undoubtedly the best in the whole of Scotland'. In 1956, Sponish Alginate Industries established a factory there, which employed 22 full-time workers and 50 part-time collectors. The factory closed for economic reasons in 1986, leaving local people dejected:

It was a great thing and should have lasted a lot longer than it did. I
don't know if it was a political matter, or how it came to an end; but it
was the one thing I could see that was going to be permanent. The more
you cut the seaweed the better it grew back in —and there was more
weight in it.

(From comments by an anonymous local person, Taigh-Chearsabhagh
Museum, Lochmaddy)

Alaria esculenta

LOCAL NAMES: bladderlocks, hen-ware, honey-ware (Orkney)
GAELIC NAMES: *mircean, muirirean, muiririn*

The inner stem was eaten, or the 'leaflets', known in Orkney as mirkles or murlins.[18, 106, 125]

Carrageen, Irish moss
Chondrus crispus

GAELIC NAME: *an carraceen*

Carrageen, boiled in milk, was made into a kind of blancmange, especially for invalids, convalescents and people with chest complaints. Lemon juice or jam were added to give flavour. It was gathered from rocks at the lowest ebb tide, washed and sun-dried until bleached white.[57] It is still collected to be used commercially as a thickening agent in ice-cream and other desserts and can be bought in health food shops.

Sea-laces
Chorda filum

LOCAL NAMES: dead men's ropes (Ayr), lucky minny's lines (Shet)
GAELIC NAME: *gille mu leann* (young man's net)

The tough stalks were stripped and used as fishing lines, nets and ropes.[18, 75, 125]

Confervae
e.g. *Cladophera, Enteromorpha*

SCOTS NAME: linarich
GAELIC NAMES: *lianach, linnearach* (pool), *luireach* (cloak)

Applied to the forehead to soothe fever or headaches, induce sleep and stop nosebleeds; also used as a plaster on burns, sores and goitres.[18, 100]

Hemanthalia lorea

GAELIC NAME: *aiomlach/iomleach* (name for cup-shaped disc from which thongs spring)

Made into sauce to serve with fish or fowl dishes.[18]

Bladder wrack
Fucus vesiculosus

SCOTS NAMES: sea-ware, black tang, lady-wrack
GAELIC NAMES: *propach/prablach* (tangled); *grobach/grob* (to dig/grub)

One of the commonest seaweeds, this was an important source of winter fodder for cattle, sheep and deer, of fertilizer for the fields and of salt for preserving cheese.[18, 136]

> *Instead of salt to their cheese they use Sea Ware (wrack) which they burn; and with the Ashes thereof they salt their cheese, by rubbing it outwardly; after some days they wash it.*[73]

On St Kilda, Martin Martin reported,

> *they use only the ashes of sea-ware for salting their cheese, and the shortest (which grows on the rocks) is used only by them, that being reckoned the mildest.*[100]

Dried wrack was used as a medicinal charm[18] and infused for inhaling:

> *If, after a fever, one chanced to be taken ill of a stitch, they* [the inhabitants of Jura] *take a quantity of ladywrack and red fog*[1] *and boil them in water; the patients sit upon the vessel and receive the fume, which by experience they find effectual against the distemper.*[100]

A folk tale from Vatersay tells of a woman, presumably a witch, stealing the milk from cows on the beach by tying them up with a stem of black tangle.[87]

In Shetland, children made water pistols by cutting or biting the end off a large bladder, flattening then immersing it until it filled with water.[135]

Tangle
Laminaria digitata

SCOTS NAMES: sea-girdles, tangle
GAELIC NAMES: *stamh/slat-mhara* (sea-wand), *doire* (tangle, Skye)

As well as being important in the kelp industry, tangle was eaten in considerable quantities. Apparently it was a favourite of children who would roast the stalks and spread them on a buttered bannock, or even chew them raw like sticks of rhubarb. Adults chewed it too, as a tobacco substitute. Medicinally, it was known to be effective against scurvy and

---

1. This might be either Yorkshire fog (*Holcus lanatus*) or red fescue (*Festuca rubra*), both common grasses but neither recorded elsewhere as having medicinal uses.

glandular diseases, long before the value of iodine was recognised. A poultice of tangle was used to clear warts.[23, 100, 125]

Pepper dulse
Laurencia pinnatofida

Pepper dulse was collected and sold with common dulse; it has a sharp flavour and so was generally eaten as a condiment to other seaweeds.[125]

Laver, sloke
Porphyria laciniata

GAELIC NAMES: *sloucan, slochdan* (*slok* = pool/slake)

> *The Natives eat it boil'd and it dissolves into Oil; they say that if a little Butter be added to it, one might live many Years on this alone, without Bread, or any other food, and at the same Time, undergo any laborious Exercise.*[100]

It was gathered in, pounded and stewed, sometimes with leeks and onions, or made into soup or sauce; Caithness fishermen made sloke jelly which they took to sea and ate with oatcakes.[18, 75, 100]

Dulse
Rhodymenia edulis, R. palmata

GAELIC NAME: *duiliasg* (water-leaf)

> *There is a common saying in Stronsa* [Orkney], *that 'he who eats of the dulse of Guiodin[1] and drinks of the wells of Kildingie, will escape all maladies except black death'.*[106]

There was widespread belief in the tonic effects of dulse, eaten raw straight from the sea and washed down with salt water. In Caithness, the ebb tide on a May morning was considered the most efficacious time for an annual dose. It was eaten raw or boiled to treat scurvy, constipation and to promote perspiration; the water in which it was boiled was also drunk. Dried, powdered dulse taken after fasting was used to treat worms. Externally it was applied fresh as a plaster for skin diseases and headaches and placed on the abdomen to help expel the placenta after childbirth.[7, 18, 52, 100, 125]

Dulse, said to be best in early summer, is one of the more palatable seaweeds, known to have been eaten by Columban monks on Iona and doubtless long before that. It can be used raw, boiled, roasted, stir-fried or

1. Place name meaning the rocky voe (creek) of Odin

dried as a savoury relish to be served with vegetables. It can also be simmered in milk to make jelly. It was cut small and mixed with butter for flavour, washed and sun-dried for chewing like tobacco. It yields brown dye.[18, 52, 73]

Sea-grapes
Sargassum vulgare (syn. bacciferum)

GAELIC NAME: *turusgar/trusgar* (journey)

Not native to Britain, but according to Cameron,

> *This weed is frequently washed by the Gulf Stream across the great Atlantic, with beans, nuts, and seeds, and cast upon the western shores. These are carefully gathered, preserved, and often worn as charms. They are called* uibhean sithein, *fairy eggs, and it is believed that they will ward off evil-disposed fairies.*[18]

Green lava, sea lettuce
Ulva lactuca

Another species used to sooth headaches and induce sleep, applied fresh to the forehead and temples as a refreshing and cooling plaster; like linarich (p. 52) it was used to heal the skin after a spearwort (*Ranunculus flammula*) plaster had been used (see p. 146).[100, 125]

Musci
MOSS FAMILY

Martin Martin recorded that on Skye, weary travellers bathed their feet in warm water in which red moss had been boiled, and rubbed them with the moss before going to bed. This may have been a species of bog moss, *Sphagnum*, which has long been used for a great variety of medicinal and household purposes. *Sphagnum* contains penicillin, and has been used since prehistoric times as a wound dressing—a Bronze Age warrior buried in Lothian had a chest wound packed with moss. Although clearly it did not save his life in this case, many other soldiers right up to the Second World War may well have owed their survival at least in part to the moss. It was referred to as a wound dressing in the exceptionally bloody Battle of Clontarf in 1014. As part of the 1940s war effort, when conventional dressings became in short supply, Girl Guides were sent to collect *Sphagnum* from their local bogs.[6, 100]

Sphagnum was also used like toilet paper and sanitary towels and was the original disposable nappy; as well as being highly absorbent, it reduces chances of infection. Until very recently, indigenous Vancouver Islanders, whose lifestyle appears to have been very similar to that of Scottish people in earlier times, collected and stored large quantites of *Sphagnum* to be used like paper towels, for wiping hands, mopping up spills and cleaning fish; they also used it for bedding. Another recorded Scottish use was between roof slates to reduce leaks and draughts and increase insulation.[27, 134]

In modern times, *Sphagnum* is popular with flower arrangers and may be seen in many hanging baskets, used to prevent them from drying out. It must however be pointed out that *Sphagnum* moss plays a vital role in conserving water on bogs, an increasingly rare habitat in Scotland that should not be interfered with by removal of any plants.

Possible prehistoric and more recent uses of other kinds of moss are described on p. 26.

Lycopodiaceae
CLUBMOSS FAMILY

GAELIC NAME: *garbhag an t-sleibhe* (rough one of the hill)

Clubmosses are curious little plants found throughout Scotland, most commonly in upland areas. Fir clubmoss (*Huperzia selago*) is the most widespread species, although apparently stag's-horn clubmoss (*Lycopodium clavatum*) was formerly found in lowland grassland and is now proving an excellent coloniser of old shale bings in West Lothian.

Medicinally, an infusion of clubmoss was used as a powerful emetic and cathartic which, unless administered with great caution, caused giddiness, convulsions and abortion. Fumigation with clubmoss was used to treat eye disease.

> *The plant Selago (probably club moss) was used by the Druids as a preservative against accidents, and the smoke of it was considered good for maladies of the eyes. It was gathered without the use of iron by the right hand passed through the left sleeve of the tunic, as though the gatherer were performing some furtive act. The clothing of the gatherer, too, had to be white, the feet bare and washed, and a sacrifice of bread and wine had to be made before the plant was collected. It was to be carried in a new napkin.*[20]

Dusting powder for the skin was very fashionable at various times throughout history; fir clubmoss was dried and ground for this purpose. According to Mary Beith, it was also regularly collected by children in Sutherland until early this century, to be steeped in a big pot of boiling water, simmered for a few hours, strained, cooled then made into a softening, soothing lotion for faces, arms and hands, and for babies' bottoms.[6, 7, 18, 61, 75, 76, 109]

Clubmosses were also a plant of protection, especially for the traveller:

> *The club-moss is on my person,*
> *No harm or mishap can me befall;*
> *No sprite shall slay me, no arrow shall wound me,*
> *No fay nor dun water-nymph shall tear me.*

> *Thou man who travellest blithely,*
> *Nor hurt nor harm shall befall thee*
> *Nor in sunshine nor in darkness*
> *If but the club-moss be on thy pathway.*
> (from *Carmina Gadelica* by Alexander Carmichael)

Clubmosses appear to have been involved in Scottish textile manufacture since at least the twelfth century (see **Textiles**), and were still commonly used in Lightfoot's time. They contain aluminium and so can replace the mordant alum (potassium aluminium sulphate), in the production of yellow and blue dye from traditional dye plants such as madder (*Rubia tinctorum*), woad (*Isatis tinctoria*), weld (*Reseda luteola*) and willowherb (*Epilobium species*). The colours produced with clubmoss as a mordant are softer and less bright than with alum but longer lasting. Archaeological excavations in twelfth century Perth have revealed what appears to have been a dyeing or textile workshop, with shoots of the stag's-horn clubmoss and alpine clubmoss (*Diphasiastrum alpinum*), along with remains of other dye plants (see **Textiles**); these, with fir clubmoss, appear to have been the three most widely used species.[52, 60, 109]

Equisetaceae
HORSETAIL FAMILY

Horsetail
Equisetum species

GAELIC NAME: *clois*

❇Fluid extracted from the barren stem after fruiting was used fresh internally as a diuretic and astringent, also to treat dropsy, kidney disorders, tuberculosis, stomach acidity and indigestion, haemorrhage and ulcers. Externally, a strong decoction was used to stop bleeding, heal wounds and reduce swelling of the eyelids.[61]

Horsetails are high in minerals including silica, iron and base elements; the shoots of some species have been eaten as vegetables since Roman times and were probably an important food in early spring, when not much else was available.[109]

Some species of horsetail, especially *E. hyemale*, were used as pot scourers; this species is now uncommon and in decline.[7] In general, horsetails are common in most parts of Scotland, in damp vegetation by streamsides.

Filicopsida
FERNS

LOCAL NAMES: trows' kairds (Ork, Shet)
GAELIC NAMES: *raineach, roineach* (perhaps from *reath*, turning, of young fronds)

Ferns generally were thought to have magic properties, including that of keeping witches away, and featured in many Gaelic charms. Although to be botanically correct ferns have spores not seeds, Scottish folklore has numerous references to the potency of fern seeds (presumably the spore-bearing body, or sorus), which worked best if gathered on Midsummer Eve.[18, 95]

It is possible that ferns were used in Scotland for cooking. On Vancouver Island in Canada, the Nitinaht Indians place fronds in layers above and below food being cooked in a steaming pit; they also use fern fronds as serving platters at feasts.[134]

Black spleenwort
Asplenium adiantum-nigrum[1]

❀The triangular fronds, usually found in rocky places, were made into cough medicine and used as a hair-wash.[61]

Wall rue
A. ruta-muraria

❀The tiny, rue-like fronds, frequently found on walls and in rock crevices, were used for many medicinal purposes: to treat coughs, shortness of breath, jaundice, ruptured spleens, rickets and kidney stones. Wall rue was believed to cleanse the lungs, purify the blood and reduce swellings. It was applied to the skin to treat ulcers, dandruff, scalp sores and in an attempt to rectify hair-loss.[61]

Maidenhair spleenwort
A. trichomanes

SCOTS NAMES: Black spleenwort, common maidenhair[2]
GAELIC NAMES: *dubh chasach* (dark-stemmed), *lus na seilg* (spleen)

A small fern found on rocks and walls in most parts of Scotland. Spleenwort was considered the best remedy for any disorder of that organ. On Skye, ale brewed from hart's tongue (*Phyllitis scolopendrium*) and spleenwort was drunk for coughs and consumption.[18, 100]

Moonwort
Botrychium lunaria

GAELIC NAME: *luan lus* (moonwort)

According to Cameron, this tiny, odd-looking fern of dry grassland was a powerful plant, held in awe by Highlanders, that could cause horses to shed their shoes if it grew in their pasture.[18]

---

1. This fern is not native to Scotland; Sutherland may have been referring to *A. trichomanes* (see footnote 2).
2. There may be some confusion about names here; the standard common name for *A. trichomanes* is maidenhair spleenwort; these names may actually refer to *Asplenium adiantum-nigrum* .

Male fern
Dryopteris filix-mas

GAELIC NAME: *marc raineach* (horse fern)

A common, large woodland fern. The powdered roots, taken in water, were considered an excellent remedy for worms. Comrie noted that the Romans used male fern root in south Lothian—this knowledge may well have been passed on.[18, 32]

Adder's tongue
Ophioglossum vulgatum

❀A small, inconspicuous fern of damp grassland. The root and leaves were used medicinally for internal wounds and bruising, vomiting, bleeding from the mouth or nose, and eye infections.[61]

Royal fern
Osmunda regalis

SCOTS NAMES: flowering fern, osmund royal

❀Royal fern was used to treat jaundice, internal blockages, wounds, bruises, rickets and lumbago. A poultice of boiled roots applied to a dislocated knee-cap was said to reduce pain and swelling, allowing the joint to return to its place. In addition, it was a magic plant; Carmichael quotes a love charm that required nine stalks of royal fern.[7, 23, 61]

This is a large fern found mainly in wet woods and on lochsides, especially along the west coast of Scotland. The spores were added to halt fermentation of mead made with meadowsweet and heather in prehistoric Rum.[7, 109]

Hart's Tongue Fern

Hart's tongue fern
Phyllitis scolopendrium

❀A distinctive fern with a solid blade found on damp rocks and banks, and sometimes walls, mainly on the west coast and in the south of Scotland. The fronds were made into ointment for piles, wounds and scalds, and ale (with spleenwort, see p. 59) for treating coughs and consumption.[61, 100, 125]

Shield ferns
Polystichum species

GAELIC NAME: *ibhig*

Large ferns of wet woodlands; the powdered roots were taken in water for worms.[18]

Bracken, brake
Pteridium aquilinum

GAELIC NAMES: *an raineach mhor* (large fern), *bun rainnich* (roots)

Although considered inferior to heather for both purposes, bracken was widely used in Scotland as bedding for people and livestock, and also for thatching, using either entire fronds or stripped stalks alone. Recent scientific research has supported the folk belief that bracken fronds contain pest-repellent qualities. In Argyll it was the commonest roofing material but not as durable as heather or straw, a bracken-thatched roof lasting only ten to fifteen years.[57, 75, 109]

✿The roots were made into ointment for wounds and ulcers and according to Lightfoot,

> *The ancients used the root of this fern, and the whole plant, in decoctions and diet-drinks, in chronic disorders of all kinds, arising from obstructions of the viscera and the spleen. Some of the moderns give it a high character of the same intentions, but it is rarely used in the present practice. The country people, however, still continue to retain some of its ancient uses, for they give the powder of it to destroy worms, and look upon a bed of the green plant as a sovereign cure for the rickets in children.*[75]

The more uses that could be found for bracken the better, as clearing it improved pasture. The roots and rhizomes were boiled to produce yellow dye, and the fronds for lime green. The whole fern was used for animal bedding, packing potatoes on their way to market and as fuel for brewing and baking. Lightfoot recommended bracken as 'green' manure and the ashes, which are high in potash, make excellent fertiliser, especially for potatoes. Balls of bracken ashes were mixed with a little water then sun-dried and used instead of soap to wash linen.[52, 75, 109]

The ash was also used in the Scottish glass-making industry before soda from sea salt became widely available, and in the mid-eighteenth century the Isle of Mull had a significant income from exporting bracken ashes.[125]

At one time many crofters augmented their incomes by selling bracken ash to the glass or soap manufacturers of Glasgow. Prior to 1750, rents might even be paid partly in bracken: in Knapdale, for example, Sir Archibald Campbell stipulated in his lease to tenant farmers that sixteen cartloads of pulled fern be delivered to his house. Bracken was protected, and only allowed to be cut after a certain date. Economically, then, it may be seen as a predecessor of kelp.[1] [10]

Since pulling and cutting of bracken has ceased in most areas, it is spreading on the lower slopes of hills, destroying heather and pasture.

Cupressaceae
CYPRESS FAMILY

Juniper
Juniperus communis

SCOTS NAME: aiten
LOCAL NAMES: aitnach (Banff, Mor), melmot/melmont berries (Mor)
GAELIC NAMES: *aiteal, aiteann, aittin/aitinn, samh*

The Scots and local names for juniper, sometimes called mountain yew, clearly derive from the Gaelic; a juniper tree is *craobh aiteil*. The adjective *aitealach*, abounding in juniper, sadly can be little used today. It is still to be found in mountainous and hilly areas, either in the open or as an understory in old pine and birch woods, but it would be a hard task nowadays to collect the sacks full of berries sent to markets in Aberdeen and Inverness during August in the nineteenth century, for exporting to Holland to make gin.[52, 76]

Juniper trees, twigs and berries were believed to have the power to avert evil and to have great powers of protection and purification. In Sutherland, juniper wood was used for teething rings so that babies were protected from harm. Sprigs of juniper were tied to animals' tails as a charm against evil. Branches were burned on the threshold at *Samhain* (Hallowe'en) to keep evil spirits away, in house and byre on New Year's morning,[2] and whenever illness and infection struck a household. The building was sealed, smoke allowed to spread throughout until all the occupants were coughing and sneezing and had streaming eyes, thereby

Juniper

1. See pp. 49-51.
2. *Samhain* was the start of the old Celtic year, so presumably this tradition was simply moved when the festival date changed.

expelling any disease they might be harbouring. Then the windows and doors were thrown open, the fumes blown away and the (human) occupants revived with whisky. A more prosaic kind of magic was the use of juniper as fuel for illegal whisky stills: it is said to burn with less smoke than other wood so reducing the risk of revealing the location to the exciseman.*50, 52, 95, 115, 117*

According to McNeill, the necessary ritual to be observed when collecting mountain yew was to divide the branches into four bundles between one's five fingers, then pull it by the root repeating the incantation:

> *I will pull the bounteous yew*
> *Through the five bent ribs of Christ*
> *In the name of the Father, the Son and Holy Ghost*
> *Against drowning, danger and confusion.*[95]

Young juniper twigs were used for smoking hams, imparting a slight turpentine-like flavour, not to everyone's taste. Baskets called sculls, and house walls were woven from juniper withies.*73, 115, 125*

❀It is known that the Romans were using juniper berries medicinally in the Lothians for purging, stomach ailments, epilepsy and purification; whether they learned from or taught locals about its properties we may never know but it was certainly a popular remedy. It has been said Highlanders used the berries to treat virtually anything, including epilepsy and snake bites. The cure was often taken in hot whisky, which perhaps explains its popularity. According to some old ballads, Mary Hamilton, one of Mary Queen of Scots' famous ladies-in-waiting, the Four Marys, unsuccessfully tried using juniper as an abortifacient. The berries were also used for tea, wine and liqueur and for yellow and brown dyes.*23, 32, 52, 110, 135*

Pinaceae
PINE FAMILY

Scots pine, Scotch fir
Pinus sylvestris

GAELIC NAME: *giubhas, giuthas* (juicy tree—it has abundant resin)

Scots pine is called in Gaelic *giuthas* or *giubhas, craobh ghiuthais*; a pine forest is *giusaichean*. King of the forest, wildman of the woods, tree of heroes, chieftains and warriors: the spirit of the ancient Caledonian pinewoods that once covered much of Scotland remains powerful. All evergreens were symbols of life and immortality, the origin of our custom of decorating the house at midwinter with greenery and the reason Scots pine was planted on warriors' graves. Pine cones were a masculine fertility symbol, often representing male genitals in legends and art. In Orkney, it was traditional to 'sain' (purify) mothers and newborn babies by whirling a flaming pine-candle three times around the bed.[50, 58]

Healing ointment for boils and sores was made from beeswax, pig fat and pine resin, while the bark was used for fever and the buds for scurvy.[6, 50]

Resinous roots and stumps of Scots pine dug from peat bogs were widely used for tapers until the end of the eighteenth century when cheap oil lamps began to replace them. Villagers went on autumn expeditions to lay in a store of the wood for dark winter evenings. The dried logs were cut into strips about 70 cm long and 1-2 cm thick, which would burn like a candle because they were so full of resin. Descriptions of the light they gave range from 'charming' to 'guttering and oily'.[27, 57] It was usually the job of the youngest members of a household to look after and replace the fast-burning 'rosety roots',

Scots Pine

> *but when the sturdy beggar or gaberlunzie man came begging his supper and quarters, the duty at once devolved to him, and he became the candlestick. Hence, in after times when a permanent stand of iron was invented, the name of 'Pier Man' was given to it, as the lineal descendant of the poor man.*[116]

The once extensive Caledonian pinewoods have been reduced to small remnants; for many centuries Scots pine timber has been used for a great variety of purposes. Individual trees could grow to a great size, 25 metres tall, 2 metres diameter, of durable wood, light and strong, knot-free, suitable for house and boat building and only slightly inferior to oak. Logan recorded (in 1832) that when the 300 year old roof of Kilchurn Castle in Argyll was dismantled, the Scots pine roof timbers were found to be as fresh and full of sap as newly imported wood.[76, 125]

Boat builders particularly valued the long, straight, pliable planks of Scots pine, and believed that they should not cut the tree when the moon was waning, because the sap was tidal and the timber would then be less resinous. Botanical research has shown that there are in fact complex fluctuations in sap flow which are not yet fully understood. Resin from Scots pine was added to varnish, paint and tar, the last used by boatbuilders for sealing planks and waterproofing the hull.[23, 50]

Another inventive use of resources was the manufacture of strong rope from the long, fibrous roots of bog pines. The fresh, wet roots were beaten until they could be separated into thread-like fibres to be spun like hemp.

The ropes were very buoyant and used for tying boats.[116]

The cones yield light brown dye.[52]

Taxaceae
YEW FAMILY

Yew
Taxus baccata

GAELIC NAME: *iubhar*

Yew is not a widespread tree in Scotland, occurring naturally mainly in the Argyll area. The Gaelic name *iubhar* is thought by some scholars to be the origin of the name of Iona, where druids were said to worship yew and use it for prophecy before St Columba arrived and expelled them (but Iona could equally be derived from *ionad naomh*, meaning holy place or sanctuary). The legendary Otherworld traveller, Thomas the Rhymer, is said to dwell safely with the faeries inside *Tom na h-Iubhraich* (knoll of the yew tree) near Inverness.[50, 95]

The *slat-dhraoidheachd*, rod of office, once used ceremonially throughout the Highlands, was traditionally made of yew, a legacy of the druids. Yew was one of the sacred woods used to bake special cakes on feast days. Planted in graveyards as an evergreen symbol of immortality, yew was the tree that grew down into dead bodies to release the soul and purify the body—sacred compost, fertility gift to the earth. An old Celtic legend tells of two lovers buried together who respectively grew into an apple and a yew tree, entwined in new life above the earth. Perhaps some of the magic power was simply related to the qualities of the hard, beautiful wood; Scottish archers were thus well-served symbolically as well as practically by their yew bows.[23, 50, 76, 95]

An ancient yew that grows at Fortingall by Glen Lyon in Perthshire is said to be the oldest tree in Europe, declared to be 3,000 years old by Sir Robert Christison in 1870. Tradition has it that Fortingall was the birthplace of Pontius Pilate while his parents were there on a peace mission with the Roman army, and that he was suckled under the tree.[1] There has been a place of Christian worship beside the tree since the seventh century

1. Notes in the adjacent church attribute this belief to Holinshed's *Chronicles*; information about the yew is taken from notes based on research by Beverley Jeffry displayed beside the tree and in the church.

AD, and it is quite possible that, as often happened, the first church was built there to sanctify a Pagan sacred grove.[1]

Pennant measured the tree in 1769 when the circumference was 17.5 metres. The yew became well known and many distinguished travellers went to visit it; unfortunately fame brought a price: curio hunters kept taking pieces of the tree and combined with the damage done by local boys who lit Beltane fires beneath the spreading branches, this caused the central trunk to fall apart in 1825. Subsequently a wall was built around the tree and the branches were propped up with stone pillars, so that now it can only be seen through gratings in the high wall. Nevertheless it is an impressive piece of natural sculpture; the tree is still very much alive and fruiting.

1. Estimates of the age are based on the great circumference of the tree. Old sketches do show a massive, intact trunk; it is perhaps possible there has been a yew tree on that spot for thousands of years, but what can be seen now may simply be trees that have suckered from branches that touched the ground around an original central parent tree, which has long since completely rotted away.

Apiacae
CARROT FAMILY

Cow parsley
Anthriscus sylvestris

LOCAL NAMES: deil's meal, dog's carvi (Shet), wild carraway (Banff)

Found in all parts of Scotland and connected with the devil in the same way as hemlock. The young plant and flowering tips produce a green or yellow-green dye which was used for dyeing Harris tweed. The dried stalks were used to make weaving bobbins.[47, 52, 57]

Hemlock
Conium maculatum

SCOTS NAMES: hech-how, humlock
LOCAL NAMES: humly rose, kaka (Ork)
GAELIC NAMES: *iteotha, mimnhear*

❋A powerful, poisonous plant, used in medicine and magic. Thirty-one hemlock seeds were found in a cache with henbane (*Hyoscyamus niger*) at the mediaeval monastic hospital site being excavated at Soutra in East Lothian; the seeds were presumably to be used as anaesthetic before surgery (see p. 170). It has sedative and anti-spasmodic properties, and was used as an antidote to strychnine and similarly acting poisons. Small doses were administered to treat teething, epilepsy, cramp, spasms, bronchitis, whooping-cough and asthma.[61, 103]

An overdose can lead to paralysis and death. In 1845 an impoverished Edinburgh tailor, Duncan Gow, died after eating hemlock in 'salad' collected from beneath the Walter Scott monument by his children aged 10 and 6.[103] Carmichael was informed that:

A cold poultice of hemlock was applied to a cancer sore. The hemlock plaster was so hot and so strong that it drew the cancer out from the bottom, the roots coming with the cancer as the roots come with the hemlock itself out of the ground. This was effective when done in time. When the disease became soft nothing could cure it.[23]

Scottish witches were said to use the plant and fairies dipped their arrows in 'dew of hemlock'.[95] It is found on waste ground in southern and eastern Scotland.

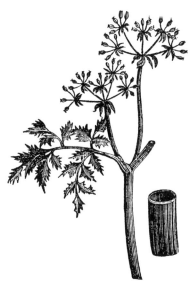

Hemlock

67

Pignut
Conopodium majus

SCOTS NAMES: arnut, earthnut, gourlins, hornecks
LOCAL NAMES: curluns (Kirk, Wigt), gowlins, knotty meal (Inv), lucy arnut (Fife), lousy arnuts (Perth, Aber), truffle (Inv)
GAELIC NAME: *braonan bhuachail* (shepherd's drop/nut)

> *The ancient Gael had a certain vegetable...about the size of a bean* [which] *enabled them to resist, for some time, the effects of a want of either meat or drink. The Highlanders, at this day, occasionally use an article that was in much esteem with their ancestors, and which, if not the above, seems to possess similar qualities. The root* braonan, *which grows abundantly in the country, is delicious, and very nutritious when boiled. It is dug from November to April, and, when dried and ground, it makes good bread. Many, also, chew it like tobacco, and allege that it allays the sensation of hunger.*[76]

Pignut is common in unimproved grassland and light woods throughout Scotland, and even today, some country children know a tasty snack can be easily obtained by the long-recorded tradition of grubbing up the small, crunchy root tuber, which has a sharp, slightly nutty flavour. No doubt in times past they were not in the slightest bit put off by the Scottish belief that if you ate too many of the Lousy Arnuts, you would get head lice.[62, 96]

Rock samphire
Crithmum maritimum

SCOTS NAME: passper (from French 'pierce-pierre')
GAELIC NAMES: *lus nan cnamh* (digesting weed), *saimbhir* (St Pierre)

❀A rare plant of cliffs and rocky places in southwest Scotland. Rock samphire was used as a salad vegetable to aid digestion, and also to treat kidney, bladder and liver problems.[18, 61, 62]

Wild carrot
Daucus carota

SCOTS NAMES: bird's nest, curran-petris
GAELIC NAMES: *curran* (root like a carrot), *muran* (plant with tapering roots)

The natives [of Harris] make use of the seeds of a white wild carrot, instead of hops, for brewing their beer; and they say that it answers the end sufficiently well, and gives the drink a good relish besides.[100]

Martin Martin recorded a case of poisoning (fortunately not fatal) on Skye when 'hemlock' was eaten instead of wild carrot; this may have been hemlock water dropwort (*Oenanthe crocata*) which has swollen roots and could therefore be mistaken for *Daucus*, though the two plants are otherwise dissimilar. Wild carrot grows best in chalky grassland near the sea and is found all around the coasts of Scotland.

❀Wild carrot was boiled to treat cancer and ulcers, or applied as a poultice, made from the roots or leaves mixed to a paste with honey, for all kinds of sores and ulcers. The plant was also used to treat dropsy, kidney and bladder problems, flatulence, dysentery, coughs and jaundice.[7,61]

The carrot was a symbol of deep and high significance, appealing to the sacred instincts of the people as no other plant did. It symbolised fertility, offspring, children. The carrot was given by a woman to a man, rarely by a man to a woman.[23]

Wild carrots were collected for the Michaelmas harvest festival in the Islands and on the west coast (see pp. 6-7).

Wild Carrot

Hogweed, cow parsnip
Heracleum sphondylium

SCOTS NAMES: buneweed, bunnen, bunwort, bunnert, cow-cakes
LOCAL NAMES: bunnle (Lan), cowkeep (Fife), cow-keeks (Berw), hemlock (Banff), keksi (Shet)
GAELIC NAMES: *gunnachan sputachain* (squirt-guns), *meacan-a-cruidh* (cow's plant), *odharan* (pale, dun, yellowish)

Common throughout Scotland, hogweed was as the name suggests used as fodder for pigs and cattle. Children used to make squirt-guns from the hollow stems; unfortunately this tradition has led to some serious injuries when children have used giant hogweed (*H. mantegazzianum*) for the same purpose. The juice of this much larger and easily distinguishable plant causes the skin to burn in sunlight; the same chemical is present in *H. sphondylium*, but in much smaller quantities and the stems are safe to use when dry.[18, 62]

Scots lovage
Ligusticum scoticum

SCOTS NAMES: scotch parsley, sea parsley
GAELIC NAME: *suinas* (growing in exposed situations)

Found all around the coast of Scotland (and in Scandinavia, but not England), Scots lovage was plucked from seashore rocks and eaten raw in salad or boiled as a vegetable. Martin and other early writers recommended it as a tonic, appetiser and against scurvy and consumption (in lamb broth with alexanders, see p. 71), but the strong, not particularly pleasant taste did not make it very popular. Martin also noted helpfully: 'The root taken fasting expels the wind.' [62, 75, 76, 100, 125]

Mary Beith states that the name lovage derives from its use as an aphrodisiac; it was also, in apparent contradiction, reputed to soothe the mind. It was used to treat animals, as a purgative for calves and for sheep with a cough. [7, 100, 125]

Spignel
Meum athamanticum

SCOTS NAMES: badminnie, micken
LOCAL NAME: bawdringie (Perth)
GAELIC NAME: *muilceann*, *muilcionn* (because aromatic, smelly)

Found mainly in central and southwest Scotland, the chunky, aromatic roots of spignel have a hot flavour like lovage and were chewed as a stimulant and to control flatulence. They were also dried and used as a spice in cooking. [18, 62, 125]

Sweet Cicely
Myrrhis odorata

LOCAL NAMES: myrrh (Aber), sweet humlick (hemlock, Berw)

Common in damp places along roadsides and in meadows in southern Scotland, and now believed to have been introduced. The whole plant is edible, tasting and smelling strongly of aniseed. It was eaten as a salad. [18, 125]

Burnet saxifrage
Pimpinella saxifraga

❋Localised on rocks and in dry grassland in the south-eastern half of

Scotland. The whole plant was gathered in July and used as a wound dressing to stop bleeding and prevent infection; it was also used to treat fever, gout and rheumatism. The fresh root, also cut in July, was used for toothache, or as a decoction for asthma and dropsy and to gargle for throat infections.[61]

Sanicle
Sanicula europaea

GAELIC NAMES: *bodan coille* (wood-tail/little old man of the wood), *buine* (ulcer)

❀Occurs in woods in most parts of Scotland. Used as an effective dressing for wounds and ulcers.[18]

Alexanders
Smyrmium olusatrum

GAELIC NAME: *lus nan gran dubh* (plant with black seeds)

❀An introduced plant with localised distribution. Alexanders was eaten as a salad or pot-herb, or in broth with Scots lovage (see above) to prevent consumption. Four seeds of alexanders were found during the excavation of the medieval monastic hospital site at Soutra.[18, 100, 103]

Aquifoliaceae
HOLLY FAMILY

Holly
Ilex aquifolium

SCOTS NAMES: hollin, holine, holing
GAELIC NAMES: *chuillin, cuileann*

Common throughout Scotland except in the far north, holly was a magical plant, hated by witches and repellent to fairies, therefore protective against evil. This is a case of sympathetic magic, attributable to its prickly nature—many prickly or thorny species were considered to have protective or repellent qualities because evil spirits would get caught up in or be unable to pass through the plant. An old Gaelic charm invokes a force against 'The wicked who would do me harm...Be it fiercer, sharper, harsher,

71

more malignant than the hard, wounding holly'.[57, 82, 95]

Holly had the added strength of being an evergreen, all of which were considered powerful species, having the seemingly supernatural ability to withstand the onslaught of winter. Houses were decorated with branches of holly at Hogmanay when fairies were likely to be abroad looking for mischief but, as was often the case with protective plants, it was considered unlucky to fell the tree. Nevertheless, holly is good for carving, having hard, white wood used for inlay and handles of weapons and tools. It was (and of course still is) commonly planted for hedges, which were stockproof as well as protecting the house or animals from evil.[57, 117]

Araceae
ARUM FAMILY

Cuckoo pint, lords and ladies
Arum maculatum

SCOTS NAMES: aron, wake robin

✿Rare in Scotland, except in the south and a few locations where it has probably been introduced. The starchy root of cuckoo pint was made into pills with diuretic, purgative and stimulant properties; it was also used to treat ringworm.[61]

Cuckoo Pint

Araliaceae
IVY FAMILY

Ivy
Hedera helix

SCOTS NAMES: bindwood, ivery, ivin
LOCAL NAME: bentwood (Berw)
GAELIC NAMES: *eidheann, eidheantach* (Arran)

✿A magical plant that grows wild in most parts of Scotland. A three-ply wreath woven from ivy, honeysuckle and rowan was placed over the lintel of the byre and beneath churns in the milk-house to protect cows and milk from witchcraft, the evil eye and the infectious disease murrain.[23, 62, 95]

Medicinal uses for the leaves, flowers and berries were known from ancient times; the plant has diuretic, astringent, tonic and stimulant qualities. It was used internally to treat many complaints including indigestion, coughs, nervous headaches, consumption, bruises, internal wounds, ulcerated lungs, flatulence, jaundice, sciatica, gout, sore mouth and throat, gangrene and kidney problems. The leaves and twigs, boiled in butter, were made into ointment for burns and sunburn. In the nineteenth century, Fife mining families used an infusion of ivy leaves as an eye-lotion and made them into a poultice for corns; a cap made from sewn-together ivy leaves was placed on the head of a child with eczema.[7, 61, 115]

Asteraceae
DAISY FAMILY

Yarrow
Achillea millefolium

SCOTS NAMES: milfoil, stanch-girs
LOCAL NAMES: hundred-leaved grass, thousand-leaf clover, wild pepper (Berw), meal-and-folie, melancholy (Shet), moleery-tea (Caithness)
GAELIC NAMES: *athair thalmhainn* (earth/ground father), *cathair thalmainn* (ground seat or chair), *earr-thalmhainn* (that which clothes the earth), *lus chasgadh na fala* (plant that staunches bleeding), *lus na fola* (blood weed)

❀This very common grassland plant has been attributed with great powers, both medicinal and magic. It was named after the legendary Greek warrior Achilles, who aparently discovered the plant's power of staunching blood (but presumably did not have any handy when the fatal arrow caught him in the heel). On Skye, yarrow was boiled in milk with the healing 'hectic-stone' (quartz) to make a remedy for consumption. In Fife, it was used for coughs and colds. Highlanders were still making an ointment from the plant earlier this century, for use on wounds and piles and to treat sheep scab. Around the same time boiled yarrow juice was being used in Lochaber to treat stomach complaints. Mary Beith makes yarrow oil to treat cuts and bruises by boiling the leaves in olive oil.[6, 61, 100, 115]

Travelling in Orkney around 1806, Patrick Neill saw large amounts of yarrow flowers laid out to dry at a cottage door; he was curious to hear it called 'meal-and-folie', but he may simply have misheard the name of melancholy, because he went on to report that it was made into tea, 'this beverage being held in high repute for dispelling melancholy'. Yarrow leaves can also be used to brew beer, which might perhaps have the same effect.[106, 110]

73

Carmichael collected a Gaelic verse with a sting in the tail:

> *I will pluck the yarrow fair ,*
> *That more benign shall be my face,*
> *That more warm shall be my lips,*
> *That more chaste shall be my speech,*
> *Be my speech the beams of the sun,*
> *Be my lips the sap of the strawberry.*
>
> *May I be an isle in the sea,*
> *May I be a star in waning of the moon,*
> *May I be a staff to the weak,*
> *Wound can I every man,*
> *Wound can no man me.*[23]

Young women who wanted to know the name of their true love cut yarrow by moonlight with a black handled knife, saying a charm such as:

> *Good-morrow, good-morrow fair yarrow,*
> *And thrice good-morrow to thee;*
> *Come, tell me before tomorrow,*
> *Who my true love shall be.*

Keeping silent from the moment she cut the plant, in order not to break the charm, she took the plant home in her right stocking, put it under her pillow and slept on it.[6,131] It could also be pulled while saying:

> *I will pull the yarrow*
> *As Mary pulled it with her two hands*
> *I will pull it with my strength*
> *I will pull it with the hollow of my hand.*[95]

Several other verses, from Aberdeen, Galloway and the Highlands, are recorded, suggesting that the practice of using yarrow to influence the course of love was widespread. When setting out on a journey, it was customary to kneel down, place the right hand on the plant and say 'In the name of the Father and Son and Spirit journey prosper'. The tips of the young plant before it flowers can be used to make yellow and gold dyes.[52, 60, 115]

Sneezewort
Achillea ptarmica

LOCAL NAMES: adder's tongue (Aber), hardhead (Ayr), moleery-tea (Caith), pepper girse, sholgirse, stolgirse (Shet)

❀Apart from the obvious use of making a person sneeze to clear blocked nasal passages, the root was also taken as a remedy for toothache—it is sharp and hot flavoured, and when chewed promotes the flow of soothing saliva.[62] Sneezewort is common throughout Scotland.

Lesser burdock
Arctium minus

SCOTS NAMES: burdocken, flapper-bags
LOCAL NAME: bardog (Shet)

❀Burdock increases the flow of urine and perspiration and, according to Mrs Grieve, was considered one of the best blood purifiers. It was also used to treat various skin complaints, kidney disorders, dropsy, gout and rheumatism. The dandelion and burdock soft drink that is still manufactured originated as a tonic.[61]

Burdock is a fairly common lowland, wayside plant of southern Scotland including Fife and Argyll. The plant produces seed cases with strong hooks designed to be spread by passing animals. Traditionally these burrs form the basis of the Queensferry *Burry Man's* costume, along with garden flowers. On the second Friday in August, an elected member of the local community (who usually does the job for several years) dons the heavy costume and walks the town boundaries in a procession that takes several hours.

Burrs are collected in sacks the week before, dried and cleaned then assembled into square or rectangular patches, each comprising around 500 burrs. On the Burry Man's Day, he starts dressing at 7 am, first putting on a set of long underwear and hood, then standing patiently while the patches are pressed on and individual burrs are carefully placed in sensitive areas, such as the oxters (armpits) and crotch. It takes two hours until all the burrs, plus flowers at the shoulders, hips and knees and a flowery hat are in place. Two men support the Burry Man, who walks slowly and stiffly around the town from 9 am to 6 pm, able to see a little through peepholes in his face mask and drink through a straw, neat whisky being his traditional tipple.

Although it occurs only once a year, being burry man is extremely demanding—it requires stamina, a strong bladder, an indifference to the discomfort caused by the more penetrative burrs, and a conviction that this ancient custom should not die out.[28]

A replica of the Burry Man can be seen in South Queensferry Museum. The origins of this custom are unknown; it was not recorded before the mid-nineteenth century but is believed by local people to be far older.

Burdock

75

It may be derived from a Pagan ritual to bring good fortune to the fishing or the harvest, or perhaps a survival of the ancient scapegoat who carried evil influences away from the community. People may have believed that the prickly burrs would catch all evil influences and malevolent spirits, to be destroyed when the outfit was burned after the Burry Man was released at the end of the day.

Wormwood
Artemesia absinthium

A strongly aromatic plant that was used mainly as a nerve tonic and to improve digestion.[61] Wormwood is rare in Scotland. It grows on rough ground, verges and waste land.

Mugwort
A. vulgaris

SCOTS NAMES: mugger, muggert, muggons
LOCAL NAMES: bowlocks, bulwand, gall-wood, grey bulwand (Shet), moogard (Caith)

Old Scottish legends and verses record an association between mugwort and mermaids, who evidently knew the healing properties of the plant in cases of consumption (tuberculosis) and persistent fever.[25, 61, 62] One mermaid, watching a young girl's funeral passing along the banks of the Clyde, lamented:

> *If they wad drink nettles in March*
> *And eat muggons in May*
> *Sae mony braw maidens*
> *Wadna gang to the clay.*[62]

Mugwort is a common wayside and wasteland plant in lowland Scotland, especially in the south. The tops of the stalks were often used instead of hops for brewing beer; indeed the name mugwort may be derived from this. It was also used as a potherb and an appetiser and dried for smoking.[7, 61, 106]

Daisy
Bellis perennis

SCOTS NAMES: bairnwort, ewe-gowan, ewe-gollan
LOCAL NAMES: benner gowan (Dumf), curl-doddy (i.e. curly-head)

(swS), golland (Caith), gowan, Mary gowlan, may gowan (Berw), koukeleri (Shet)

❋Daisies were used medicinally to make ointment for wounds and to treat liver inflammation, fever and scurvy.[61] The widespread Scottish name of bairnwort refers to the fun children have making daisy-chains. The tradition of pulling daisy petals one by one to find out whether someone loves you is of course still well known—*s/he loves me, s/he loves me not*, the final petal bearing the answer.

Bluebottle, cornflower
Centaurea cyanus

LOCAL NAMES: bluebottle (Berw), blaver (Berw, Rox), blawort (Berw, Rox, Angus, nS), blue gommets (Stir, Aber, Mor), blue blawort (Aber)

❋Cornflowers were used to treat plague, poison, wounds, fevers, inflammation, weak eyes and mouth ulcers.[61, 62] Once a common agricultural weed, cornflowers are still found growing wild in some parts of Scotland, but usually, it appears, as an alien brought in as part of a bird seed mix.

Black knapweed
Centaurea nigra

SCOTS NAME: horse knot
LOCAL NAME: tassel (Berw)
GAELIC NAME: *cnapan dubh* (black knob)

Found in all parts of Scotland, the whole plant was used to produce yellow, bright green, green and rich dark brown dyes.[52]

Corn marigold
Chrysanthemum segetum

SCOTS NAME: manelet
LOCAL NAME: yellow gowan (Caith, nS)
GAELIC NAMES: *dithean-oir, neoinean*

Thought to have arrived in Scotland during the Stone Age as an agricultural weed, corn marigold is found in lowland and coastal parts of Scotland. The flowers can be used for yellow dye and inspired a Gaelic love song:

Your hair was like the flower that grows in the barley,
When you put a comb in it the sheen of gold could be seen.[52, 62, 132]

Thistle
Cirsium species (see also *Sonchus* species)

SCOTS NAME: thrissel
LOCAL NAMES: tistle (Ork, Shet), bur thistle (*C. vulgare*, Ayr), carl doddie (curly head, *C. heterophyllum*, Angus)
GAELIC NAMES: *an cluaran deilgneach* (prickly thistle), *cluaran, diogan, foghnan, giogan*

Thistles are commonly believed to have become the emblem of Scotland because of the somewhat unlikely story that in the eleventh century, invading Danes were repelled when they landed on a beach of the scratchy plant, so that their yells awoke the locals who sprang to their own defence. The motto that usually accompanies the thistle badge, *Nemo me impune lacessit*, can be roughly translated as 'no one attacks me and gets away with it'. Thistles appeared on coins minted under James III in 1470, and the plant had certainly become the emblem of the Scottish royal family by 1503, when James IV married Margaret Tudor. William Dunbar commemorated the occasion with a poem *The Thrissil and the Rose*.[122, 135]

Several different species have been called *the* Scottish thistle but it is doubtful if most Scots know or care which one is which. Three species of *Cirsium* are very common in Scotland: creeping thistle (*C. arvense*), marsh thistle (*C. palustre*) and spear thistle (*C. vulgare*, but this species has no thorns). Melancholy thistle (*C. heterophyllum*) is widespread but less common. Lightfoot wrote that dried flowers of spear thistle (*C. vulgare*) were used in some countries as rennet to curdle milk, but does not state if this was the case in Scotland.[75]

Strong coloured dyes can be obtained from thistles; as Su Grierson points out, a good use for an undesirable garden weed. The plant should be picked just before the flowers open; the tips of spear thistle used with indigo give emerald green; stems, leaves and flower heads together give yellow (sow thistle) or green (marsh thistle with an iron mordant).[52, 60]

Hemp agrimony
Eupatorium cannabinum

LOCAL NAME: filaera (Berw)

❧Found in damp areas in some coastal districts of Scotland, hemp agrimony has tonic properties and was used for purifying the blood; a tea made from the leaves was drunk to relieve catarrh and flu.[61]

Cudweed
Gnaphalium species

❀Sutherland refers to 'mountain cudweed', giving the species as *G. norvegicum*, but this is a rare plant, found mainly in northwest Scotland, with no recorded medicinal use. He may have been referring to *G. uliginosum*, common in damp muddy areas, used internally and as a gargle for quinsy, inflammation of the throat or tonsils.[61]

Ox-eye daisy
Leucanthemum vulgare

SCOTS NAMES: gowan, horse gollan/gowlan
LOCAL NAME: muckle kokkeluri (Shet)

❀[1]Ox-eye daisies were used as a tranquilliser and to treat whooping cough, asthma, coughs, catarrh, wounds, bruises, ulcers, skin diseases and jaundice.[61] It grows wild in most parts of Scotland.

Butterbur
Petasites hybridus

LOCAL NAMES: burn-blade (stream leaf, Kirk, Wigt), eldin-docken (Berw, Rox), son before the father (flowers precede leaves, Clack)

A distinctive, common plant in many lowland and coastal areas of Scotand. The leaves appear after the brush-like flesh-pink flowers, and can reach a metre in diameter, forming clumps in damp places. They were used in many places to wrap butter. It was an ingredient in a love charm collected by Carmichael (see **foxglove**, p. 165).

Ragwort
Senecio jacobea

SCOTS NAMES: beaweed, benweed, bowlocks, bundweed, stinking weed, weebo
LOCAL NAMES: ell-shinders, fizz-gig, ragweed (Berw, Loth, Ayr, Aber), sleepy dose (Banff), stinking alisander (Stir), stinking davies (Fife) yellow weed (Berw)
GAELIC NAMES: *buadhlan buidhe* (overcome, yellow), *buadhghallan* (stripling/branch that overcomes), *guiseag bhuidhe/ cuiseag* (yellow-stalked plant)

The ragwort or ragweed was much prized by the old people. They stored

1. Recorded by Sutherland as *Bellis major*, greater wild white daisy: it seems most likely he was referring to the ox-eye daisy.

79

it among the corn to keep away mice...The fairies (some say the sluagh, host) sheltered beside the ragwort on stormy nights; and [they] rode astride the ragwort in voyaging from island to island, from Alba to Erin, from Alba to Manainn, and home again. In the Outer Isles, for want of better material, the stem of the ragwort was used for making creels. It was also used as a switch for cows, horses and children. The following is the verse addressed by the first wife to the second wife for ill-using the children of the mother in the grave.

> *'Thou ragwort! Thou ragwort!*
> *And thou woman who plied the ragwort!*
> *If the dead of the grave should rise,*
> *The plying of the ragwort would be remembered.'*

(From *Carmina Gadelica* by Alexander Carmichael)

Other records report ragwort as being ridden by witches.[95] Burns wrote:

> *Let Warlocks grim, an' wither'd Hags*
> *Tell how wi' you [Devil] on ragweed nags,*
> *They skim the muirs an' dizzy crags*
> *Wi' wicked speed.*

Ragwort is common in grassland throughout Scotland. In the Hebrides, whole ragwort plants were uprooted and became the focus of a school playground chasing game.[9]

❀The juice of ragwort is astringent and was used to treat burns, eye inflammation, sores and cancerous ulcers, as a gargle for an ulcerated throat and mouth and for bee stings. A poultice made from the green leaves was applied for rheumatism, sciatica and gout, while a decoction of the root was taken for internal bruising and wounds.[61]

The whole plant can be used to produce bronze, yellow and green dyes.[52]

Groundsel
S. vulgaris

LOCAL NAME: wattery drums (Shet)
GAELIC NAMES: *am bualan* (the remedy), *grunnasg, lus Phara liath* (grey Peter's weed—looks old even in spring)

❀Groundsel leaves were so valuable as a poultice for skin problems, it merited the Gaelic name of simply 'the remedy'. Martin recorded the use on Skye:

To ripen a tumour or boil they cut female jacobea small, mix it with some fresh butter on a hot stone, and apply it warm; and this ripens and draws the tumour quickly, and without pain; the same remedy is used for women's breasts that are hard or swelled.[100]

Mary Beith describes another method of preparing a poultice, by pouring boiling water over washed leaves, leaving them to steep, then applying them warm; the strained water was also used for chapped hands.[6, 7] Groundsel is common in most parts of Scotland in disturbed or cultivated ground.

Sea wormwood
Seriphidium maritimum

With similar properties to *A. absinthum* but acting less powerfully.[61] Sea wormwood is rare in Scotland, occurring along the coast from Angus to East Lothian.

Golden rod
Solidago virgaurea

GAELIC NAME: *fuinseag coille*

✿Used since ancient times to heal broken bones. Martin recorded the use on Skye of an ointment made from equal parts of betony (*Stachys officinalis*), St John's wort (*Hypericum perforatum*), and golden rod, chopped, crushed and mixed with sheep fat or fresh butter. On Lewis he observed an ointment made of golden rod, all-heal (probably *Prunella vulgaris*) and fresh butter being used for gangrene.[100] Golden rod occurs in most parts of Scotland.

Sowthistle, milk thistle
Sonchus species

SCOTS NAMES: swine thistle, swinies (Berw)

✿Common throughout Scotland, this plant was was used as a tonic.[61] Lightfoot wrote:

The tender leaves strip'd of their spines, are by some boiled and eaten as garden stuff. An emulsion of the seeds has sometimes been used to thin the blood and cure stitches and pleurises but at present is rarely practised.[75]

Feverfew
Tanacetum parthenium

Introduced in the Middle Ages for its great medicinal value. Feverfew leaves and flowers were used as a tonic and to treat constipation, flatulence, colic, menstrual disorders, nervousness, depression, coughs, wheezing, insect or rodent bites, and as a pain killer.[61] Although it is not native, the plant is included here for interest because it is a common wayside weed enjoying renewed popularity as both a prophylactic and cure for migraine and headaches; I have heard of desperate people eating daily feverfew sandwiches although it tastes rather bitter and is easier to take in tablets bought from the chemist.

Dandelion
Taraxacum species

SCOTS NAMES: doon-head clock, horse gowan, milk gowan, piss-a-bed, witch gowan, yellow gowan
LOCAL NAMES: bitter aks, eksis girse (Shet), bum-pipe (Banff, Lan), devil's milk-plant (Kirk), stink davie (Clack)
GAELIC NAMES: *bearnan bride* (*bearn* notch-in leaf, *brigh* sap), *am bearnan Brighde* (notched plant of Bridget), *bior nam bride* (sharp, tooth-like), *fiacal leaohain* (lion's teeth)

❀One of our most common plants, dandelion roots and leaves were used medicinally for their diuretic, tonic and stimulant properties. In nineteenth century Fife, mining folk used an infusion of dandelion root to cure stomach ache. Dandelion leaf sandwiches were eaten in Glencoe to cure ulcers.[48, 61, 115]

If this was indeed the plant of the goddess/saint Bride/Bridget (rather than the sappy plant), that would explain its powerful attributes. Carmichael collected a blessing of earth's bounty that included dandelion (see p. 7), and wrote that a:

> *magic hoop was made of milkwort, butterwort, dandelion and marigold. It was from three to four inches in diameter, and it was bound by a triple cord of lint—for lint also had magical properties—in the name of the Father, the Son and the Spirit, and placed under the milk-vessel, to prevent the substance of the milk from being spirited away.*

The young leaves are tasty in salad, can be boiled like spinach or added to soup, or even made into a beer-like tonic drink, while the flowers make good wine. The roots can be roasted and ground for coffee (Wilma Paterson, in *The Country Cup*, gives recipes for tea, coffee, beer and wine).

A variable yellow dye can be obtained from the plant.[52, 60]

Sea mayweed
Tripleurospermum maritimum

SCOTS NAMES: dog's chamomile, may-weed

❦No recorded medicinal use for this plant has been found.

Coltsfoot
Tussilago farfara

SCOTS NAMES: dishilago (tussilago), Son afore the Father (flowers appear before leaves)
LOCAL NAMES: cow-heave (Selk), dove-dock (Caith), foal's foot/foal-foot (Berw, Rox), tushy-lucky gowan (Dumf)
GAELIC NAMES: *cluas liath* (grey ear), *duilliur, gorm liath* (greyish green), *spuing* (tinder-leaf)

❦The flowers and/or leaves were made into an infusion, syrup or decoction for coughs, including whooping cough, asthma and other chest complaints. Nineteenth century Fife miners used coltsfoot for coughs and colds.[75, 96, 115]

The plant is common in grassland and waste land throughout Scotland, and is one of the first flowers to appear in spring. According to John Cameron,

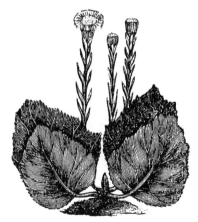

Coltsfoot

> *The leaf, dipped in saltpetre[1] and then dried, made excellent tinder or touchwood. It was used for lighting fires. The leaves were smoked before the introduction of tobacco, and still form the principal ingredient in British herb tobacco.*[18]

The leaves produce green/yellow dye.[52]

1. A white powder used in making gunpowder.

83

Berberidaceae
BARBERRY FAMILY

Barberry
Berberis vulgaris

SCOTS NAME: berber
GAELIC NAMES: *barbrag* (brilliancy of a shell), *preas nan gear dhearc* (sour-berry bush), *preas deilgneach* (prickly bush)

An uncommon shrub of hedges and scrubland found in a few scattered locations in Scotland and almost certainly introduced rather than native. Martin recorded that the roots could be boiled and drunk for jaundice, while the acid, astringent berries were sometimes preserved. In 1736 the cookery book writer Mrs McLintock was pickling barberries and making barberry comfits.

Martin reported that the roots gave yellow dye while Jean Fraser obtains orange dye from the stems, green from the roots, neither requiring mordant to make them colourfast.[52]

Betulaceae
BIRCH FAMILY

Alder
Alnus glutinosa

SCOTS NAMES: aller, allertree, aar, arn
GAELIC NAMES: *fearn(a)*, *drumanach*

A very common tree of damp places in Scotland. Reputed to have been one of the sacred woods of the druids, alder was known in folklore as the symbol of secrecy and places of refuge, providing privacy for legendary lovers and safety for outlaws.[50, 95] The wood is resistant to rotting and was used to make clog soles and the piles of waterside structures, including crannogs, the small artificial islands built in many Scottish lochs as refuges for people and livestock (see p. 29).

The leaves were made into a soothing plaster for feet swollen by travel, while an infusion of the bark is astringent and was used as a tonic and a gargle for sore throats. Black and brown dyes can be made from the tannin-rich bark and twigs [52, 76]

Birch
Betula pendula, B. pubescens

SCOTS NAME: birk, birken tree
GAELIC NAMES: *beatha, beith*

The lovely and extremely common birch tree formerly had a valuable place in the Scottish domestic economy. It features in many folk stories, and birch was usually used for the peeled white wand carried by the corn sheaf made to represent Bride at a spring festival in the Highlands and Islands (see **primrose**, p. 142). It was considered unlucky 'to pu' the birks sae green', and seeing green birch in a dream presaged ill, while birch growing with briars on the grave of two lovers indicated that death had not divided them.[122]

Birch is a colonising species and was one of the first trees to reappear after the last Ice Age. From prehistoric times, the bark may have been used in Scotland to make containers similar to those the carried by the Iceman who lived and died over 5,000 years ago in the Alps (see p. 25). Birch bark is easily removed, flexible and strong even when dried and is still used to make beautiful supple baskets in Scandinavian countries. The Iceman's containers were cylindrical buckets sewn together with fine strips of bast (probably the bark of lime trees, *Tilia* species); one had been used to carry live embers.[126] Birch sap was boiled down to make tar, the widely used glue of prehistoric people. Lightfoot mentions birch-bark rope being used to tie down thatch.[75]

The wood was used for many household utensils, the branches for shinty sticks, and fine sprays for brooms, ropes and withies. The leaves and twigs yield bright yellow dye, while the bark was rolled into candles, beaten into paper and used for tanning. Rorie extolled the virtues of birch as excellent fuel, even when damp, 'a charming companion'.[115] A charity called Highland Birchwoods started a new venture in 1995 to grow shiitake mushrooms, from Asia, on birch logs, for supply to gourmet restaurants. Based on research carried out by Aberdeen University, it is hoped the project will become a crofting business, with crops of up to 2 kilos per log and selling at £7.50 per kilo. Crofters, small farmers and tree nurseries in Inverness, Kyle, Argyll and Dornoch are already experimenting with growing the mushroom.[107]

❀Birch leaf tea was drunk to relieve rheumatism, and fresh birch sap, collected in spring, is a pleasant drink, believed by Highlanders to be beneficial for the kidneys and bladder; it also makes delicious wine, still or sparkling, long favoured by home wine makers and now being marketed by a few Scottish wineries.[125]

Boraginaceae
BORAGE FAMILY

Hound's tongue
Cynoglossum officinale

❁Used to treat a variety of ailments from coughs, colds, dysentery, piles, scalds, burns and gangrene to hair loss and rabies.[61] The plant has a very localised, mainly east coast distribution in Scotland.

Comfrey
Symphytum officinale

GAELIC NAME: *meacan dubh* (large or dark plant)

John Cameron wrote: 'The root of comfrey abounds in mucilage, and was considered an excellent remedy for uniting broken bones'.[18] *S. officinale*, the native species used medicinally (as indicated by the name *officinale*) is less common than *S. tuberosum*, which forms large patches in damp woods in southern Scotland, and may not be native. *Symphytum x uplandicum*, now the commonest roadside comfrey, is a relatively recent introduction. It was used in the nineteenth century as a forage crop for livestock.

Brassicaceae
CABBAGE FAMILY

Shepherd's purse
Capsella bursa-pastoris

SCOTS NAME: mother's heart
LOCAL NAMES: lady's purses (Berw), rofle the lady's purses (Banff)
GAELIC NAME: *lus na fola* (the blood herb)

❁Tea made from the leaves of shepherd's purse was considered to be one of the best treatments for internal bleeding. The plant was also used externally on wounds, bleeding noses, piles, bruises and strains, in addition to being prescribed for diarrhoea, jaundice, rheumatism, bladder infections, dropsy and scurvy.[61] Shepherd's purse is a very common weed throughout Scotland.

Wavy bitter-cress
Cardamine flexuosa

GAELIC NAME: *biolair*

A very common little plant of damp woods and rocky places, used to produce grey dye.[52]

Lady's smock, cuckoo flower
C. pratensis

LOCAL NAME: carsons (growing on carse, low rich damp land, swS)
GAELIC NAME: *biolair ghriagain*

❧A pretty flower common in damp grassland throughout Scotland, used to treat epilepsy, fevers and scurvy.[7, 62]

Scurvy grass
Cochlearia officinalis

SCOTS NAMES: screeby, spoon-wort
GAELIC NAMES: *a maraich* (sailor), *carran* (thing for scurvy)

❧A small fleshy plant common on salt marshes, dunes and cliffs in all coastal parts of Scotland. Many medicinal uses are recorded for scurvy grass, as well as the obvious one. Scurvy, a disease characterised by livid spots and total exhaustion, is caused by vitamin C deficiency and was common whenever people did not have access to regular supplies of fruit and vegetables. The use of scurvy grass as a remedy was known in Roman times. Shetland islanders found it effective, according to Martin Martin. He reported several other uses of the plant. It was chopped and applied fresh for sharp stitch-like pains. On Skye, an infusion of scurvy grass with fresh butter added was taken as a purge; it worked gently and so was taken for up to a fortnight. On St Kilda it was also used as a purgative, mixed with melted bird fat. Of Jeskar [i.e. Fisher] off Fladder, he wrote:

This rock affords a great quantity of scurvy-grass, of an extraordinary size, and very thick; the natives eat it frequently, as well boiled as raw: two of them told me that they happened to be confined there for a space of thirty hours, by a contrary wind; and being without victuals, fell to eating this scurvy-grass, and finding it of a sweet taste, they ate a large basketful of it, which did abundantly satisfy their appetites until their return home. They told me also that it was not in the least windy, or any other way troublesome to them.[100]

Watercress
Rorippa species

SCOTS NAMES: well-girse/karse/kerse (spring/stream cress)
GAELIC NAMES: *biolair* (dainty/causes nose to smart), *biolair Moire* (cress of Mary), *durlus* (water plant)

✳Common in slow-moving streams, ditches and marshes in lowland and coastal parts of Scotland, watercress leaves were used medicinally to treat scurvy and other skin diseases, and also tuberculosis. It was given to women to cure childlessness, and Cameron wrote of an old charm used while cutting watercress to enchant neighbours into giving the person half their milk and cream; perhaps one of these uses was the reason it was known as a magic plant on Skye.[6, 18, 23, 61]

It was and still is commonly used in salad and soup, having an appetising peppery flavour, but it should always be washed carefully and not collected from areas where sheep graze because snails of the liver fluke parasite feed on it.[96]

Charlock
Sinapis arvensis

SCOTS NAMES: runch/runchik/runchie, scaldricks, skellocks, wild mustard, yellow weed
LOCAL NAMES: runch-balls (Rox, Ork, Shet), wild kale (Kirk, Wigt, Lan)
GAELIC NAMES: *amharag* (raw), *marag bhuidhe* (yellow sausage, i.e. pod), *praiseach garbh* (rough pot-herb), *sceallan* (shield), *sgealag* (biting)

Common throughout Scotland in cultivated and waste places, it was popular as a pot-herb wherever it grew.[57, 96, 100]

Hedge mustard
Sisymbrium officinale

SCOTS NAME: back-cresses

✳Found mainly on the east side of Scotland, hedge mustard was used medicinally as a powerful purgative to treat worms and obstructions of the intestines, also for rheumatism and jaundice.[61]

Field penny cress
Thlaspi arvense

✿A widespread but uncommon weed in lowland Scotland and on some of the islands, this plant was used as an antidote to poison.[61] The name refers to the large round seed, the size of an old silver threepenny piece.

Campanulaceae
BELLFLOWER FAMILY

Harebell
Campanula rotundifolia

SCOTS NAMES: blaver, blaewort, bluebell, harebell, lady's thimble, old man's (i.e. devil's) bell , thimbles
LOCAL NAMES: blue blavers (Rox), gowk's thimbles/thumles (i.e. cuckoo's thimbles), milk-ort (nS), witch bells (sS), witches' thimbies (Lan)
GAELIC NAME: *brog na cubhaig* (cuckoo's shoe)

An exquisite little flower common throughout Scotland. The association with cuckoos is curious, as harebells flower in July and August after the bird has left Scotland. The cuckoo season actually mirrors that of the bluebell or wild hyacinth, *Hyacinthoides non-scriptus*, which does flower in spring; the two plants may have been confused with each other. Fairies made hats from the flower, and it was said to tinkle a warning to hares when danger was near. Wild white specimens were considered lucky but in parts of Buchan the devil's flower was not picked.[62, 122, 135]

Caprifoliaceae
HONEYSUCKLE FAMILY

Honeysuckle
Lonicera periclymenum

LOCAL NAMES: lady's fingers (Rox), woodbind, woodbine (Renf)

Common throughout Scotland, this was a magical plant used to avert any evil powers around on May Day and at other dangerous times. A three-ply wreath of honeysuckle, ivy and rowan placed over the lintel of the byre

and beneath churns in the milk-house protected cows, milk and butter.[23]
Rorie wrote:

> *In eighteenth century Moray, children who were suffering from 'hectic
> fever', as well as consumptive patients, were passed thrice through a
> circular wreath of wood-bine, which was cut during the increase of the
> March moon and let down over the body from the head to the feet. In
> 1597, a certain Janet Stewart stood her trial for witch-craft, one charge
> laid against her being that she had healed sundry women 'By taking ane
> garland of green wood-bynd, and causing the patient pas thryis throw it,
> quhilk thereafter scho cut in nyne pieces and cast it in the fire'.*[115]

He does not say what she was treating them for or what her fate was
but it is noteworthy that the unfortunate woman's crime was to have
healed the sick women.

An infusion of the flowers was used to treat coughs and sore throats,
asthma and bronchitis, freckles and sunburn. The flowers can also be
made into tea and wine.[7, 110]

Elder
Sambucus nigra

SCOTS NAMES: boun-tree, boon-tree, bour-tree, bore tree, borral
GAELIC NAMES: *droman, dromanach, ruis*

Elder

Elder, often known as bour-tree in Scotland, is very common and was
second only to rowan for protection against witchcraft and evil spells. It
was often planted at the back of a house, with rowan at the front, and milk
and freshly baked cakes were left to cool beneath the bour-tree for safe-
keeping. A cross made from elder was hung on stables and byres to protect
the animals inside.[50, 52, 95] In the nineteenth century, according to Marian
McNeill,

> *the driver of a hearse had his whip-handle made of bour-tree to avert
> evil. But the bour-tree was more than a mere protector. The green juice
> of the inner bark applied to the eyelids of a baptised person gave him the
> power of 'seeing' things (presumably on the Quarter Days[1]) and if he
> stood under a bour-tree near a fairy hill on Hallowe'en, he could see the
> fairy train go by.*[95]

1. The Pagan quarter days marking the changing seasons were Christianised as Candlemas
(February 2), Whitsun (May 13), Lammas (August 1) and Martinmas (November 11), but
belief persisted that on these days the veil separating the natural and supernatural worlds
became so thin, there was serious danger of evil powers or enchantment affecting earthly
dwellers.

90

There was a belief that the cross Jesus died on was made of elder wood (rather unlikely, considering the small size and crooked shape of elder; other legends say it was aspen, *Populus tremula*). Robert Chambers recorded the following rhyme:

> *Bour-tree, bour-tree, crookit rung,*
> *Never straight and never strong,*
> *Ever bush, and never tree*
> *Since Our Lord was nailed t'ye.*[25]

It was considered unlucky to cut elder; nevertheless the timber was used for furniture, ornamentation and inlay. On Colonsay, McNeill recorded that boys who hoped to become pipers made practice chanters from hollowed out young branches. Mary Beith suggests the name bour- or bore-tree actually derives from the ease with which elder can be hollowed out to make pipes, for blowing or smoking, and pop guns.[6, 50, 96]

❀Almost every part of the tree had a medicinal use; the whole plant is strongly purgative, emetic and diuretic. The bark and root were used to treat dropsy (heart and kidney disorder), epilepsy, asthma and croup. The leaves were made into ointment for bruises, sprains, chilblains and wounds, dropsy, inflamed eyes, blocked nose and nervous headache. The flowers treated wounds, burns, chilblains and other skin problems, scarlet fever, measles and other diseases that cause rashes and spots, pleurisy, constipation, colds, sore throat, flu, inflamed eyes, pain, headache and piles. The berries made remedies for rheumatism, syphilis, constipation, colic, diarrhoea, epilepsy and piles, and elderberry wine made a palatable medicine for catarrh, flu, asthma, coughs, colds, fever and sciatica.[6,61]

The berries yield blue and violet/purple dye, the leaves yellow and green, the bark grey/black; it was important in Harris tweed manufacture. The berries are still widely used for making wine and syrup, and the flowers for tea, wine and 'champagne', cordial and for adding flavour to punch, fruit juice and preserved fruit.[52, 60]

Caryophyllaceae
PINK FAMILY

Mouse-ear
Cerastium species

❀Used to treat wounds (see p. 16).

Pearlwort
Sagina species

LOCAL NAME: meldi (meal plant, Shet)
GAELIC NAMES: *lus beannaichte* (blessed plant), *molus, mothan*

S. procumbens is an extremely common, inconspicuous little plant found throughout Scotland on lawns, paths, waste ground and riverbanks; other *Sagina* species are more localised. Pearlwort was ground into flour in the Shetland Isles.[62] However, the plant was best known for its magic powers, attributed to blessings of the plant by Christ, St Bride or Bridget and St Columba, because it was believed to be the first plant Christ stepped on when he came to earth, or when he rose from the dead.[23] Alexander Carmichael recorded several Gaelic incantations for plucking the 'gracious *mothan*,[1] plant most precious in the field', bestowing on the gatherer holiness, wisdom and eloquence, and protection against the evil eye.

> *Pluck will I the* mothan,
> *As ordained by the king of life,*
> *To overcome all oppression,*
> *And the spell of evil eye.*
>
> *I will pluck the gracious* mothan,
> *Plant most precious in the field,*
> *That mine will be the holiness of the seven priests,*
> *And the eloquence that is within them.*
>
> *While I shall keep the pearlwort,*
> *Without wile shall be my lips,*
> *Without guile shall be mine eye,*
> *Without hurt shall be mine hand,*
> *Without pain shall be my heart,*
> *Without heaviness shall be my death.*[23]

The plant was hung above the door to prevent fairies from entering the house and spiriting away the inhabitants. The *lus beannaichte* (blessed plant) placed under the right knee of a woman during childbirth soothed her mind and body and protected both mother and baby from fairies, providing the woman removed all rings from her fingers, to ensure they would not interfere with the plant's action. In the byre it protected cows, calves, and milk, and was placed in the front hooves of the bull before

1. In one note Carmichael says 'I am not sure what the plant [*mothan*] is—perhaps the bog violet?' while in another he translates it unequivocally as pearlwort, a 'rare' plant of moorland and hill which would fit *S. subulata* or *S. sanguinoides*

mating to protect both cow and future calf at the vulnerable moment of conception. It was also kept under the milk churn, in a bag with iron nails for combined effectiveness. When a cow grazed on pearlwort, protection extended to her calf, milk, and all who drank the milk. Women wore the plant sewn into their bodice, and men had it sewn in their vest under the left arm. Carrying the plant or drinking milk from a cow who had eaten it ensured immunity from harm, even for one being tried for a crime of which they were guilty.[23]

It was said to be a potent love charm; girls drank the juice, or wetted their lips with it, to attract lovers, and the unwary lad who kissed a lass with a piece of pearlwort in her mouth was bound to her forever:

> When the mothan *is used as a love-philtre, the woman who gives it goes*
> *upon her left knee and plucks nine roots of the plant and knots them*
> *together, forming them into a* cuach *(ring). The woman places the ring*
> *in the mouth of the girl for whom it is made, in name of the King of the*
> *sun, and of the moon, and of the stars, and in name of the Holy Three.*
> *When the girl meets her lover or a man whom she loves and whose love*
> *she desires to secure, she puts the ring in her mouth. And should the man*
> *kiss the girl while the* mothan *is in her mouth he becomes henceforth her*
> *bondsman, bound to her everlastingly in cords infinitely finer than the*
> *gossamer nets of the spider, and infinitely stronger than the adamant*
> *chain of the giant.*[23]

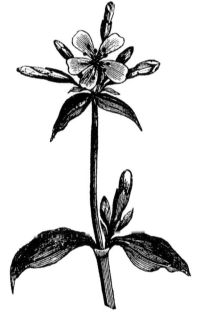

Soapwort

Soapwort
Saponaria officinalis

GAELIC NAME: *gairgean-creagh*

A pretty wayside plant found occasionally in southern and central Scotland (probably introduced); the crushed leaves produce a lather which was used not only to cleanse but also to treat skin problems.[18]

Bladder campion
Silene vulgaris

SCOTS NAME: cowmack
LOCAL NAME: cow-cracker (Dumf)

According to Grigson, bladder campion was known as 'cowmack' in Scotland because it was believed cows that grazed on it would welcome the bull's attentions.[62]

93

Corn spurrey
Spergula arvensis

SCOTS NAME: yarr
LOCAL NAME: meldi (meal plant, Shet)

A very common arable weed and wayside plant throughout Scotland. Like pearlwort, this plant was known as meldi in Shetland where it was ground into meal.[62]

Chickweed
Stellaria media

SCOTS NAME: chickenweed
LOCAL NAMES: arva/arvi, chickenwir (Shet)
GAELIC NAME: *fliodh/fliogh* (an excrescence)

✿This is a very common plant of bare or cultivated ground throughout Scotland, with many medicinal uses. Martin reported that on the Isle of Skye, chickweed was used with what sounds like tender loving care:

> *To procure sleep after a fever, the feet, knees, and ankles of the patient are washed in warm water, into which a good quantity of chick-weed is put, and afterwards some of the plant is applied warm to the neck, and between the shoulders, as the patient goes to bed.*[100]

The fresh leaves were also made into ointment for inflammation, ulcers and piles, chilblains, rashes, rheumatism and stiff joints, or applied as a poultice on abscesses and sore or swollen breasts. A decoction was taken for constipation and an infusion for coughs and hoarseness; chickweed water was drunk for obesity and insomnia, and also used as eyewash.[6, 7, 61, 135]

Chenopodiaceae
GOOSEFOOT FAMILY

Sea beet
Beta vulgaris ssp *maritima*

GAELIC NAMES: *betis, biotas*

This plant has only a localised distribution in a few coastal areas of Scotland and is nowhere common, but Lightfoot reported 'The young leaves boil'd are wholesome and good greens.'[75]

Fat hen
Chenopodium album

SCOTS NAMES: meldweed, common white- or frost-blite
LOCAL NAMES: midden mylies (nS), myles (Berw)
GAELIC NAME: *praiseach fiadhain* (wild pottage)

Archaeological evidence indicates that fat hen was being eaten in the Bronze Age in Scotland, and it remained a common vegetable until spinach was introduced; on Islay, Lightfoot saw this plant being boiled and eaten.[62,75] It is nowadays regaining popularity with people interested in wild foods. A plant of waste and cultivated ground, common throughout Scotland.

Good King Henry
Chenopodium bonus-henricus

SCOTS NAMES: English mercury, wild spinage, allgood, smear docken
LOCAL NAMES: midden mylies (Selk), smiddy leaves (Berw)
GAELIC NAMES: *praiseach brathair* (friar's potherb)

Lightfoot enjoyed the young leaves of Good King Henry as spring greens, while a hundred years later Cameron recorded the leaves still being eaten as spinach where nothing better was available.[18, 75] It is found mainly in the south-eastern half of Scotland and a few coastal districts further north.

Saltwort
Salsola kali

✿A prickly succulent plant that grows on sandy seashores. The juice and seed-vessels of saltwort were used as a diuretic.

Saltwort

Clusiaciae
ST JOHN'S WORT FAMILY

St John's wort
Hypericum species

LOCAL NAME: St Peter's wort (Ork)
GAELIC NAMES: *achlasan Chaluimchille* (armpit package of Columba), *allas Muire* (image of Mary), *eala bhuidhe* (yellow), *lus na Maighdinn Muire* (Virgin Mary's herb), *lus na fala* (blood wort, Glen Roy)

95

Believed to be the special plant of St Columba, because of its association with his favourite saint, John the Evangelist, and with the Virgin Mary; hence this plant is attributed with strong powers of protection. This may represent the adoption by Christianity of an ancient belief: St John's wort is thought to have been used to light sacred Beltane (May 1) bonfires in Pagan times, chosen perhaps for its flame-like buds—and it was on 6 May that Christians honoured St John the Evangelist (the patron saint of Scotland before St Andrew) until his feast day was changed to 27 December in the Middle Ages. Pagan beliefs also survived in the use of St John's wort for Midsummer's Eve[1] divination rites, and preventing fairies from spiriting people away while they slept.[95, 125, 133]

Lightfoot wrote:

> *The superstitious in Scotland carry this plant about with them as a charm against the dire effects of witchcraft and enchantment. They also cure, or fancy they cure their ropy milk, which they suppose to be under some malignant influence by putting this herb into it and milking afresh upon it.*[75]

In Alexander Carmichael's time, the late nineteenth century, it was

> *one of the few plants still cherished by the people to ward away second-sight, enchantment, witchcraft, evil eye, and death, and to ensure peace and plenty in the house, increase and prosperity in the fold, and growth and fruition in the field.*[23]

He recorded several Gaelic poems relating to the plant, e.g.:

> *Arm-pit package of Columba, kindly*
> *Unsought by me, unlooked for!*
> *I shall not be lifted away in my sleep*
> *And I shall not be thrust upon iron...*
>
> *Better the reward of it under my arm*
> *Than a crowd of calving kine;*
> *Better the reward of its virtues*
> *Than a herd of white cattle.*

and:

> *St John's wort, St John's wort*
> *My envy whosoever has thee*
> *I will pluck thee with my right hand*
> *I will preserve thee with my left hand*

St John's Wort

1. Midsummer's Eve is close to the feast day of St John the Baptist, 24 June.

Whoso findeth thee in the cattle field
Shall never be without kine.[23]

St John's wort had to be found by accident to be effective and was then tucked under the left armpit, popularly thought of as a trend started by the great Columba himself, but most likely in fact simply the place it was put as a poultice where it would be most effectively absorbed by the body.[7, 62]

❀Martin refers to the use on Skye of St John's wort in ointment for bonesetting, along with equal quantities of speedwell and golden rod, chopped and crushed in sheep fat or fresh butter.[100] Lightfoot wrote:

An oil or tincture of the flowers is esteemed a good vulnerary. The express'd juice or infusion of the same is reckoned good to destroy worms, to resolve coagulated blood, and to promote urine.[75]

According to Fraser, it was sometimes used in brewing beer and put in whisky for flavouring, giving it a dark purple tinge. The flowers give red dye.[52]

Convolvulaceae
BINDWEED FAMILY

Sea bindweed
Calystegia soldanella

❀A rare coastal plant which was used as a purgative.[61]

Cornaceae
DOGWOOD FAMILY

Dwarf cornel
Cornus suecica

GAELIC NAME: *lus-a-chraois* (plant of gluttony)

The berries have a sweet, waterish taste, and are supposed by the High-landers to create a great appetite.[18]

Grows mainly on moorland in the Highlands of Scotland.

97

Corylaceae
HAZEL FAMILY

Hazel
Corylus avellana

GAELIC NAMES: *alltuinn, calldainn, callduinn, caitlin, colluinn* (wood, grove), *coll*

❀Hazel has several Gaelic names, *calltuinn* or *coll* being the commonest. John Cameron suggests New Year's Night, January 1, is called *oidche coille* because hazel starts flowering in January.[18]

It is associated with many old Scottish beliefs. The tree was sacred to the Celtic sea god Manannan and the penalty for unnecessary cutting of hazel was death. Hazel nuts were the fruit of wisdom, eaten by druids seeking prophetic powers, and the tree may have been, along with rowan, more important in Scottish druidic rites than oak. Eating hazel nuts was said to give bards their knowledge of epic legends and ability to write poems and songs. An ancient legend tells that the salmon, a sacred fish, acquired its red spots from swallowing nuts from the nine hazels of knowledge that fell into the water where it swam in a sacred pool; the knowledge was then passed on to the person who ate the salmon.[50, 105, 82, 95]

Hazel was also sacred to witches, who sometimes used it for broom sticks, because it symbolised female wisdom. On the other hand, finding two nuts naturally joined together, called St John's nut, was a good omen and it could be thrown at witches, presumably to protect oneself against the evil eye.[18, 62, 75]

Hazelnuts were used in divination rites on *Samhain* (Hallowe'en). The feelings of one's sweetheart could be ascertained by asking questions of the nut, then throwing it into the flames and watching the way it burned or jumped to reveal the answer; this practice was still being tried early this century. Babies born in autumn were considered fortunate because they could have hazelnut milk as their first food and sick children were fed an elixir of nut milk mixed with honey.[50, 95, 96]

Hazel was also associated with Thunor (Thor), god of fire, and therefore of thunder and lightning, because its wood was used to make fire by friction. The young St Kentigern (or Mungo) was said to have used a hazel bough to obtain fire from heaven when the sacred fire of his monastery was extinguished by his playmates for a prank. Druids and early Christian bishops carried hazel wands; a hazel walking stick gave the bearer protection against evil and in the hands of a magician could confer invisibility. Hazel rods were formerly used to detect veins of gold, lead, coal and other minerals, while water diviners commonly use hazel twigs for dowsing. The wood was by some considered unlucky, said to symbolise loss and misfortune; a tradition that survived into the last century was to present a piece of hazel wood to a lover one wished to forsake.[82, 85, 76, 95, 105]

Hazel wood was used for tool-handles, shepherds' crooks, shinty sticks and balls, while the pliable, strong and rot-resistant stems were made into baskets, farm and lobster creels, hurdles, house walls (wattle) and the walls and roofs of animal shelters.[96, 116] Carmichael recorded an old belief in Eigg that hazel (as well as willow and pine) should not be cut when the moon was waning:

> *The sap of the wood goes down into the root, and the wood becomes brittle and crumbly, without pith, without good.*[23]

Crassulaceae
STONECROP FAMILY

Stonecrop, wall-pepper
Sedum acre

GAELIC NAME: *grafan nan clach* (stone's pickaxe)

✤Common in most parts of Scotland, this plant was used to treat worms, scurvy and scrofula (tuberculosis of lymph glands in the neck). It was also eaten in salad.[61, 96]

White stonecrop
S. album

SCOTS NAMES: small house leek, yellow prick madam

✤Naturalised in parts of Scotland except the Highlands and Islands, the leaves and stalks were used for treating inflammation and piles.[61]

Roseroot
S. rosea

LOCAL NAME: priest's pintel (Banff)

✤The plant is widespead on mountains and sea cliffs in the Highlands and Islands, but the medicinal use is not known. Grigson explains that 'In

Stonecrop

99

Banffshire it had the ironic name of mixed sweetness and opprobium, priest's pintel', meaning priest's penis. This presumably alludes to the succulent leaves, which are thick, stiff and often tipped with deep pink.[62]

Orpine, livelong
S. telephium

SCOTS NAMES: healing leaf, orpy-leaf
LOCAL NAME: orppies (Berw, Rox)

❀Localised (probably introduced) in the south and east of Scotland, orpine was used to treat diarrhoea, piles, wounds, fever, haemorrhages, heavy menstrual bleeding and sterility in women, kidney disorders, cancer and scrofula.[61, 62]

Houseleek
Sempervivum tectorum

SCOTS NAME: sengreen
LOCAL NAMES: foose (Berw, Rox, Angus, Aber, Mor), healing blade/ leaf (Clack), hockerie-topner (Dumf)
GAELIC NAMES: *lus gharaidh* (garden-wort), *lus nan cluas* (the ear plant), *tin gealch, tineas na gealaich* (moon-sick)

An odd looking plant, rare in Scotland but recorded occasionally since ancient times and possibly naturalised. Houseleek had a number of medicinal uses. Cameron wrote:

> *the juice of the plant applied by itself, or mixed with cream, is used as a remedy for the ear-ache...for various diseases, particularly those of women and children, and head complaints.*[18]

The Gaelic name translated as moon-sick may be associated with the plant's use for women's diseases, menstruation being so closely related to the cycles of the moon, although Mrs Grieve's detailed account of its uses fails to mention any specifically female ailments. It was also used to soothe shingles and burns and to cool fevers.[7, 61]

Navelwort, wall penny wort
Umbilicus rupestris

SCOTS NAMES: jack-in-the-bush, kidney-wort, lover's links, maid-in-the-mist, walpenny woort

✿Found in Argyll and the southermost Hebridean islands. The juice of the plant was used to treat epilepsy, inflammation of the liver and spleen, and the leaves for piles, kidneys, gout, sciatica, chilblains and wounds.[61]

Cyperaceae
SEDGE FAMILY

Sea–clubrush
Bolboschoenus maritimus

GAELIC NAME: *brobh* (quern, hand-mill)

The large, nutritious roots were fed to cattle and in times of scarcity ground into meal for people to eat.[18]

Sea sedge, sea matgrass, sand sedge
Carex arenaria

GAELIC NAMES: *gallsheilisdear/seilisdear amh* (raw sedge)

Common in sandy areas throughout Scotland. Murdo McNeill recorded that on Colonsay, cattle tethers were made from the long creeping roots.[96]

Common spike-rush
Eleocharis palustris

GAELIC NAME: *luachair*

Very common on marshy ground and the edges of ponds and lochs. The flowers yield green dye.[52]

Bulrush, clubrush
Schoenoplectus species

GAELIC NAME: *curcais, cuilc* (a cane, when cut), *ghobhal luachair* (forked rush)

Bulrushes (now officially renamed clubrushes) are found in silty water at the edge of lochs, ponds and rivers and were used for making ropes, baskets, mats, chair seats and for thatching. In Orkney and Shetand, trows, or trolls, rode through the air on bulrushes.[18, 75, 95]

Tufted scirpus, deer's hair, heath clubrush
Trichopherum cespitosum

GAELIC NAMES: *ciob/cipe/ciob cheann dubh* (black-headed food), *cruach luachair* (hill-rush)

The main food for cattle in the Highlands in spring.[18]

Dipsacaceae
TEASEL FAMILY

Teasel
Dipsacus fullonum

SCOTS NAMES: great white teasel, venus-basons

❀The root and flower heads were used medicinally for jaundice, liver, stomach ailments, eyewash and cleansing of 'warts, wens, cankers, fistulas' (Mrs Grieve, quoting Culpepper). Teasel is locally common only in a few places in the south and east of Scotland. The name comes from the use of the spiny flower of the closely related species *D. sativus* to card, or tease, wool in preparation for spinning, but this species is rare. It was (and still is) cultivated in Somerset for this purpose.

Field scabious
Knautia arvensis

SCOTS NAME: blue bonnet
GAELIC NAME: *gille guirmein* (blue lad)

❀Found mainly around the coasts of Scotland, in the Central Belt and south eastern areas, the plant (excluding the roots) was made into ointment for skin disorders including scabs, sores, ulcers, gangrene and dandruff. It was also used to treat fever, coughs, pleurisy, breathlessness and other lung problems, for pains and stitch in the side.[61]

Devil's bit scabious
Succissa pratensis

SCOTS NAMES: blue bonnets, curl-doddy (i.e. curly head), devil's bit
GAELIC NAME: *ura bhallach*

❀Common throughout Scotland, the whole plant was made into tea for coughs and fevers, to reduce internal inflammation and to purify the blood; an infusion was also used on skin sores and dandruff.[61]

Grigson recorded that:

children in Fife spoke a rhyme to the Devil's Bit or Curl-doddy,

> *Curl-doddy, do my biddin*
> *Soap my house and hool my midden,*

as if the plant gave them power to summon a brownie to sweep the house and shovel the dung and drudge for them in the brownie's manner.[62]

The leaves yield yellow dye.[52]

Droseraceae
SUNDEW FAMILY

Sundew
Drosera species

SCOTS NAME: red rot
GAELIC NAMES: *geald-ruidhe/ dealt ruidhe* (very red dew), *lus na fearnaich* (plant with shields), *ros an t'solais* (sun-rose/flower)

❀The caustic digestive juices of this beautiful insectivorous bog plant have been used for various human purposes. The text *Regimen Sanitatis Salernitanum*, used by Gaelic medical practitioners in the fifteenth to seventeenth centuries (see p. 14), recommended boiling the leaves in asses' milk to treat whooping cough. Lightfoot wrote:

The liquor which exudes from the hairs of the plant, is said to take away warts and corns...The Highlanders believe that the rot in sheep is often occasioned by their feeding on this herb, which opinion is very ancient. [75]

while Murdo McNeill reported:

The whole plant is acid, and sufficiently caustic to erode the skin; but some ladies mix the juice with milk so as to make it an innocent and safe application to remove freckles and sunburns.[96]

According to John Cameron, it was used by ancient Celts as hair dye. He does not specify the shade acquired, but the plant yields red and purple dyes, so the effect may have been eyecatching.[18, 52]

Empetraceae
CROWBERRY FAMILY

Crowberry
Empetrum nigrum

SCOTS NAMES: berry-girse (grass), crawcroups
LOCAL NAMES: blackberry (Caith), knauperts (Banff)
GAELIC NAMES: *dearcan feanaig, fionag* (wine-berry), *lus na fionnag* (crow plant)

Crowberry is a common little evergreen shrub of upland areas of Scotland, often found growing with members of the heath family, which it resembles. Grigson tells us this plant takes its name from the small, black, bitter berries it bears, fit only for crows to eat; however Highland children and sometimes adults ate them, although over-indulging was said to cause headaches. The berries were used medicinally to treat septic sores. James Logan, in a long-winded explanation of the 'proper' Gaelic name *fionag*, wine-berry, felt certain that good wine could be produced from the berries without adding sugar, but does not appear to have actually tasted any.[18, 62, 76, 96, 125]

In 1806, at Deerness in Orkney, Neill saw strong ropes made from crowberry shoots being used by farmers for a variety of purposes. The berries produce dark purple dye.[18, 52, 96]

Ericaceae
HEATH FAMILY

Bearberry *Arctostaphylos uva-ursi*

LOCAL NAMES: brawlins (nS), craneberry-wire, creashak (Ross), dog-berry (Aber), gnashaks (Banff, Mor), nashag (Caith), rapper-dandy (Berw and elsewhere)
GAELIC NAME: *grainnseag*

The fascinating variety of Scots names for this plant, which occurs in many parts of the Highlands, does not shed much light on its uses, which seem to have been mainly in tanning leather, the plant being rich in tannin. The leaves were made into a tonic for bladder and kidney disorders. Yellow-green and blue-green dye can be obtained using the whole plant, and blue-green from the berries. The berries are not worth eating, being bitter—fit only for bears and dogs—though relished by grouse.[52, 62]

Heather[1]

Of all Scottish wild plants, the prize usefulness must surely go to heather. In a typical dwelling in many parts of Scotland until this century, heather might have been found in the walls, thatch, beds, fire, floor mats, ale, tea, baskets, medicine chest and dye pot, being used to sweep the house and chimney, to feed and bed down sheep and cattle and to weave into fences around the farm.

Nowdays heather is considered by many to be as much an emblem of Scotland as the thistle, without the realisation that most heather moorland is an artificial and degraded landscape created by deforestation and maintained by over-grazing of sheep and deer and burning for grouse management. Nonetheless, heather is part of the Scottish image and even the vocabulary, with expressions such as *heather lowper* for a hill or country dweller and *heather piker* as a contemptuous term for a very poor or miserly person in northeast Scotland.[26]

Houses often had heather packed down with mud in the walls, as well as heather thatch, described by Logan in 1832:

> *The usual covering for the houses in Scotland is feil or divot, i.e., turf cut thinly... generally covered with heath...[it is] cheap and lasting...It can be used alone, and with timber of a very ordinary description. It also takes very little trouble to keep in repair; and, if...well executed, it is equal to slates, and will last 100 years...Many churches were formerly covered with heath...Its only disadvantage is being heavier than straw and rushes.[76]*

—and that it caught fire easily.[27, 76, 125]

Whatever material houses were thatched with, it was common to see the thatch tied down with ropes made from heather and weighted with stones. Heather rope was found in the 4,000 year old village of Skara Brae in Orkney (see p. 28). Often two people made the rope—one fed in the heather while the other walked backwards twisting the developing rope clockwise on a stick. It was a job to occupy the long winter evenings, when people gathered for a ceilidh in the home of a storyteller such as Angus MacLellan:

1. Heather is a generic name used for the three species that occur in Scotland: heather or ling (*Calluna vulgaris*), bell heather (*Erica cinerea*), and bog heather (*E. tetralis*). The two *Erica* species are often called heaths to distinguish them from *Calluna* heather.

*He would bring in a load of heather when it was getting dark and the
lamp was lit and he'd be there till eleven o'clock and you couldn't see
him at last for the heather rope all around him—coiled round his chair...he
was telling tales and singing songs all the time there.[80]*

Many other uses were found for heather rope, said to be stronger than
straw rope. In 1764 John Walker recorded that Hebridean farmers sur-
rounded their fields with heather rope two or three inches thick laid on
the ground to keep wild geese from feeding on the crops; he said the geese
would only cross the rope if they were extremely hungry. In Sutherland
and Caithness, heather rope was being used in the nineteenth century to
shake frost off corn to prevent blight. It stood up well to immersion in sea
water, and was used to tie up boats and to gather kelp (see p. 50).[57, 76, 136]

David Lambie of the Heather Centre in Perthshire has carried out
extensive research on uses of heather. The brushwood, with juniper, was
used as insulation and soundproofing in cavity walls. The roots served as
nails or pegs for hanging slates, and after the Second World War, the
shortage of timber for flooring led to the establishment of a small factory
by Loch Lomond to produce floor tiles from compressed heather stems.
The process became uneconomic when timber restrictions were lifted but
the method was developed for the manufacture of the curious and distinctive jewellery made by the Heather Gems company in Blair Atholl.[74]

Many other uses have been recorded by Lambie. Long heather stems
were used to weave rough kitchen mats with various designs. On Islay,
mats woven from young heather were called *peallagan*. Long stems were
also used to make baskets to be carried on the back or used as horse
panniers:

*In Orkney, one particular form of basket was called a 'Heather Cubby'.
These baskets were made in various forms but the most common one was
woven from long, fine, straight heather stalks, not rough or crinkly, and
was used for carrying turnips from the shed to the byre for the cattle.
Carried on the back, they were also used to bring peats inside from the
stack. Another type of basket was called the 'Sea Cubby'—so called
because it was specially used to carry home fish.[74]*

Heather was used to make several other kinds of basket for carrying
fish, and also to pack the fish inside for travel to market.

One of the more unusual and fascinating uses discovered by Lambie is
that of heather mixed with scraps of fleece in medieval times to make
footpaths and later to form a layer between the brushwood base and the
gravel surface of roads and tracks. Heather tops were placed in the bottom
of field drains to filter silt and prevent them from clogging up.

It is likely that heather has been used for bedding since prehistoric times. Archaeological excavations of an Iron Age settlement in Glen Bracadale have found concentrations of heather shoots and flowers that suggest this use.[6] Heather beds have come in for some extravagant praise. First, George Buchanan, tutor to James VI, observed in the sixteenth century (as quoted by Mary Beith),

In this manner they form a bed so pleasant, that it may vie in softness with the finest down, while in salubrity it far exceeds it; for heath, naturally possessing the powers of absorption, drinks up the superfluous moisture, and restores strength to the fatigued nerves, so that those who lie down languid and weary in the evening, arise in the morning vigorous and sprightly.[6]

Both Martin Martin and John Lightfoot found heather beds on Skye fragrant, refreshing, health-restoring and almost as soft as a feather mattress. To make a heather bed, the longest, straightest stalks of young heather in full flower were pulled up and laid out to dry. They were then packed in the bed (often no more than a wooden frame against the wall to hold the heather in) with all the tops uppermost and leaning slightly towards the bed head. The effect has been likened to a Turkish carpet, and the fragrance from the nectar rich flowers was said to be soporific.[74] Sometimes the heather was mixed with ferns.

Another use of heather was observed in Harris in 1853 by Osgood Mackenzie. Calling on a thatched house in Harris in search of fresh milk one morning, he witnessed a scene that was no doubt routine to the inhabitants, but which impressed him so much he never forgot it. He had to wait while the good wife who 'like all the Harris people, had most charming manners', served breakfast to her family:

There was a big pot hanging by a chain over the peat fire, and a creel heaped up with short heather, which the women tear up by the roots and with which they bed the cows. The wife took an armful of this heather and deposited it at the feet of the nearest cow...to form a drainer. Then, lifting the pot off the fire, she emptied it on to the heather; the hot water disappeared and ran away among the cow's legs, but the content of the pot consisting of potatoes and fish boiled together, remained on top of the heather. Then from a very black looking bed three stark naked boys arose one by one, aged, I should say, from six to ten years, and made for the fish and potatoes, each youngster carrying off as much as both his hands could contain.[84]

Eventually Mackenzie got his milk, but the scene he had witnessed had unfortunately rather spoiled his appetite.

A variety of drinks have been made with heather since prehistoric times. Archaeologists excavating on Rum found, on a fragment of pottery, traces of what they believe to have been a drink made with heather flowers. Moorland tea made from dried heather tops with bramble leaves, blaeberry leaves, speedwell, wild thyme and wild strawberry was associated with Robert Burns. Various legends exist about heather ale[1] and Picts who preferred death to parting with the recipe, as immortalised by R. L. Stevenson in his famous poem *Heather Ale*:

> *From the bonny bells of heather,*
> *They brewed a drink long syne,*
> *Was sweeter far than honey*
> *Was stronger far than wine.*
> *They brewed it and they drank it*
> *And lay in blessed swound*
> *For days and days together*
> *In their dwellings underground...*[128]

Nevertheless the art of brewing it survived, mixing two parts of heather tops with one part of malt, both for the pleasant honey flavour and to assist fermentation. An Act of Parliament passed in the eighteenth century prohibited brewers from making ale with anything other than hops and malt, but hops do not grow in the cool Scottish climate and recipes for heather ale continued to be passed down in Highland families. In the nineteenth century James Logan wrote that,

> *it was an almost invariable practice, when brewing, to put a quantity of the green tops of heath in the mash tub, and when the plant is in bloom it adds much to the strength and flavour of the beer. The roots, also, will improve its qualities, for they are of a liquorice sweetness, but their astringency requires them to be used with caution.*[76]

Logan was particularly fond of heather honey, which was used in mead. The wooden fermentation containers formerly used in whisky distilleries were scrubbed with heather besoms and new stills were washed with an infusion of heather to sweeten them.[74]

In the 1980s Bruce Williams of Glasgow began experimenting with an old Gaelic recipe for *leann fraoich*, heather ale, which uses heather flowers and leaves of bog myrtle *Myrica gale*. It is now in commercial production, brewed at the West Highland Brewery in Argyll and marketed as *Fraoch*.

❁Medicinally, an infusion of heather tops was used as a tonic and to treat consumption and coughs, nerves, depression and heart complaints. Heather tea, liniments and ointments were good for arthritis and rheumatism,

---

1. A name sometimes also used to refer to whisky.

and chopped with egg white it made a head poultice for insomnia.[6]

Heather shoots were used to tan leather when nothing else was available, and to dye wool, giving

> *various shades of yellow and orange, some of which tints are brilliant, though possessing little permanency...For use in dyeing the plant should be mown, or cut, when in flower, carefully dried, and stacked until required. The brilliant orange and green tints given by some of the Highlanders to the woollen thread used in the manufacture of their tartans were frequently obtained from Heath tops, and in the Hebrides these dyes have been used from time immemorial.*[125]

Bundles of heather were used to heat ovens in the absence of better fuel, while households that could afford coal cleaned the chimney with two or three roots of heather (or whin) wrapped around a stone, dropped down the lum on a rope then pulled up and down. A great variety of heather brushes or besoms were made, for sweeping floors, cleaning dishes, even brushing horses; a good living could be earned from making them.[125, 140]

Heather, ling
Calluna vulgaris

SCOTS NAME: hather
LOCAL NAMES: dog heather (Aber), he-heather (Berw), hedder (Ork, Shet)
GAELIC NAME: *fraoch*

As well as all the uses described above, heather was used to obtain yellow, grey green, orange, brown and bronze dyes.[52]

White heather was said to mark the resting places of fairies. Beacons of burning heather were used to summon the clans to battle.[122]

Bell heather
Erica cinerea

SCOTS NAME: she-heather (Berw)
GAELIC NAMES: *fraoch bhadhain* (tufted heath), *fraoch an dearrasain* (heath that makes a rustling or buzzing)

Used for many of the same purposes as other heathers, including thatch, tannin, ale and bedding. It yields purple dye.[52]

Bog heather, cross leaved heath
E. tetralix

SCOTS NAME: he-heather (Berw)
GAELIC NAMES: *fraoch frangach* (French heath), *fraoch an ruinnse* (rinsing heath)

Also used for the same variety of purposes as the other heathers, but a bunch of bog heather stems made the best kind of scouring brush, which might explain the Gaelic name.[18]

Blaeberry, bilberry, whortleberry
Vaccinium myrtillus

GAELIC NAMES: *fraochan* (that which grows among the heather), *dearchan-fithich* (raven's berries), *gearr-dhearc* (sour berry), *lus-nan-broileag, lus nan dearc* (berry plant)

❀It is said in the Highlands that blaeberries have been known as a cure for kidney stones since the fourteenth century, a cure attributed to the doctor Fearchar Lighich, originally a cattle drover from Glen Golly. Both Martin and Lightfoot recorded the astringent blaeberries being made into syrup for diarrhoea. Lightfoot also found Highlanders eating them in milk and pies and making jelly to mix with whisky as a treat for visitors. Blaeberry leaf tea was said by Neill in 1806 to be indistinguishable from real tea when properly gathered and dried.[6, 75, 100, 106]

Blaeberries can be used to dye purple, blue, violet, brown or sage green.[52]

Cranberry
V. microcarpum

An increasingly rare bog plant due to loss of habitat. The fruit is nowadays best known as a sauce made with the larger berries imported from the American species *V. macrocarpon*, but in the eighteenth century Lightfoot noted that Longtown, in the Borders, was

> remarkable for the great trade carried on during the season of cranberries; when for four or five markets, from twenty to twenty-five pounds worth, are sold each day at three pence a quart, and sent in small barrels to London.[75]

Cranberries were sometimes added to the special *struan* bannock baked in the Hebrides at Michaelmas (see p. 7).

Euphorbiaceae
SPURGE FAMILY

The juice from most of this family of plants is poisonous.

Dog's mercury
Mercurialis perennis

GAELIC NAME: *lus Ghlinne Bhracadail*

A plant of woods and shady places in all parts of Scotland except the far north, used by ecologists as an indicator species of old woodland—even where the trees have disappeared, dog's mercury hangs on in ditches and hedgerows, and is slow to colonise new plantings.

Martin Martin found this plant being used on the Isle of Skye as a purgative to induce both vomiting and diarrhoea, and to make poultices. Such poultices, made from the juice of the whole plant collected in flower, were applied to swellings and to cleanse sores, but it is now considered dangerous for internal use and has even caused death when eaten in mistake for Good King Henry, also sometimes known as mercury (see p. 95). Lightfoot was disturbed when he observed an infusion of the plant being used on Skye to promote salivation; he felt this was dangerous because the plant is so strongly emetic.[62, 75, 100]

Fabaceae
PEA FAMILY

Kidney vetch
Anthyllis vulneraria

LOCAL NAMES: dog's paise (Banff), Lady's fingers (Lan)
GAELIC NAMES: *cas an uain* (lamb's foot), *meoir Mhuire* (Mary's fingers)

Found in coastal parts of Scotland, locally common on coastal dunes, waste ground and base-rich pasture. Kidney vetch was used to treat wounds and also added to hay.[96, 136]

Broom
Cytisus scoparius

Broom

GAELIC NAMES: *bealaidh/bealuidh* (plant that Belus favoured), *giolach sleibhe* (reed/cane/leafless twig of the hill), *sguab* (a brush made from broom)

> *The original broom, whether for domestic or magical purposes, was a stalk of the broom plant with a tuft of leaves at the end.*[95]

As well as being the domestic floor sweeping broom, a stalk of this plant with its tufted branchlets was associated with magic. This may go back to the time of the druids, worshippers of the sun god Belus, for whom yellow, the colour of broom flowers, was sacred.[18] Broom was sometimes used for the peeled white wand carried by the corn sheaf made to represent Bride at the spring festival in the Highlands and Islands (see p. 142). The flowers were recommended by a witch in the ballad *The Broomfield Hill*, for a 'lady bright' to send her gallant knight to sleep:

> *Take ye the blossom of the broom,*
> *The blossom it smells sweet,*
> *And strew it at your true-love's head,*
> *And likewise at his feet.*[115]

❀Broom has narcotic properties; in large quantities it acts like hemlock and can be deadly. The tops were used to treat dropsy, bladder and kidney complaints and as a heart tonic and regulator. According to Mary Beith, in the Highlands a bunch of broom was tied around the neck to staunch nosebleeds.[7, 61, 115]

The seeds can be dried and ground for coffee and the flowers made into wine.[110] Mrs McLintock's recipe for pickled broom buds is as follows:

> *Gather your Broom-buds about the first of May, pick them clean, sew a Linen Bag, put them in, lay them in a strong pickle of salt and Water, let them lie 5 or 6 Days, change the water every Day, boil them in salt and Water, till they be as green as Grass; then take as much wine Vinegar as you think will cover them, with a little Nutmeg, Cloves, Mace, Ginger; boil all with your Vinegar, and drain the Buds clean from the Water, and put them among the Vinegar, and let them boil awhile; so bottle them up.*[93]

Yellow and green dyes can be obtained from the flowers. Occasionally broom was used for thatch, though only as a last resort, being not very durable and preferable only to turf. Surprisingly fine furniture with beautiful grain was made from broom veneer and inlay; examples, made in Dundee, can be seen in Blair Castle, Perthshire.[27, 52, 57, 96]

Bitter vetch
Lathyrus linifolius

SCOTS NAMES: heath-vetch, heath-pea, wood-pease,
LOCAL NAMES: caperoiles, cormeille, corra-meile (nS), knapperts, napple
GAELIC NAME: *cairmeal* (*cair*—of the moss, *meal*—enjoy)

In northern parts of Scotland and the Hebridean islands, the tuberous
rhizomes of this very common heath and moorland plant were dug up and
eaten, either fresh and raw, or roasted after being dried in bundles hung
under the roof thatch. According to Martin, islanders on Mull were inclined to drink a great deal of whisky in wet weather—a pleasant enough
way to pass a dreich day when no outdoor work could be done—and used
to chew the root of this plant afterwards, to sweeten their breath and, he
was told, to prevent drunkenness.[100] A liquorice-flavoured alcoholic drink
called cairm was made from the dried, powdered root, described by Lightfoot:

> *The highlanders have a great esteem for the tubercles of the roots; they*
> *dry and chew them in general to give a better relish to their liquor; they*
> *also affirm them to be good against most disorders of the thorax, and*
> *that by the use of them they are enabled to repel hunger and thirst for a*
> *long time. In Bredalbane and Rossshire they sometimes bruise and steep*
> *them in water, and make an agreeable fermented liquor with them. They*
> *have a sweet taste, something like the roots of liquorice, and when boiled,*
> *we are told, are well flavour'd and nutritive, and in times of scarcity*
> *have served as a substitute for bread.*[75]

Restharrow
Ononis repens

SCOTS NAME: purple restharrow without prickles
LOCAL NAMES: lady-whin, sitfast (Mor), wild liquorice (Dumf, Inv, Mor)

❀Found in dry grassy places in lowland and coastal areas of Scotland, this
plant may have been used for the same purposes as its close relative, *O.
arvensis*, to treat kidney stones and delirium.[61]

Red and white clover
Trifolium species

SCOTS NAMES: cow-cloos, plyvens, soukies, soukie soo
LOCAL NAMES: claver (Ayr), cow-grass (Rox)
GAELIC NAMES: *seamar chapuill* (mare's clover), *sugag* (for the sweet
nectar), *tri-bilean* (trefoil/three-leaved)

A wild plant that has been brought into cultivation as nutritious fodder. It also has magic associations, the much-sought four-leaved clover or sham-rock[1] being thought to confer protection. At the Lammas Fair in Kirkwall, Orkney, young men were advised to put a four-leaf clover in one of their boots, presumably to keep themselves out of trouble.[101] Carmichael re-corded incantations describing the 'shamrock of good omens' and of power,

Thou Shamrock of promise on Mary's Day,
Bounty and blessing thou art at all times

but like other magic plants, it only worked if found by chance, not searched for. People buried the soft spongy substance coughed up by new-born foals in the hope that shamrock would grow from it.[23, 62]

The nectar-rich flowers have long been favoured by children for a sweet snack. Some people still add clover flowers to salads for colour and flavour. They can also be made into tea and wine.[18, 110]

Gorse, whin
Ulex europaeus

GAELIC NAME: *conasg* (prickly)

Gorse is highly nutritious and used to be important fodder for horses and cattle. The leaves can only be grazed when young and tender in the spring, but it was cultivated to be cut and crushed for winter use when other food was scarce.[69]

Wine can be made from the flowers, which also yield yellow and green dyes; it was traditional to use them to dye Easter eggs in Morayshire. In Fife, it was considered unlucky to give anyone gorse flowers.[52, 96, 110, 135]

Tufted vetch
Vicia cracca

SCOTS NAMES: cat-peas, wild fetches, wild tare
LOCAL NAMES: blue girse (Shet), fitchacks (Aber)
GAELIC NAME: *pesair nan luch* (mice pease)

Common in all lowland parts of Scotland, this vetch was thought to pro-vide excellent pasturage.[136]

1. Several other plants have also been identified by various authors as the shamrock, includ-ing bogbean (*Menyanthes trifoliata*), wood sorrel (*Oxalis acetosella*), watercress (*Rorippa* species) and lesser yellow trefoil (*Trifolium dubium*). The name 'shamrock' appears to be derived from the Irish *seamroge*, meaning 'little clover'.

Fagaceae
BEECH FAMILY

Beech
Fagus sylvatica

Although not native to Scotland, beech has long been naturalised here and is very common. The nuts (known as mast) were fed to pigs, and also dried and ground as a coffee substitute. Beech leaves have been made into wine and liqueur.[42, 110]

Oak
Quercus petraea

GAELIC NAMES: *daire, darach, darag, darroch, dru, dur*

The commonest Gaelic names for oak are *daire* or *darag* (also meaning tree stump); *diure* is an oak grove, while the word for oak timber, *darach*, also means the hull of a boat, often of course made from oak. The names derive from the same root as *druidh* (*draoi, draiodh*), magician, philosopher, learned one, and *dur*, door, symbolising the magic door through which one might enter the Otherworld, the Land of Faerie.[95]

Oak features significantly in many stories of gods, goddesses, mythical and legendary characters. It was revered by Celtic people throughout Europe as the symbol of supreme power due to its size and strength and association with the mysterious and magic mistletoe plant (see pp. 175-6), although there is evidence that in Scotland hazel and rowan were believed to be more powerful still. Druids made crowns from oak leaves, used the branches for their staffs and the wood to carve sacred effigies. Sacred fires with oak wood are still lit on Beltane (May 1) and at the midsummer and midwinter solstices. No ancient Scottish feast was considered complete without a massive oak log to burn. This association of oak with fire may be because tall oak trees occasionally attract lightning. It was once believed the mistletoe seed was placed in the tree by lightning, where a bolt from the Thunder God touched.[50, 62, 76, 95]

Oak groves were traditional places of worship, their power usurped by early Christians who sited churches and monasteries in them, often using the timber for building. St Columba was said to have loved and respected oak trees, avoiding felling them when possible, although he built an oak chapel on Iona using wood from the great oak woods on Mull. Highland people baked cakes with oak fuel on Thursdays, Columba's day.[23]

Oak

115

Missionary monks travelling between Ireland and Scotland in the period from 500 to 1,000 AD used coracles with oak frames covered by skins tanned with oak bark.[133] One story tells of St Brendan receiving a divine message to replace the traditional skin-covered coracle with an oak boat that served him well. The Lords of the Isles maintained their power with fleets of swift oak boats. Whether it was believed the strength came from magic powers or simply durable, elastic wood, very many oak trees have ended their days as buildings, war-ships and fishing boats over the centuries. In addition, the wood has been used to make fine furniture, doors, wheels and barrels.

Oak bark was widely used for tanning leather, especially to make red shoes; large quantities of bark were sent from the West Highlands to Glasgow to support the leather industry. On his tour in 1772, Pennant observed in Perthshire, 'considerable natural woods of oak: they are cut down once in twenty years for the sake of the bark, which is here an important article of commerce'. The bark has been used to produce brown dye, while bark with acorns and/or galls added yields black dye. The galls, or oak apples, were used to make ink.[50, 52, 96, 111]

✿The inner bark is astringent and mucilaginous and was applied to wounds on horses. Tanners are said to have derived some protection against tuberculosis from the tannin in oak bark. Oak twigs were used as toothbrushes; the tannin simultaneously strengthened the gums and acted as an antiseptic. Oak bark was also used medicinally as a tonic and to treat ague, haemorrhage, malaria, diarrhoea, dysentery, sore throat, vaginal discharge, bleeding gums and piles.[61, 96]

Martin Martin recorded a curious use for oak on Skye and Tiree:

> *A rod of oak, of four, five or six, or eight inches about, twisted round like a with,[1] boiled in wort,[2] well dried, and kept in a little bundle of barley straw, and being steeped again in wort, causeth it to ferment, and procures yeast: the rod is cut before the middle of May, and is frequently used to furnish yeast; and being preserved and used in this manner, it serves for many years together. I have seen the experiment tried, and have been shown a piece of a thick with, which hath been preserved for making ale with, for about twenty or thirty years.[100]*

Other drinks made with oak include acorn coffee, leaf tea and leaf wine.[110]

As well as being used for fuel, both in the home and ceremonially, vast quantities of oak were made into charcoal for iron-smelting, especially

1. i.e. withy, as in basket making
2. fermenting beer

116

from the woods in Argyll at Bonawe, Taynuilt and Furnace. Fortunately these forests were properly managed and consequently have survived to the present day. Oak sawdust from barrel making was considered fine fuel for smoking herrings into kippers.[98]

Fumariaceae
FUMITORY FAMILY

Fumitory
Fumaria officinalis

GAELIC NAME: *lus deathach-thalmnainn* (earth-smoke plant)

Fumitory

❀This very common small, scrambling plant was used medicinally to treat internal obstructions, especially liver complaints, and for skin problems such as scurvy, leprosy and cradle cap, and also as a tonic and diuretic.[61]

The Gaelic name refers to the belief that smoke from burning this plant had the power to exorcise evil spirits.[9]

Gentianaceae
GENTIAN FAMILY

Centaury
Centaurium erythraea

SCOTS NAMES: feverfoullie, gentian
GAELIC NAMES: *ceud bhileach* (hundred-leaved), *teantguidh*

❀A small, very localised, mainly coastal plant of dry grassland and dunes, except in north east Scotland where it is rare. Centaury had various medicinal uses, as a tonic, to cleanse the blood and kidneys, for indigestion and colic, jaundice, wounds, sores and rheumatism. According to Grigson, the plant was called gentian in Scotland because it had the same medicinal effect as the roots of great yellow gentian (*Gentiana lutea*), which were imported and sold as a strong tonic to treat general debility and digestive problems.[57, 61, 62]

117

Felwort, Autumn gentian
Gentianella amarella

LOCAL NAME: dead man's mittens (Shet)

Used as a tonic since Roman times, felwort is localised in base-rich pasture and sand dunes. The local name is thought to derive from its appearance because the half-open buds appear like finger-nails protruding from the turf.[32, 120]

Field gentian
G. campestris

LOCAL NAME: ridin' girse (Shet)

Field gentian is locally common in grassland and sandy areas. In Shetland, it was fed to cows that were slow coming into season—a bovine aphrodisiac.[135]

Geraniaceae
GERANIUM FAMILY

Storksbill
Erodium cicutarium

Storksbill is found mainly around the coastal parts of Scotland. Murdo McNeill recorded that on Colonsay, the tap-root was used to obtain reddish brown dye, which was an attractive shade but faded.[96]

Herb Robert
Geranium robertianum

SCOTS NAME: cancer wort
GAELIC NAMES: *lus-an-eallain* (cancer weed), *lus an rois, righeal cuil* (fly reprover)

❀Herb Robert is very common in all parts of Scotland. Both this species and bloody cranesbill (*G. sanguineum*) were held in high regard by Highlanders for their medicinal properties. The whole plant was chopped and made into an infusion to treat cancer, wounds and skin diseases.[18, 96, 131]

Bloody Cranesbill
Geranium sanguineum

GAELIC NAME: *creachlach dearg* (red wound healer)

Found mainly in coastal districts to the south and east of Scotland, bloody cranesbill was used similarly to Herb Robert.[18]

Graminae
GRASS FAMILY

Bent grass
Agrostis species

LOCAL NAME: bread-and-cheese (Elgin)
GAELIC NAMES: *muirineach* (*muir*, ocean; *ineach*, generosity); *muran*

A good example of a plant put to many uses in areas where resources were very limited, such as the more exposed parts of the west coast. Uist was in fact called 'country of the bent-grass: *mhurain a' seoladh*' in many traditional songs. Bent was used for thatch, sometimes mixed with straw. It had to be replaced annually and so no elaborate techniques were used; it was simply raked into place and when removed, after a year of impregnation with peat smoke, made reasonable fertilizer.[57]

Tightly bound tubes of bent sewn in coils were made into bee skeps and *ciosans*, leak-proof containers 30 cm or more high, for storing meal, grain or anything dry. Isabel Grant describes several other uses:

Bent grass was also woven into bags for holding meal and grain and, with a different weave, into pads that were put under pack saddles, and it was also fashioned into the most excellent brushes...On the Long Island [Lewis] very shapely collars of bent grass have only gone out of common use in the [twentieth century]...They were made of several rings of the plaited grass, sewn edge to edge and of course did not open.[57]

An example of such a collar can be seen in the Scottish Agricultural Museum at Ingliston, by Edinburgh Airport.

Bent grass was called 'bread-and-cheese' by children in Elgin who used to chew it—and perhaps still do.[135]

Meadow foxtail
Alopecurus pratensis

GAELIC NAME: *fiteag* (food, refreshment)

This common and widespread grass was valued for hay.[75]

Marram grass, matweed
Ammophila arenaria

GAELIC NAMES: *muirineach* (*muir*, ocean; *ineach*, generosity); *muran*

Used and named the same as bent grass (p. 119), on Colonsay marram was considered to be one of the best and most durable thatching materials. It was also used for binding oat-straw baskets. A common grass of sand dunes, marram has creeping roots and has long been propagated to bind sand on the shore, in order to reduce erosion.[96, 98]

In his delightful book of childhood memories *Crowdie and Cream*, Finlay MacDonald recalls collecting *mealtrach*, marram grass roots, for scrubbing floors (see p. 31). Marram grass was also used to make combs for separating the weaver's weft and beating the warp.[47]

False oat grass
Arrhenatherum elatius

SCOTS NAME: pight aits

A common grass with large seeds, this appears to have been a remarkably valuable plant in the Orkney Isles:

> *The wild oat grass with which the lands of Orkney were much infested until modern times was called 'Pight aits'. It grew and ripened fast, and was said to make good bread if it was cut, before the Picts threshed it out. The plant had another useful quality: it could be made into excellent ale which never caused drunkenness.*[101]

Wild oat, bearded oat grass
Avena fatua

GAELIC NAMES: *coirc dubh* (black oats), *coirc fiadhain* (wild oats)

Although this grass was introduced it is now naturalised on arable and waste ground and is included here to note one of the more unusual recorded plant uses. Lightfoot wrote: 'The beard of this is well known to make a very sensible hygrometer' (an instrument for measuring humidity).[75]

Crested dogs tail
Cynosurus cristatus

GAELIC NAMES: *conan* (dog's grass), *goinear, goin fheur*

Common throughout Scotland, crested dog's tail was considered to be excellent grazing for sheep and deer.[75]

Couch grass
Elytrigia repens

❀Nowadays the gardener's persistent pest, it was used to treat bladder and kidney disorders, gout and rheumatism.[61]

Sheep's fescue
Festuca ovina

GAELIC NAME: *feur chaorach* (soft sheep grass)

Growing abundantly in upland areas, this is a fine sweet grass long valued as sheep pasture and still important to farmers.[18, 75]

Darnel
Lolium temulentum

❀Used as a sedative, and to treat headaches, sciatica and meningitis.[61] The name 'darnel' was once used as a generic term for a number of corn field weeds. Sutherland was in fact mistaken in believing *L. temulentum* to be native; it was introduced from the Mediterranean, and became a common agricultural weed. It is now rare, having been nearly eradicated by farmers because it carries the ergot fungus that can poison humans and cause blindness and abortion in cows.

Purple moor grass
Molinia caerulea

SCOTS NAME: purple melic-grass
GAELIC NAMES: *bunglas, punglas* (blue root)

A very common grass of wet moorland, used in Skye for thatching.[57] Lightfoot found fishermen there making rot-resistant ropes for their nets from this grass.[75]

Reed
Phragmites australis

GAELIC NAME: *cuilc*

✤On Lewis, Martin found people making fermented cough medicine from reed roots boiled in water to which yeast had been added.[100]

Common in marshy areas and along loch shores, the main use for strong reed stalks was for thatching; it was roped on in bundles, often mixed with wild iris or oat straw. Reed thatch lasted twenty-five to thirty years.[27, 98]

Green dye can be obtained from the very young flower heads.[52]

Fairies used 'bog-reed' to make arrows which they tipped with flint and dipped in hemlock (p. 67).[95]

Meadow grasses
Poa spp

In the eighteenth century, according to Lightfoot, the three meadow grasses (*Poa trivialis*, *P. angustifolia* and *P. pratensis*) were highly esteemed for hay; they are still used for grazing and lawns.

Grossulariaceae
CURRANT FAMILY

Blackcurrant
Ribes nigrum

SCOTS NAME: wineberry
LOCAL NAME: blackberry (Berw)

A widespread shrub of damp woodland, usually a garden escape. The berries make delicious pies, cordial, wine and liqueur.

Redcurrant
R. rubrum

SCOTS NAME: wineberry
LOCAL NAMES: rizzles, russles (Kirk,Wigt)
GAELIC NAME: *dearcan dearga*

As well as jelly, wine, cordial and Meg Dods' 'currant shrub liqueur', redcurrants were made into a syrup called 'rob' for sore throats. The twigs produce brown dye.[42, 52, 110] Locally common, redcurrant usually occurs in woodland as a garden escape but is thought to be native.

Gooseberry
R. uva-cripsa

SCOTS NAMES: honeyblob, groser, groset
LOCAL NAMES: grozzle, gruzel (Rox, Dumf)

Fairly common in woods and hedges, native in wetter areas but often a garden escape. Gooseberries are used like redcurrants and also made into a kind of champagne.[110]

Mary Beith writes:

The prickles were used as charms to remove warts and styes. A wedding ring was laid over the wart...[which was then] pricked through the ring with a gooseberry thorn. Ten such thorns were plucked, the other nine simply being pointed at the part affected, and then thrown over the shoulder.[7]

Iridaceae
IRIS FAMILY

Yellow iris, flag
Iris pseudacorus

SCOTS NAMES: seggen (sedges), water-skegg
LOCAL NAMES: cheeper (from making a noise with the leaves, Rox), dug's lug (dog's ear, Shet), saggon (Lan)
GAELIC NAMES: *bog-uisge* (rainbow), *seilisdear/ seileasdear/ siolastar* (plant of light)

❀The rhizome acts as a powerful cathartic, and was used to treat diarrhoea, period pain, coughs, convulsions, dropsy, snake bite and other poisoning, bruises, toothache, weak eyes, ulcers and swellings.[61] Martin found people on Skye made poultices from iris rhizomes mixed with water and salt butter.[100] Such uses were known to the Romans who occupied the south of Scotland and may have shared their expertise with local healers. Comrie quotes an ancient Gaelic medical manuscript believed to have been used in the fifteenth century which said of iris:

This plant is hot and dry in the second degree. If its root is gathered in the end of spring it preserves its virtue for two years. It has a laxative, diuretic value, and removes the obstructions of the spleen, the kidneys and the bladder. It is a powerful remedy against troubles of the spiritual organs, and stomach ailments that proceed from flatulence. Its powder put on sores checks proud flesh and cleans them.[32]

The dried, powdered roots were made into snuff to clear head colds, or crushed to extract the juice which was then spooned into the nostrils:

This strange application is immediately followed by a kind of salivation, or copious defluxion of rheum from the mouth and nostrils, which often effects a cure, but not without great danger of the patient's taking cold during the violence of the operation.[75]

Bright green dye was extracted from the leaves, while the roots yielded dark blue, grey and black dye, all used in the Harris tweed industry. The roots were also made into ink. In the Orkneys, iris was sometimes added to oat straw to bulk out thatch.[52, 75, 98]

It is possible to make a kind of coffee from the seeds, collected in late summer then roasted and ground. The roots were dried and made into snuff. Children in Shetland made toy sailing boats, called seggie boats, from the leaves by making a small lengthwise slit halfway along a leaf, then bending the tip over and through to create a sail above and keel below.[18, 110, 135]

This very beautiful plant is common in wet meadows and ditches, by lakes and on the west near the sea.

Juncaceae
RUSH FAMILY

Rushes
Juncus species

LOCAL NAME: trow bura (heath rush, Ork, Shet)
GAELIC NAME: *luachar* (splendour, brightness)

Rushes had many domestic uses in earlier times, from strewing on the earthen floor to be swept out occasionally with all the crumbs and other household debris, or making pot scrubbers and the sweeping brushes themselves, to thatching roofs.

One of the most important uses was as wicks for lamps; *J. effusus* was collected with a 'rashie rake', and then it was a tedious job, often given to children, to peel the green outer skin away from the white pith without breaking it, leaving one narrow strip to hold it together. The pith was then drawn through melted fat, left to set then hung up to dry. It was dipped and burned in fish liver oil (whale oil was used where available, e.g. Dundee and Montrose) or mutton fat in a small shallow iron dish called a *cruisgean*, or crusie lamp.[18, 27, 75, 96, 116]

A rope to tether animals could be quickly made from rushes but was not very strong. Martin saw rushes being used to hang herring from heather ropes to dry on roof tops in Skye. Lightfoot recorded rush baskets being made from *J. conglomeratus* and *J. effusus* for children to play with.[57, 75, 100]

Lamiaceae
LABIATE FAMILY

Ground ivy
Glechoma hederacea

SCOTS NAME: grundavy

❀The whole plant, in decoction or as an infusion, was used as a tonic and to treat kidney disorders, indigestion, coughs, headaches, consumption, snake bites and bruises. Snuff made from the dried leaves was also used to relieve asthma and headaches.[7, 62, 110] The plant is more common in the south eastern part of Scotland, where it occurs in woodland forming a dense, creeping mat (like ivy) across the ground.

Red deadnettle
Lamium species

SCOTS NAME: red archangel
LOCAL NAMES: daa-nettle, dee-nettle (i.e. deaf), okkerdu (Shet)

❀Found throughout Scotland growing in disturbed soil. Red deadnettle was used externally to treat bleeding and wounds; it was also made into tea for fever, chills and kidney problems.[61]

Water mint
Mentha aquatica

❀Water mint was used to treat diarrhoea, colds, influenza, menstrual problems, and severe vomiting.[61]

125

Wild marjoram
Origanum vulgare

❋Wild marjoram was used as a mild tonic and to treat toothache, measles, spasms, indigestion, swellings, rheumatism and headaches. It was also made into liniment to rub on strained muscles.[61] It occurs as a rare casual mainly in the south eastern part of Scotland; although Sutherland believed it to be native, it is now thought to have been introduced from North Africa or southwest Asia.

Self-heal, all-heal
Prunella vulgaris

LOCAL NAMES: heart o' the earth, prince's feather (Berw, Rox)
GAELIC NAMES: *dubhan ceann chosach* (sponge-headed kidney), *dubhan pceann-dubh, dubhanuith, lus a chridh* (heart-weed), *slan lus* (healing plant)

❋Common throughout Scotland. A variety of medicinal uses for this plant are recorded:

> *A popular remedy for chest ailments, it was collected in summer, tied in bundles, and hung up in the kitchen roof to dry for winter use. The plants were boiled in milk and strained before using; butter was added.*[96]

On Lewis, Martin recorded that an ointment made of golden-rod, all-heal, and fresh butter was applied to septic wounds.[100] The whole herb has astringent, styptic and tonic properties. It was also used to treat sore throats, as a gargle for mouth ulcers, an infusion for internal bleeding and a compress for piles and wounds, and to remove obstructions of the liver, spleen and kidneys.[18, 61]

Betony
Stachys officinalis

Although a rare plant in Scotland except the far south, according to Mary Beith its use was widespread in Gaelic medicine and she suggests it must have been widely cultivated in herb gardens for its usefulness as a nerve tonic and for headaches, known since the time of the ancient Celts.[7] Mrs Grieve states that the common name betony is derived from the Celtic roots *bew*, a head, and *ton*, good, i.e. good for headaches. The whole plant was used.[61]

The leaves were eaten as salad and made into tea.[7]

Marsh woundwort
S. palustris

SCOTS NAMES: maskert, swine's maskert
LOCAL NAMES: cockhead (Lan), hound's tongue (Mor), swinen arnit
(i.e. earth-nut, from tubers on the rhizome, Banff), swine's beads, swines
murricks (i.e. bulbs,tubers, Shet)
GAELIC NAME: *lus nan sgor*

A dye plant: yellow and blue can be obtained from the whole plant and
red when it is used with tormentil roots (see p. 153).[52] Widespread in
lowland and coastal areas of Scotland.

Wild (wood) sage
Teucrium scorodonia

The plant is found throughout Scotland. Martin wrote:

> *A quantity of wild wood sage, chewed between one's teeth, and put into
> the ears of cows or sheep that become blind, cures them, and perfectly
> restores their sight, of which there are many fresh instances both in Skye
> and Harris, by persons of great integrity.*
>
> *...wild sage chopped small, and eaten by horses mixed with their
> corn, kills worms. The horse must not drink for ten hours after eating it.
> The infusion of wild sage after the same manner produces like effect.*[100]

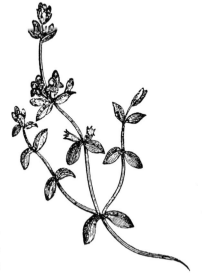

Thyme
Thymus polytrichus ssp. *britannicus*

SCOTS NAME: mother of thyme
LOCAL NAME: tae-girse (tea grass, Shet)
GAELIC NAMES: *lus an righ* (king's plant), *lus mhic righ Bhreatainn*
(plant belonging to the king of Britain's son)

> *It has a pleasant aromatic scent, and is esteemed a good nervine. An
> infusion of it by way of tea is reputed to be an almost infallible cure for
> that troublesome disorder, the incubus, or Night-mare.*[75]

❀A very common creeping plant of calcareous grassland throughout Scotland. Said to give courage and strength by the smell alone, the name
thyme is derived from the Greek for courage, strength; hence it is the
plant of kings and princes. Tea made from the dried leaves was also drunk
as a tonic. The tops yield purple dye.[18, 96]

Thyme

Lentibulariaceae
BUTTERWORT FAMILY

Butterwort
Pinguicula vulgaris

LOCAL NAMES: butter-plant (Selk), earning-grass (i.e. curdling, Lan), ekel-girse (Ork, Shet), rot grass (Berw), sheep-root (Rox), sheep-rot (nS), yirnin-girse (Shet)
GAELIC NAME: *badan-measgain*

This was a magical plant in the Scottish islands. People who carried it were protected from witches; cows that had eaten it were immune to elf-arrows. It was woven with other flowers into a magic hoop to place under the milk pail and protect the milk from fairies (see p. 82). There is a story of a house on Colonsay where women were keeping watch over a new born baby to prevent fairies stealing it and leaving a changeling—a sickly, fey fairy child—in its place. Two fairies came to the cradle and, to their dismay, they could not take the child because its mother had eaten butter made from milk of a cow that had eaten butterwort.[62, 96]

The name *earning-grass* in Lanarkshire came from the plant's use instead of rennet to make cheese.[135]

Liliaceae
LILY FAMILY

Ramsons, wild garlic
Allium ursinum

SCOTS NAMES: ramps, ramson
LOCAL NAME: wild leek (Berw)

Ramsons is often abundant in woods and damp shady places and some people enjoy the pungent garlic flavour in salads. It was used widely in the Highlands and Islands to treat kidney stones, either eaten fresh or drunk as an infusion. Martin recorded in Harris and Skye that:

> *wild garlic is much used by some of the natives, as a remedy against the [kidney] stone: they boil it in water, and drink the infusion, and it expels sand powerfully with great ease.*

An infusion was also drunk as a tonic for cleansing and strengthening the blood; the leaves were used in poultices for drawing out pus.[7, 62, 100]

Lily of the valley
Convallaria majalis

❀A rare plant in the wild, found only in a few parts of central Scotland and Grampian. Lily of the valley was used medicinally as a diuretic and heart tonic; it acts similarly to foxglove (p. 164) but is less powerful and less poisonous.[61]

Bluebell, wild hyacinth
Hyacinthoides non-scriptus

SCOTS NAMES: craw-taes, gowk's hose (cuckoo's socks)
GAELIC NAME: *brog na cubhaig* (cuckoo shoe)

Common in deciduous woodland, hedgerows and shady banks throughout Scotland, this is indeed the flower of cuckoo season, springtime. Bluebells yield red dye; glue can also be obtained from the roots.[52]

Herb paris
Paris quadrifolia

LOCAL NAMES: deil-in-a-bush (Perth), true-love (leaves in two pairs, Dumf)

❀A poisonous, narcotic plant found in scattered locations in ancient woodland across Scotland. The whole plant was used in small doses to treat bronchitis, coughs, rheumatism, cramp, colic, heart palpitations, septic wounds, tumours, inflammations, and as an antidote for mercury and arsenic poisoning.[61]

Linaceae
FLAX FAMILY

Purging flax, fairy flax
Linum catharticum

LOCAL NAME: laverock's lint (Lan)
GAELIC NAMES: *lion na bean sith* (fairy woman's flax), *lus caolach* (slender

weed), *mionach* (bowels), *miosach* (having medicinal properties)

Common throughout Scotland. Used medicinally for its cathartic effects, including as an abortifacient.[7, 18]

Flax, linseed
Linum usitatissimum

GAELIC NAME: *lion* (thread)

Flax was introduced to Scotland in the fifteenth century and soon was widespread, replacing nettle fibres which had previously been used in the manufacture of linen. In its turn, flax was replaced by imported cotton during the nineteenth century. Flax seed was also valuable for its oil, used medicinally and for feeding livestock. It has been reintroduced as a crop in recent years.[96, 116]

❀Flax was used to make poultices for ulcers, inflammation, burns, scalds, boils and abscesses. It was also taken internally as a laxative and for coughs, colds, urinary infections, kidney problems and pleurisy.[61]

Lythraceae
LOOSESTRIFE FAMILY

Purple loosestrife
Lythrum salicaria

GAELIC NAME: *lus an sith chainnt* (peace-speaking plant)

❀Found mainly in the south and west of Scotland along rivers and ditches. This plant was used medicinally to treat diarrhoea and constipation, dysentery, vaginal discharge, fever, lung and liver complaints, infant cholera, wounds, sores, eye and throat infection, and glandular diseases.[18, 61]

The name loosestrife may be derived from the Greek *lusimachion*, 'ending strife', due to the belief that the unrelated plant yellow loosestrife (*Lysimachia vulgaris*), with which purple loosestrife was mistakenly associated by the early taxonomists, would end strife between a horse and ox yoked to the same plough. The Gaelic name may simply be derived from this as well.[61]

Malvaceae
MALLOW FAMILY

Marsh mallow
Althaea officinalis

GAELIC NAMES: *fochas* (mocking), *leamhad* (vexatious)

Cameron records marsh mallow as being used for lung complaints and as a remedy for itchiness but as this species only occurs as a rare casual in Scotland, it is likely it was cultivated in physic gardens. The abundant mucilage found throughout the plant has made it an important remedy since ancient times for inflammation and irritation of various kinds, both internal and external. The Gaelic names may also refer to this use.[61]

Marsh Mallow

Dwarf mallow
Malva neglecta

GAELIC NAME: *ucas frangach*

The roots of dwarf mallow (which is naturalised and found mainly in the central belt of Scotland) are similarly mucilaginous and were boiled to make a lotion to bathe sore breasts. The Gaelic name may translate as gill of the stone fish, from the appearance of the delicate pink petals.[18]

Menyanthaceae
BOGBEAN FAMILY

Bogbean
Menyanthes trifoliata

SCOTS NAMES: bog nut, marsh-trefoil
LOCAL NAMES: buckbean (Rox), gulsa-girse (jaundice grass), trefold (Shet)
GAELIC NAMES: *luibh mhor, lui'-nan-tri-beann* (three-leaved plant), *lus nan laogh, milsean monaidh* (sweet plant of the hill), *ponair chapull* (mare's bean), *tri-bhileach, tribhealeach*

Perhaps the most lovely of all our wetland plants, the frilled, snow white (sometimes pink) flowers of bogbean can be seen in late spring and early summer in bogs and shallow loch margins in many areas of Scotland.

131

Fresh juice or tea made from the leaves, stem or root of bogbean was highly regarded as a tonic or remedy for colic, ulcers and other stomach complaints, tuberculosis, jaundice, constipation, coughs, asthma and heart disorders. The leaves were also used as a poultice for boils and burns.[6, 48, 57, 75, 96, 131]

The plant was used for dyeing green.[52]

Myricaceae
BOG MYRTLE FAMILY

Bog myrtle
Myrica gale

SCOTS NAMES: gale, myrtle, Scotch gale
LOCAL NAME: sweet gale (Renf)
GAELIC NAMES: *rideag, roid*

Bog myrtle is strongly aromatic and was used in various ways to repel pests, in bedding and stored linen and around the house. An infusion of leafy tops of bog myrtle was drunk to treat intestinal worms in children. Some hillwalkers and forestry workers still put a sprig of bog myrtle in their hat or hair to drive midges away, and recent scientific research at the Scottish Agricultural College has proved that midges are indeed repelled by the smell of the plant. A company called Scotia Pharmaceuticals is manufacturing a cream on the basis of this, initially using wild bog myrtle gathered by crofters but with plans to establish a plantation on Skye if the venture proves successful.[52, 81, 96, 110, 125]

Another company, Efamol, already working on the Isle of Skye, is testing bog myrtle oil as a way of controlling house mites that can aggravate asthma, and as non-toxic pest control for aphids, fungus and potato blight. Results so far are promising and the company foresees the possibility of growing bog myrtle in plantations from which the leaves could be cropped like tea.

The magic powers of bog myrtle are illustrated by a story told by David Rorie. An eighteen-month old child who was fractious and not thriving, after a resentful beggar woman had cast the evil eye on her, was passed eighteen times through a burning hoop, then taken home and put to bed under a sprig of the bog myrtle, which was left in place for a month. By then she had significantly improved in both health and temper; six months later she was fully recovered.[115]

The leaves were used to flavour ale before hops were available and are still added by some home-brewers. The bark was used for tanning leather. The stiff catkins or cones were boiled to produce a waxy scum which was made into aromatic candles. Yellow, orange, brown and green dyes can be obtained from the plant and it was used to dye Harris tweed until the 1970s. Bog myrtle is widespread in peat bogs.[52, 96, 98, 110]

Nymphaeaceae
WATER LILY FAMILY

White water lily
Nymphaea alba

LOCAL NAME: cambie-leaf (nS)
GAELIC NAMES: *cairt-locha, duileag bhaite bhan* (drowned white leaf, or white leaf of drowning), *gucagan-baite*

❀The roots were used internally for dysentery, diarrhoea and gonorrhoea and externally for bleeding, while a poultice of the leaves and roots was used on boils, ulcers, swelling and inflammation. In a remedy found in Argyll, possibly dating from the seventeenth century, the roots boiled in vinegar were recommended as a plaster to remove corns. In parts of the Highlands, it was believed that white water lily was used by fairies to weave spells and enchant people.[7, 61, 95]

However, it was as a dye plant that white water lily was best known; the roots were cut up and boiled to dye black, blue or dark brown, used in the Harris tweed industry. Because the plant tends to grow in deep mud, a special raft was required to collect the roots, which were cut with a hook then lifted out—with great difficulty![52, 57, 75, 96, 98]

Oleaceae
OLIVE FAMILY

Ash
Fraxinus excelsior

GAELIC NAMES: *craobh uinnseann* (long-lasting wood), *uinsinn*

Ash in Gaelic is called *uinnse*; the wood of the ash tree is *uinnseann*.

Fraxinus means firelight, ash being traditionally used as a Yule log. In ancient Nordic myths ash was *Yggdrasil*, the World Tree, with roots that linked the sources of wisdom, fate and magic; thus it was the Tree of Life with power to protect against charms and enchantment.

An eighteenth century, probably older, Highland tradition was recorded by both Pennant and Lightfoot in each of their accounts of the journey through Scotland that they made together (see p. 20). They described midwives giving newborn babies sap from a green stick of ash held in the fire so that the juice oozed out onto a spoon held at the other end. It seems to have been a way of giving the child the strength of the ash tree and protecting it from evil spells; the custom may have derived from an ancient belief that the first man was created from an ash tree, the tree of life (the origin of the first woman is less clear—different accounts refer to alder, elm or rowan. These ancient myths of humans being created from trees contrast with the Biblical one in which they are nearly destroyed by eating forbidden fruit from the Tree of Knowledge). Druids carved magical images from ash roots and the branches were used for divination, best cut at midsummer when the tree's vigour and power were at their height. Ash was traditionally used for the handle of a witch's broom, the twigs being birch bound with willow.

🐍Snakes were believed to be afraid of ash; John Cameron quotes an old Gaelic saying: 'The serpent will go through fire, rather than through the leaves of the ash'. Ash leaves were therefore considered good protection against snake bite, and were also used to treat anyone unfortunate enough to have been bitten. Both leaves and bark have many recorded medicinal uses, relating to their astringent, diuretic and purgative effects, that might well have led to the use of this tree to treat snake bite. The bark was also used to treat fever, obstructions of the liver and spleen and rheumatic arthritis; bark ash was rubbed on scabby and leprous heads. The leaves treated gout, rheumatism, dropsy, obesity, kidney stones and jaundice, while the fruits (keys) were ground and taken for flatulence.[61]

Ash was traditionally the wood used to make a shepherd's crook, perhaps reflecting another common belief, that a stick of ash would never hurt cattle being herded with it. The tough, elastic wood was ideal for spear and tool handles, boats and oars, wheels, ploughs, furniture, fence posts and sports implements. It was coppiced: five year old growth supplied sticks for supporting garden peas or beans; after ten years, a spear shaft; after twenty, an oar.[50, 62, 96]

Ash sap makes a pleasant drink, and the keys can be pickled.

Orchidaceae
ORCHID FAMILY

Early purple orchid
Orchis mascula

SCOTS NAMES: Adam and Eve, bull's bag, bull-seg, craw-taes (crowtoes), crowfoot
LOCAL NAMES: Aaron's beard, adder's grass, Cain and Abel (two tubers), cock's kame, dead man's fingers/hand, deil's foot, hens, hen's kames (Berw), baldeeri, boldeeri, curlie-doddy (curly head, Shet), beldairy (Aber), bog hyacinth (Kirk), fool's stones (Ork), puddock's spindles (kite's legs, Perth)
GAELIC NAMES: *lus an talaidh* (the enticing plant), *moth urach* (*moth*—male, *urach*—earthy)

🐝A nourishing porridge called salep, made from the starchy, tuberous roots of early purple orchid, was given to invalids and convalescents, as well as those suffering from gastro-intestinal irritation, diarrhoea and bilious fevers. The roots form two storage tubers, which were collected in late summer when fully developed. They were blanched and skinned, then dried, to be eaten boiled in milk or water; they were so nutritious, just a few grams a day was said to be sufficient to sustain a person for several days.[61, 96; 125]

Early Purple Orchid

Grigson explains that the word salep comes from the Arabic *khusy ath 'lab*—testicles of the fox—and that in Forfarshire the dried tubers were carried as love talismans. The scientific name of this plant reflects the ancient observation that the roots resemble testicles, and it is not surprising that this has led to its use as a magic charm for enticing a lover. The two root tubers are of different sizes; the larger is said to represent the man, the smaller the woman. In order to predict the chances of winning a particular person's love, the plant was pulled up with the roots before dawn, the aspirant facing south while doing so. The appropriate tuber was then placed in spring water, still before sunrise; if it sank, marriage with the object of desire was certain. On the other hand, to find out whom one would marry, powdered orchid root placed beneath the pillow would send dreams of the destined lover.[62, 95]

Alternatively, in Aberdeenshire and other parts of northern Scotland, the custom was to dry and grind to a powder the correct part of the root,

1. It is likely that much of this information also applies to *Dactylorhiza* species, which used to be in the *Orchis* genera and are much more widespread than the early purple orchid.

then get the desired one unknowingly to eat it, after which they would find you irresistible. However, care was required—the wrong half would render you repulsive to them and even if it was successful, love generated in this way would be dissipated by marriage. In addition, it should be noted that, to the dismay of modern lovesick swains, it is now illegal to disturb wild orchids in any way whatsoever.

Oxalidaceae
WOOD SORREL FAMILY

Wood sorrel
Oxalis acetosella

SCOTS NAME: Lady's clover
LOCAL NAMES: cuckoo's meat (swS), cuckoo-sorrel (sS), gowk's meat (nS), sour clover (Berw)
GAELIC NAMES: *biadh nan coinean* (bird's foot), *samh* (shelter—where it grows; summer)

This very common woodland plant, always welcomed as one of the earliest to appear in the slow northern spring, was said to have been sacred to the Celts and druids, symbolising a secret doctrine. It may have been chosen because its leaves occur in threes, a magic number, making the shape that later appears in many Celtic knotwork patterns and that was also used by St Patrick as the symbol of the Holy Trinity (see footnote on p. 114).[125]

❀The plant has diuretic and cooling properties and was used for tonic and cleansing treatments, urinary disorders and fever. On Arran, Lightfoot was told that it was infused and drunk as an effective treatment for fevers. It was included in herb poultices applied to scrofula, wounds, swellings and inflammation, and was eaten to prevent scurvy or treat mouth ulcers. Wood sorrel contains oxalic acid, giving it the sharp, appetising flavour of rhubarb, and was also used to improve appetite and quell nausea. However, Mrs Grieve cautions against its use for people with gout or rheumatism.[61, 75, 96]

The leaves make a refreshing snack to nibble on long walks. They add flavour to salads, lemonade or lemon balm tea.[110]

Wood Sorrel

Papaveraceae
POPPY FAMILY

Poppy
Papaver dubium

GAELIC NAMES: *cromlus* (bent weed), *fothros* (corn rose), *meilbheag/beilbheag* (a little pestle—capsule), *paipean ruadh* (red pap)

❀Poppies grown in Britain are only slightly narcotic but the juice was added to children's food to soothe and make them sleep and in South Uist the flowers were made into a liquid for teething troubles. Mrs McLintock gives a recipe for 'Syrop of Red Poppies'. Roots of poppies and other wild flowers were added to the water when washing newly-woven linen, for more effective cleansing.[7, 18, 61, 76, 93]

Plantaginaceae
PLANTAIN FAMILY

Buckshorn plantain
Plantago coronopus

❀Buckshorn plantain grows on rocks or in short turf near the sea. The whole plant including the roots was used to treat fever; the leaves were made into eye wash.[61]

Ribwort plantain
P. lanceolata

SCOTS NAMES: curl doddy, fechters (fighters)
LOCAL NAMES: kemp (to fight), kempseed (Selk), soldiers, headman (Perth), Johnsmas-flooer (Shet), ribgrass (Kirk, Wigt)
GAELIC NAMES: *lus an t'slanuchaidh, slan lus* (healing plant), *snaithlus*

❀Widely used until recent times as a healing herb, ribwort plantain was pounded into pulp to make a poultice for wounds, swellings and sores or to be added to ointments. The plant was also believed to have magic powers of divination: in Shetland at midsummer, two lovers would each pick a Johnsmas-flooer (so called because it begins to flower around St John's day, 24 June), remove the florets and place them under a flat stone.

If the plant grew more florets before the picked ones withered, the couple would marry.[18, 57, 96, 101]

The Scots names fechters, kemp, soldiers and headmen derive from a game children played, in which the flowering heads were made to attack each other until the losers were all decapitated.[62]

It was valued as nutritious pasture.[57, 136]

Great plantain
Plantago major

SCOTS NAMES: healing blade, rat's tails, ripple-girs, wabran-leaf
LOCAL NAMES: bird's meat (Aber), Johnsmas pairs/flowers, waaverin-leaf (Shet), waybread (Berw, Rox, Kirk, Wigt), way-burn leaf (Lan)
GAELIC NAMES: *cuach Phadraig* (Patrick's bowl/cup), *slan-lus* (plant of healing)

Great Plantain

❀A cooling, astringent and styptic plant of healing, the leaves of which were used whole externally for poultices applied to wounds, burns, stings, scalds and sores. Sometimes the leaves were warmed and beaten between the palms so that the ribs could be extracted leaving a smooth surface; the poultice drew the pus from boils and sores and had to be renewed every few hours. Internally a decoction of the leaves or root was taken for fevers, dysentery and bowel problems, stomach complaints and intestinal worms.[57,61,62,96,100,125]

The interweaving of magic with medicine led one unfortunate healer to be accused of witchcraft for using this plant: in 1623, Bessie Smith was forced to appear before the Presbytery of Lesmahagow, where she confessed that she had been guilty of attempting to cure 'heart fevers' by giving people wayburn leaves to eat for nine mornings, with a charm to be spoken.[95]

The name waybread may simply derive from the very widespread distribution of this plant—it is always to be found along the way, being tolerant of the compacted soil beside paths.

Polygalaceae
MILKWORT FAMILY

Milkwort
Polygala serpyllifolia

This common little grassland and heathland plant was woven with other plants into a magic hoop to protect the milk from enchantment (see p. 82).

Polygonaceae
DOCK FAMILY

Black bindweed
Fallopia convolvulus

SCOTS NAME: spades (from shape of leaves, Berw)

Thought of as a common agricultural weed, growing in amongst planted corn, in fact black bindweed has starchy seeds that in themselves have nutritional value and were formerly harvested and eaten along with the crop. Indeed, in prehistoric times black bindweed may have actually been the crop; a seed and seed impression have been found with wheat and barley grains of the late Bronze Age in Morayshire. As Grigson points out, archaeologists recognise that in primitive agriculture the distinction between 'wild' and 'domesticated' plants is often negligible (see p. 5). Black bindweed is common on arable and marginal land except in north west Scotland.[62]

Great bistort
Persicaria bistorta

LOCAL NAME: snake weed (Banff, Lan)

A strongly astringent and styptic plant. The root, powdered or in decoction, was used for an amazing number of medicinal purposes including diarrhoea, dysentery, cholera, bowel problems, piles, bleeding from the lung, stomach or nose, diabetes, fever, ague, wounds, ruptures, bruises, jaundice, plague, smallpox, measles, stings, bites, sores, ulcers, sore throat, gum infection and worms. Mrs Grieve gives several recipes for its use, including *Infants' Diarrhoea Syrup*, *Decoction for Piles* and *Gargle for Ulcerated Tonsils*.[61]

The plant may well have been introduced to Scotland but is widespread though not common. In 1806, Patrick Neill visited Orkney, where he found bistort, among other plants, growing in the physic garden of Dr Sutherland (see p. 21).[106]

Great Bistort

Spotted knotweed, water pepper
P. hydropiper

SCOTS NAME: hot arsmart
GAELIC NAME: *lus an fhogair* (the plant which expels or banishes)

139

❀The somewhat graphic Scots name may derive from the effect of this plant on the bowels when eaten; medicinally, as the Gaelic name suggests, it was used to treat dysentery, flatulence and piles, as well as gravel in the kidneys or bladder, colds, coughs, epilepsy, gout, sore mouth, gangrene, ulcers, piles, inflammation, toothache and whitlows.[61]

Water pepper is common in marshes and beside rivers and lochs except in the north of Scotland. Yellow and gold dye can be obtained from the chopped plant.[52]

Persicaria, redshank
P. maculosa

SCOTS NAMES: dead arsemart, spotted arssmart, useless
LOCAL NAMES: flooering soorik, yellowin girse (Shet)
GAELIC NAME: *lus chrann ceusaidh* (herb of the crucifixion tree)

❀The medicinal uses of this common agricultural weed are not known, but the Scots name arssmart suggests it may have once been use similarly to *P. hydropiper* (see above). Legend says persicaria got the red spots on its leaves from the blood of Jesus because it grew beneath the cross, hence the Gaelic name. Yellow dye can be obtained from the whole plant.[52, 62]

Knotgrass
Polygonum aviculare

LOCAL NAMES: deil's lingels (thongs, Berw), finzach (Banff), swine's grass (Berw, Rox)

❀Another common agricultural weed. Knotgrass has astringent and styptic properties and was used for diarrhoea, piles, bleeding, kidney stones, intestinal worms, nosebleed, sores, colic, wounds and nervous complaints.[61]

Sorrel
Rumex acetosa

SCOTS NAME: sourock
LOCAL NAMES: lammie sourocks, sourlick, redshank (Rox), soorik (Shet)
GAELIC NAMES: *samh, sealbhag, sealbhag ruanaidh*

❀Used as a poultice on sores, bruises and abscesses. For the last, the leaves were boiled with mistletoe and fenugreek.[18, 32] Martin demonstrated his own healing skills in the following account of the advice he gave an overweight St Kildan:

Sorrel

One of them that was become corpulent, and had his throat almost shut up, being advised by me to take salt with his meat, to exercise himself more in the fields than he had done of late, to forbear eating of fat fowl and the fat pudding called giben, and to eat sorrel, was very much concerned because all this was very disagreeable, and my advising him to eat sorrel perfectly a surprise to him; but when I bid him consider how the fat fulmar eat this plant he was at last disposed to take my advice; and by this means alone in a few days after, his voice was much clearer, his appetite recovered, and he was in a fair way of recovery.[100]

The acidic leaves of this common grassland plant are still popular in salads and sauces. At one time they were used to take rust stains out of linen. The plant yields red dye.[52, 96, 131]

Dock, docken
Rumex species

GAELIC NAME: *copag*

The astringent leaves of docken are still widely used to rub on nettle stings, but traditionally a far more effective poultice was made of the roots, cleaned, peeled and crushed into a pulp. This was also applied to bee stings. The roots were boiled and mixed with equal parts of beeswax and fresh butter to make a healing ointment.[6]

On St Kilda and no doubt elsewhere dock leaves used to be eaten as greens. Bunches of dock leaves were fed to cows to encourage them to stand still during milking. In the Orkneys, trows (trolls) rode through the air on docken stems. A more practical use by resourceful Shetlanders was in making baskets known as 'dockens', using stalks 60 cm long as the upright framework bound together with marram or bent grass. An example of this kind of basket can be seen in Lerwick Museum.[4, 98, 100, 101]

The roots give a black dye, the leaves yellow or warm brown.[52]

Primulaceae
PRIMROSE FAMILY

Scarlet pimpernel
Anagallis arvensis

LOCAL NAME: poor man's weather glass (Lan)

❀Recommended to treat wounds in the sixteenth century (see p. 16). The Lanarkshire name (variations of which were used throughout Britain) refers to the fact that the flowers, which open from about 8 am to 3 pm, tend to close in wet and humid weather.[62] This small, prostrate annual is becoming less common, and now occurs mainly in the north of Scotland.

Cowslip
Primula veris

GAELIC NAMES: *brog na cubhaig* (cuckoo's shoe), *muisean* (low rascal, devil)

> *It was formerly boiled, and an ointment or distilled water was made from it, which addeth much to beauty, and taketh away spots and wrinkles of the skin, sun-burnings and freckles, and adds beauty exceedingly.*[18]

❀The yellow flower has sedative properties and was used to treat nervous conditions, insomnia and headaches. Cowslip wine was also used as a sedative and the syrup for palsy (paralysis accompanied by uncontrollable tremors). The roots were used for muscular rheumatism.[61] Cowslips, found in calcareous grassland, are uncommon in Scotland.

Primrose
Primula vulgaris

SCOTS NAMES: May spink, pimrose
LOCAL NAMES: buckie-faalie (Caith), May-flooer (Shet)
GAELIC NAMES: *sobrach, sobrag* (pleasure, delight, joy)

Alexander Carmichael noted that the primrose, common in woods and grassland throughout Scotland, was mentioned frequently in popular rhymes and was greatly relished by children as a summer snack. He also described a delightful Hebridean spring ceremony with obvious pagan roots. On Bride's Eve[1] girls:

> *fashion a sheaf of corn into the likeness of a woman. They dress and deck the figure with shining shells, sparkling crystals, primroses, snowdrops, and any greenery they may obtain.*[23]

---

1. 1 February, St Bride's Day, was one of the Scottish quarter days that marked the changing seasons, derived from the ancient feast of Imbolc and transformed into Candlemas by the Christian Church, but retaining its symbolism of the growing light of spring and fresh growth stirring.

The figure, called Bride or *Brideag*, Little Bride, was carried in procession to every house by the maidens, themselves dressed in white with their hair loose, symbolising purity and youth. They were given gifts for Bride of more decorations or, from mothers they visited, a specially made bannock, cheese or roll of butter. The girls then feasted behind a closed door with Bride displayed prominently in a window; young men later had humbly to ask permission to gain entry and pay obeisance to the figure.

❀The whole plant including roots was used medicinally as a sedative and to treat worms, rheumatism, gout, paralysis, headaches and wounds.[61] Comrie quotes from a manuscript in Edinburgh University Library, *Ane Gude Buik of Medycines Callit the Treasure of Puir men*, copied in the late sixteenth century (and suggesting the handwriting of medical folk was as indecipherable then as now!):

To purge the heid
Take the joyce of prymrose, and the mylke of ane knowe, as I supose it
should be ane kow. And with ane pen blaw it into they nose thrysle, and
it sall purge the heid and make the [w]*hole.*[32]

The flowers can be made into wine and tea.[110]

Brook-weed
Samolus valerandi

SCOTS NAME: water pimpernel

Brook-weed is found in streams and wet flushes near the coast, apart from in the northeast of Scotland. According to Pliny, *Samolus*, collected using the left hand without looking behind, was placed by druids in their cattle's water troughs to protect the beasts against infectious diseases.[32]

Ranunculaceae
BUTTERCUP FAMILY

Although little used in herbal medicine today, the properties of the buttercup family were well-known in earlier times. Because of their poisonous and acrid nature, most members of this family need careful handling and are rarely used internally. While people seldom poison themselves with *Ranunculus* species because they taste so unpleasant, livestock will eat them when young or if other food is scarce, but usually recover.

Wood anemone
Anemone nemorosa

SCOTS NAME: darn-grass (for giving cattle a disease called the darn)
LOCAL NAMES: wild jessamine (Dumf), windflower (Peeb)

A widespread plant of woods, also found on upland grassland and moorland where it may be a relic indicating previous woodland cover. The juice from wood anemones was used in the nineteenth century to dye Easter eggs. It provided a safe refuge for fairies to take their beauty sleep or shelter from rain, as the flower closes at night and at the onset of wet weather.[61, 122]

Marsh marigold
Caltha palustris

LOCAL NAMES: blogda, bludda, blugga (horse-hooves, Shet), golland (Caith), kingcup (Lan), water golland/gowland (sS), wildfire (Kirk), yellow gowlan (nS)
GAELIC NAMES: *corrach-shod, lus-buidhe-bealltain, lus Muire*

❀In medieval times marsh marigold was used to treat skin rashes, but the plant is strongly irritant. An infusion of the flowers was used to treat fits and a tincture of the whole plant in flower was drunk for anaemia.[61, 62]

Found throughout Scotland, it was woven into magic hoops to protect milk (see p. 82). The flowers yield a yellow dye.[52]

Hellebore

Hellebore
Helleborus species

Although introduced to Scotland, stinking hellebore *H. foetidus* and green hellebore *H. viridis* both grow in the south and east. This plant was used in ancient times as arrow poison and was cooked with venison to make it sweet and tender.[76, 96]

Buttercups
Ranunculus species

LOCAL NAMES: crowfoot (Lan), golland (Berw), kraa-tae (Shet), sitsticker, yellow gollan (sS)
GAELIC NAMES: *cearban* (raggy), *gair* (a smile), *cean* (live, elegance)

Meadow buttercup
R. acris

LOCAL NAME: gowan (Wigt)
GAELIC NAME: *cearban feoir* (grass rag)

Crushed leaves of meadow buttercup were tied in rags (*cearban*) over boils and infected skin to raise a blister and extract septic fluids.[18, 96] (See also *R. flammula*).

Lesser celandine, pilewort
R. ficaria

SCOTS NAME: foalfoot (Ayr)
GAELIC NAMES: *grain-aigein, searraiche* (little bottle-roots)

Meadow Buttercup

Cameron defines the Gaelic name *grain-aigein* as that which produces loathing, but Mrs Grieve calls the plant *grian*, the sun, because of the flower's habit of opening from about 9 am to 5 pm, when the sun is shining. The tuberous roots were grubbed up to be eaten in hard times.[61]

❀The knobbly little roots were also crushed and applied as juice (for which care was needed in handling because it could cause healthy skin to blister) or made into ointment for external growths, lumps, corns and piles. This use derives from the ancient 'Doctrine of Signatures', whereby early herbalists were inspired by the appearance of certain plants to use them to treat the disease or part of the body they resembled. Although it might be surmised that at least sometimes the similarity was noticed after the plant's efficacy had been determined, in the case of *R. ficaria* a very useful remedy was discovered by whichever means; the plant is also known as pilewort and an ointment made from the roots might still be the first treatment a modern herbalist would suggest for haemorrhoids.[6, 96]

Lesser spearwort
R. flammula

SCOTS NAMES: butterplate, goosetongue, wilfire
GAELIC NAMES: *buidheag, glas-leun* (green swamp), *lasair-leana* (swamp flame)

Common in wet areas, lesser spearwort had several medicinal uses. Martin found it in infusion being drunk as a purgative; it had to be mixed with melted butter to prevent it burning the throat. On the Hebridean island of Brorera, he noted that:

The vulgar are accustomed to apply Flammula Jovis [the scientific name of R. flammula at that time] for excavating noxious humours, such as cause the headache, and pains in the arms or legs; and they find great advantage by it. The way of using it is thus: They take an quantity of it, bruised small and put into a patella [limpet shell], and apply it to the skin, a little below the place affected: in a small time it raises a blister about the bigness of an egg which, when broke, voids all the matter that is in it; then the skin fills and swells twice again, and as often voids this matter. They use the sea-plant linarich [see p. 52] to cure the wound.[100]

Lightfoot suggested this practice was widespread throughout the coastal areas of the Highlands.[75]

The plant was used as a substitute for rennet in cheese-making.[96] Purple dye can be obtained from the plant's tips.[52]

Celery-leaved crowfoot
R. sceleratus

GAELIC NAME: *torachas biadhain* (possibly 'food of which one would be afraid')

The whole plant is very corrosive, and beggars use it to ulcerate their feet, which they expose in that state to excite compassion.[96]

This plant is not common in Scotland, being found in wet areas mainly in the south and coastal districts.

Lesser meadow-rue
Thalictrum minus

GAELIC NAME: *ru beg* (to flow)

The Gaelic name indicates the strongly cathartic effect the roots of this plant have when used medicinally, so powerful it was used to induce abortion. It was also said to have been effective for rheumatism. On North Uist, red dye was obtained from the roots.[7, 18, 52, 96]

The plant is widespread in lowland and coastal districts of Scotland, on machair and riverbanks.

Globe flower
Trolius europaeus

SCOTS NAMES: cabbage daisy, lapper gowan, locker gowlan, lockin
gowan, luggie gowan, witches' gowan
LOCAL NAME: bull-jumping (Kinrs)
GAELIC NAME: *leolaicheann*

A lovely flower, once common in upland and mountainous areas but de-
clining because of grazing pressure and now found mainly in the north
west of Scotland. People went out in groups to gather globe flowers for
festivals. Children used the flowers as drinking cups.[18, 62]

Resedaceae
MIGNONETTE FAMILY

Dyers rocket, weld
Reseda luteola

SCOTS NAME: yellow rocket
GAELIC NAME: *lus buidhe mor*

The whole plant except the roots can be used to dye wool lemon yellow,
golden yellow, orange yellow or olive green. It was used in producing
Harris tweed; however, as this plant is uncommon, occurring in eastern
and southern Scotland, it must have been grown specially or imported
from England where it is fairly common on chalk grassland.[52]

Rosaceae
ROSE FAMILY

Agrimony
Agrimonia eupatoria

GAELIC NAME: *mur-druidhean* (*mur*—sorrow; *druidh*—magician, druid)

Agrimony is found in dry grassy places in most areas except the north
west of Scotland. The Gaelic name of this plant, *mur-druidhean*, may
derive from the use of agrimony by healers to treat spiritual troubles.
Ferquhar Ferguson, tried for witchcraft on Arran in 1716, admitted using

Agrimony

agrimony to cure elf-shotten people. (Judging by the number of remedies recorded this was a common affliction of earlier times.) Ferguson was guided in his treatment by a voice heard while sleeping, which instructed him to pull the plant in the name of the Holy Trinity.[18, 85]

❀Agrimony has astringent, tonic and diuretic properties, and a decoction of the root and leaves was used to treat skin and liver disorders including jaundice.[61] Wilma Paterson uses it to make tea and wine.[110]

Lady's mantle
Alchemilla vulgaris

LOCAL NAMES: dew cup, duck's foot (Berw), elf-shot (Kirk, Wigt)
GAELIC NAME: *copan an druichd* (dew cup)

❀Long considered to be one of the best wound herbs, an infusion or decoction of the leaves or root was used for bleeding, swelling, bruises and ruptures as well as for vomiting and diarrhoea. The large leaves collect drops of morning dew and it was a widespread tradition to use this pure water for a refreshing face wash.[61]

It was also a powerful remedy for domestic animals that had fallen ill after being shot by the arrows of malevolent elves. Water containing juice from the plant was both sprinkled on the sick beast and given it to drink.[62]

Lady's mantle is found in meadows throughout Scotland.

Parsley piert
Aphanes species

LOCAL NAMES: bowel-hive grass (Berw), parsley-breakstone (Orkney and elsewhere)

❀Common in dry grassland in coastal districts of Scotland, parsley piert has diuretic and cooling qualities; an infusion of the herb was taken as a remedy for dropsy, kidney and bladder disorders. On Colonsay, it was used to treat inflammation of the bowel (bowel-hive) in children, especially in the north; it was also eaten raw or pickled.[61, 96]

Hawthorn
Crataegus monogyna

SCOTS NAME: haw-berry
LOCAL NAMES: haw, haw-bush (Dumf), has tree (Dumf, Loth, Lanark, Ayr)
GAELIC NAMES: *preas nan sgeachag, sgiteach, sgithich*

Although the tree had several uses—black and fawn dye can be obtained from the bark, the hard, rot-resistant wood was used for carving and tool handles, the leaves were added to tea, the blossoms and berries made into wine and liqueur—nevertheless, hawthorn was once considered to be so sacred that using any part of the tree was treated as a violation. This taboo survives in the belief still occasionally encountered that it is unlucky to bring hawthorn blossom into the house. It was planted in circles forming sacred groves where priestesses of the pre-Christian Mother Goddess religion worshipped and was associated with graves of important people, who were either buried in such consecrated groves or had hawthorn planted around their burial mounds. This may be linked to the belief that thorny plants are efficient 'spirit catchers'.[50, 52, 110, 125]

A decoction of the flowers and leaves was drunk to soothe sore throats and to correct high or low blood pressure.[7]

Meadowsweet
Filipendula ulmaria

SCOTS NAMES: lady- or queen-of-the-meadow, meduart
LOCAL NAMES: blackin-girse (Shet), meadow-queen (Renf, Perth)
GAELIC NAMES: *lus Chuchulainn, rios Chuchulainn* (belt of Cuchulainn)

❀Common in damp places throughout Scotland. Meadowsweet contains salicylic acid—an ingredient of aspirin—and the whole plant was used to treat malaria and other fevers. Mary Beith has observed the scent of meadowsweet alone effectively clearing headaches. The Gaelic name associating the plant with the legendary warrior Cuchulainn is derived from the story of his treatment with meadowsweet baths to cure uncontrollable fits of rage or fevers. It was certainly used to treat fevers in South Uist, where meadowsweet was also employed as a fragrant strewing herb for floors, with bog myrtle.[7, 52, 62, 110]

The common name comes from using the flowers to flavour mead, a use known to go back at least to the Bronze Age (see p. 4). They can also be made into tea and wine. The plant yields yellow, green, black and rosy red dyes.[39, 52, 110]

Dropwort
F. vulgaris

❀Similar to meadowsweet but grows in drier, calcareous grassy areas mainly in the Fife area. The roots, powdered or in decoction, were used to treat kidney problems and breathlessness, wheezing, sore throat and congestion.[61]

Wild strawberry
Fragaria vesca

GAELIC NAMES: *subh, subhan laire* (ground sap), *suth thalhmain* (earth's sap/delight), *tlachd subh* (pleasant fruit)

❀Wild strawberry plants can be found throughout Scotland in woodland clearings and along banks. Records show that they were a regular delicacy at the court of James IV. The tiny, irresistably sweet wild strawberry is not just a delicious fruit, however; the berry was used to treat rheumatic gout and sunburn and as a cosmetic to colour pale cheeks and lips. Tea made from the dried leaves and roots is astringent and was drunk after diarrhoea or dysentery.[61, 68, 110]

Herb bennet, wood avens
Geum urbanum

❀Common in woods and hedgerows in most parts of Scotland. This plant has astringent, styptic and antiseptic properties and a decoction or infusion of the root or herb had many medicinal uses including as a tonic, for worms, diarrhoea, dysentery and other stomach problems, bleeding, sore throat, fever, colds and headache.[61]

Crab apple
Malus sylvestris

LOCAL NAMES: scrab, scrogg (i.e. scrubby, Berw, Rox)
GAELIC NAME: *ubhal-fiadhaich*

Hallowe'en rituals such as apple-dooking and throwing apple peel, removed in one long strip, over a girl's shoulder to reveal the initial of her future husband, are the survival of Celtic *Samhain* (old New Year, 1 November) rites of divination and prophecy. Apples were the fruit of life, passport to the Celtic Otherworld or Land of Faerie, the fruit that guided the ancient hero Cuchulainn across the Plain of Ill-luck on his way to the military college in Skye. An early Christian legend relates that when St Servanus tossed his pastoral staff across the Firth of Forth (whether this was for a show of strength or simply staking a claim, I do not know), it took root where it landed and grew into an apple tree.[95, 136]

Apple blossom, a sign of spring, was associated with various aspects of the maiden/mother goddess in many parts of Europe and used in fertility rites. Cut an apple crosswise through the centre, and each half dispays a five-pointed star, symbol of the goddess of love, of the five stations from birth to death, of the five days of ovulation and of menstruation in the female cycle and hence the emblem of immortality.[105, 136]

The use of apple juice internally to cool fevers is still well known; it also used to be applied externally to soothe sprains and cramps. Mary Beith records that a decoction of apples and rowan berries, sweetened with brown sugar, was used to cure whooping cough in the Highlands, and the sensible advice in the medieval medical manuscript used by Gaelic doctors, *Regimen Sanitas* (Rule of Health, see p. 14) included cleaning the teeth with apple skins and eating a roasted apple, before going to bed, to induce sleep, and before heavy meals to aid digestion.[7, 52]

Yellow dye can be obtained from the bark and was used in Harris tweed production.[52]

Silverweed
Potentilla anserina

SCOTS NAMES: dog-tansy, moor-grass, moss-crop
LOCAL NAMES: fair-days (Berw), fair-grass (Rox), goose-grass (Berw, Rox),swine's grass (Ork), swine's murriks (roots, Shet)
GAELIC NAMES: *an seachdamh aran* (the seventh bread), *brisgean/ briosglan/ brislean* (brittle)

The small, creeping herb silverweed is found in all coastal districts of Scotland and often far inland on waste ground, roadsides, in meadows and the hollows of sand dunes. The common name refers to the fine silvery hairs on the leaves (especially beneath).

It was known in Gaelic as *an seachdamh aran*, one of the seven breads of the Gael, referring to its great importance in the diet of people in the Highlands and Islands of Scotland before the mid-eighteenth century when potatoes became common. A lovely description collected by Alexander Carmichael describes the year-round importance of 'The blest silverweed':

> *Honey under ground,*
> *Silverweed of spring.*
> *Honey and condiment*
> *Whisked whey of summer.*
> *Honey and fruitage*
> *Carrot of autumn.*
> *Honey and crunching*
> *Nuts of winter.*[23]

The root (called *brisgean, brisgein, briosglan* or *brislean*, meaning brittle) was considered palatable and nutritious and continued to be eaten even after potatoes were available, especially in times of famine. Lightfoot wrote in 1777:

In the islands of Tirey and Col they are much esteemed, as answering in some measure the purposes of bread, they having been known to support the inhabitants for months together, during a scarcity of other provisions. They put a yoke on their ploughs, and often tear up their pasture grounds, with a view to eradicate the roots for their use; and as they abound most in barren and impoverished soils, and in seasons that succeed the worst for other crops, so they never fail to afford a most reasonable relief to the inhabitants at times of greatest scarcity. A singular incidence this of the bounty of providence to these islands![75]

Boiled or roasted, the roots taste rather like parsnips; raw, they have a crunchy, slightly nutty flavour. Martin described them being eaten with melted giben (fowl fat) on St Kilda. They were sometimes dried and ground to make porridge or bread. In some places silverweed was grown as a vegetable crop, plants with larger roots being selected for cultivation. At Lag nan Tanchasg in Paible, North Uist, it was said a man could could sustain himself on a square of ground his own length growing *brisgein*. Suitable *morfhearann* (common land) was allocated by lottery in the same way as fishing grounds at sea and fish landed on the shore. The roots could be traded for corn or meal of the same quantity and quality.[23]

❀*Potentilla* means 'little powerful one'; the plant has astringent, anti-catarrhal, diuretic and anti-inflammatory properties. Medicinal uses for the dried leaves of *P. anserina* were in a gargle or mouthwash for sore throats, mouth ulcers or gum infections, or to be taken internally or applied as a compress for haemorrhoids, heartburn or stomach ache.[61, 66]

Grigson suggests it was a belief in sympathetic magic that led to another use for the leaves, as the original jogger's inner-sole, because the plant flourishes even when trampled and was said to keep the feet of long-distance carriers or messengers cool and dry. This may be so: the felted hairs would absorb moisture and might add some springiness to the wearer's step.[38, 62]

Tormentil
Potentilla erecta

SCOTS NAMES: blood-root, shepherd's knot
LOCAL NAMES: eart-barth (earth-bark, Shet), ewe-daisy, flesh-and-blood (Berw)
GAELIC NAMES: *barr braonan-nan-con* (dog's briar bud), *braonan fraoch* (possibly bud in heather), *braonan bachlag* (earth-nut), *leanartach* (follow—because it is so common)

❀A small plant, very common on moors and grassland throughout Scotland.

The name tormentil derives from the medicinal use of the plant to relieve the torment of stomach ache. The plant has astringent and styptic properties and a decoction or infusion of the root, fresh or dried, was used for diarrhoea, piles, fever, sore throats and eyes, cholera, ulcers and sores. Archaeologists excavating the midden of a mediaeval monastery at Jedburgh found great quantities of tormentil pollen mixed with the eggs of whipworm, an intestinal parasite that causes severe diarrhoea. This appears to be clear evidence of a herbal remedy, possibly administered with the monks' food.[61, 62, 103]

Tormentil

The remedy was still well known in Lightfoot's time:

A decoction of those roots in milk is also frequently administered by the inhabitants of the...islands in diarrhaeas and dysenteries, with good success; but perhaps it would be most proper not to give it in dysenteries till the morbid matter be first evacuated. A spirituous extract of the plant stands recommended in the sea-scurvy, for to strengthen the gums and fasten the teeth.[75]

In the Western Isles the plant was also chewed to heal sore lips, while in Perthshire the plant was boiled to make a cooling lotion for sunburn.[7, 135]

The roots, thick tubers two or three centimetres across, contain red juice which was widely used in dyeing red and tanning leather and fishing nets. For all these purposes, they were best gathered in late spring, and were said to be better than oak bark for tanning. On the islands of Tiree and Coll, so much ground was destroyed by digging the roots up that at one time (possibly late nineteenth century) the inhabitants had to be prohibited from collecting them.[61, 100, 106, 125]

When visiting Skye in 1772, Lightfoot wrote to his patron the Duchess of Portland:

The Wretchedness & Poverty of the People is such as I shall astonish your Grace in the Account of it. Every Man tans & dresses his own Leather and makes his own Shoes. He tans it with the Roots of Tormentil for there is scarcely a tree to be seen in the Island to afford Bark.[14]

While voyaging in the Hebrides in 1844, Hugh Miller was given a pair of shoes, 'deep madder-red' in colour:

They were altogether the production of Eigg, from the skin out of which they had been cut, with the lime that had prepared it for the tan, and the root by which the tan had been furnished, to the last on which they had been moulded...There are few trees, and, of course, no bark to spare, in the island; but the islanders find a substitute in the astringent lobiferous root of the Tormentilla erecta, *which they dig out for the purpose*

153

among the heath at no considerable expense of time and trouble. I was informed...that the infusion of root had to be thrice changed for every skin, and that it took a man nearly a day to gather roots enough for a single infusion.[102]

Tormentil roots and rushes were the main food of Orkney pigs, according to Neill writing in 1806. The root was used in exorcism rituals in Orkney.[101]

Creeping cinquefoil
P. reptans

SCOTS NAMES: five-leaved grass, common cinquefoil

✽Similar to tormentil but creeping, as the name suggests, far less common and possibly not native. The plant has astringent and styptic properties and the roots and leaves were used to treat fevers and malaria.[61]

Gean, wild cherry
Prunus avium

SCOTS NAME: sirist
LOCAL NAME: merry-tree (Shet)

This lovely tree is found in most parts of Scotland except the far north west. Various alcoholic drinks were flavoured with the cherries, including whisky, ratafia and brandy. The bark dyes shades ranging from cream to tan, while the roots dye purple-red.[42, 52, 110]

Bird cherry
P. padus

SCOTS NAME: hagberry
LOCAL NAME: hackberry (Berw, Rox, Dumf, Perth)

✽An infusion or decoction of cherry stalks was taken for bronchitis, anaemia and diarrhoea.[61]

The fruit is small, black, and with an austere, bitter taste; but though unpleasant when eaten, is used in Scotland to give flavour to gin, whiskey, and other spirits.[125]

Bird cherry has a similar distribution to gean in Scotland.

Blackthorn
P. spinosa

Blackthorn

SCOTS NAME: bulister
GAELIC NAMES: *airne* (sloe), *preas nan airneag* (sloe bush), *sluach*

❀Blackthorn grows wild throughout Scotland. Long associated with dark forces and sometimes used in rites of black witches, the hard, strong wood and shape of blackthorn made it ideal for walking sticks and weapons and perhaps this led to the parallel belief that, like other prickly plants (which would catch and hold malevolent spirits), the tree had protective and defensive powers against evil. It was planted around fields as much for this as for its thorns, and the protection could be pleasantly absorbed through drinking sloe gin or wine, the former also being a remedy for diarrhoea. Slightly purgative tea was made from the leaves and flowers and the bark was used to reduce fever.[50, 61, 110]

The berries produce pink and grey-blue dyes, whilst the bark yields shades of red-brown to orange.[52]

Wild rose
Rosa species

SCOTS NAMES: -hips: dog-hips, hedgy-pedgies
-plant: briar
LOCAL NAMES: -hips: puckies, dog-hippans (Aber), choops (Rox, Dumf, Ayr), hawps (nS), hippans (Mor), buckie-lice (sS)
-plant: briar-rose (Berw, Rox), klonger/klunger (Shet)
GAELIC NAME: *muca-faileag* (berries)

❀In the seventeenth century, Kirkwood wrote:

> *To cure a broken bone they take a Brier and cleave it almost from one end to the other, and put therein a charm* [words]...*this brier they put upon the wall above the sick person's bed; and as the rod joyns so will the bone.*[73]

More reliable medicinal uses for the astringent leaves, flowers and hips of dog rose were to treat diarrhoea, dysentery, colic, coughs, tuberculosis and kidney stones.[61] In the Highlands, Mary Beith writes,

> *Decoctions of rose wood and leaves, with poultices of the leaves and fresh butter locally, were used in conjunction with infusions of stonecrop or herb Robert (taken internally) to treat erysipelas, a condition itself known as the 'rose'* [characterised by fever and inflammation of the face and head].[7]

Rose hips have long been made into wine, syrup, tea and jam; Mrs McLintock gives an old recipe for a 'Conserve of Dog-Hips'. Many former Girl Guides remember being sent out during the last war to collect sacks full of rose hips for making into syrup with a high vitamin C content, at a time when fruit was scarce. The petals can also be made into tea and wine.[93, 110]

Black dye is obtained from the roots.[52]

A white rose is the emblem of the Stuarts; Jacobites wore them on 10 June, the birthday of Bonnie Prince Charlie.

Cloudberry
Rubus chamaemorus

SCOTS NAMES: knoutberry, knotberry, nub
LOCAL NAMES: averin, evron (Banff, Mor), fintock (Perth), noops (Berw), nub-berry, nub (Dumf)
GAELIC NAMES: *feireag, foighreag, lus nan eighreag, oireag, oighreag*

A low-growing plant of high, cloudy places, with large, raspberry-like leaves that form conspicuous patches in wet peaty areas in the hills in most parts of Scotland. The large, red-orange berries were eaten as a dessert.[75]

Blackberry, bramble
R. fruticosus

LOCAL NAMES: gatter-tree, lady's garters (Rox); for the fruit: blackbides (Kirk, Wigt), black bowours (Berw), black boyds (wS), brambles (Perth), garten-berries, gatter-berry, lady garten-berries (Rox)
GAELIC NAMES: *an druise beannaichte, dreas, dris muine* (thorn/prickle/ sting), *grian mhuine* (thorn that basks in the sun), *smear phreas* (bush that smears), *smeuran*

Called *an druise bennaichte*, the blessed bramble, because it was said Jesus used a bramble switch when riding his donkey into Jerusalem and when driving the moneylenders from the temple. Highlanders made wreaths of ivy, bramble and rowan to protect themselves from evil. Bramble was sometimes used for the peeled white wand carried by the corn sheaf made to represent Bride at a spring festival in the Highlands and Islands (see p. 142).[23, 62, 96]

❀The leaves were placed on burns and swellings and a syrup from the berries was drunk to relieve sore throats and bronchial catarrh. An infusion of bramble leaves was used by nineteenth century Fife mining families to treat diarrhoea. Wine and cordial were made from the berries and tea from the leaves.[62, 110, 115]

The berries yield rose pink, blue, purple, grey/blue, red and orange dyes.[52] Pipes for smoking tobacco were traditionally carved from bramble wood.

Raspberry
R. idaeus

SCOTS NAMES: hindberry (eaten by deer), rasp, sivven
LOCAL NAME: wood-rasp (Selk)
GAELIC NAMES: *preas subh chraobh* (bush with sappy sprouts), *suibhean*

❧A common shrub throughout Scotland. Raspberry leaf tea was drunk for colds and influenza and widely used to ease the pain of childbirth.[110]

Raspberry

In the isle of Skye the juice or a syrup of the fruit is frequently used as an agreeable acid for making of punch, instead of oranges or lemons. A distill'd water from the fruit is cooling, and very beneficial in fevers.[75]

The fruit is of course delicious and most years abundant. It can be used to flavour liqueur, brandy and wine. Mrs McLintock gives a recipe 'To make a Geil of Rasps'.[93, 110]

Stone bramble
R. saxatilis

SCOTS NAME: roebuck
GAELIC NAME: *caora gad miann* (berry of the desirable cluster)

A slender, delicate, creeping plant that grows on basic soil in woods, on scree slopes etc., localised in scattered locations throughout Scotland. The berry is small and differs from other *Rubus* species in having fewer, larger segments. Lightfoot found a kind of mead being made from them: 'Ruffians ferment [the berries] with honey, and extract a potent spirit from them'.[75] It was said to grow abundantly around Loch Rannoch, where the fruit was collected to eat, although this is an area of acid soils where one would not expect to find much stone bramble.[125]

Great burnet
Sanguisorba officinalis

GAELIC NAME: *a bhileach losgain* (*losgain*—burning)

In Scotland, great burnet is quite rare and occurs only in the south, though

157

the plant is fairly common in some parts of northern England. As both the English and the Gaelic names indicate, the leaves were used on burns and swellings.[18]

Rowan, mountain ash
Sorbus aucuparia

SCOTS NAMES: quicken, roddin, roddin-tree
GAELIC NAMES: *caorunn, coille* (wood enchantress/wood-ash), *craobh chaoran* (berry-tree), *luis* (drink), *uinseag*

Rowan trees can still be seen growing beside many cairns, stone circles and Scottish houses both old and new, attesting to long belief in its magic powers.[1] Rowan was thought more potent than any other tree against evil or bad luck—presumably because it bears bright red berries, the colour of blood and thus of life itself. The wood was incorporated into nearly every object that might need protection: house and byre, butter churn and barrel, yoke and plough, cart and boat, spinning wheel and mill wheel, and finally the coffin. An old Scots word for the cross-beam in the chimney is rantree, from rowan tree, the wood of which it was often made. Making love under any tree, but especially a rowan, was supposed to cure barrenness and would most likely result in a male child.[18, 62, 75, 95, 115]

A rowan switch was used to herd sheep and cattle, while a sprig of rowan tied to the cow's tail (often with red string) protected milk and beast, and on a horse's tail kept the evil eye from travellers. Early this century, belief in this precaution was still firmly adhered to: MacKenzie wrote in 1914 of encountering a farmer's son on Arran who remembered once taking a cow to Lamlash for sale, and removing the rowan knot from her tail along the way—no doubt a modern young man sceptical of old superstitions. The cow promptly lay down and refused to move until a woman threw a bucket of urine over her. The cow then got up and immediately made for home. Next morning, with the rowan knot secure, she walked to Lamlash with no problem.[75, 85, 95]

On the chancy quarter days (see p. 90), a rowan wand was placed above the doors of the house and out-houses, and personal protection was ensured by carrying a twig in the pocket. At Beltane (May 1) the whole house would be decorated with rowan branches and all sheep and lambs made to jump through a rowan hoop. A wreath of ivy, woodbine (honeysuckle) and rowan was placed above the doorway of the byre and under vessels in the dairy to safeguard both cows and milk from witchcraft, the

1. McNeill quotes three poems attesting to the protective powers of rowan.[95]

evil eye and the infectious disease murrain. Women and children made protective necklaces from the berries, and rowan wood was used as fuel to bake special cakes for festivals.[23, 95, 122]

More practical uses for rowan berries were in dyeing (black and orange) and making a fermented cider-like drink or punch as well as the familiar rowan jelly. The bark was made into a poultice for adder bites and a decoction of rowan berries with apple and sugar was taken for whooping cough.[7, 18, 52, 75, 85, 125]

Rubiaceae
BEDSTRAW FAMILY

Crosswort
Cruciata laevipes

❀Crosswort was used medicinally as an appetiser and for internal and external wounds, blockages of the stomach and bowel, for ruptures, rheumatism and dropsy.[61] It is a wayside plant, common in southern and central Scotland.

Goosegrass, cleavers
Galium aparine

SCOTS NAMES: bloodtongue (draws blood on tongue), robin-run-in-the-hedge, sticky willie
LOCAL NAME: tongue-bluiders (Berw)
GAELIC NAME: *garbh lus* (rough weed)

Poultices made from the whole plant, crushed or finely chopped, were applied to skin problems. An infusion of the leaves makes a soothing tea to relieve colds and promote restful sleep, while the seeds can be roasted to make a kind of coffee.[6, 110]

Sticky willie is often used in childrens' chasing games. Murdo McNeill recorded the use of this very common plant as a strainer in the preparation of flummery, a dish made by boiling oatmeal down to jelly.[96]

The plant yields red dye.[52]

Woodruff
G. odoratum

SCOTS NAMES: white-flowered woodroof, woodrep
LOCAL NAMES: sweet-grass (Berw), witherips (Banff)

❀Woodruff is locally abundant in rich woodland. The aromatic leaves were used as a strewing herb, as a poultice for wounds and made into tea or cordial to soothe stomach and liver complaints, insomnia and nervous irritation, fever, colds and consumption. Left to steep for a few hours, the whole plant adds a delightful flavour to fruit juice, wine and punch.[61, 62, 110]

Lady's bedstraw
G. verum

SCOTS NAMES: keeslip (cheeselip, from use as rennet), Lady's bed
GAELIC NAMES: *bun na ruamh, leabadh ban sith, lus an leasaich* (rennet plant), *ruamh* (red), *ruin*

❀Lady's bedstraw was used to treat urinary and kidney problems, epilepsy, hysteria, skin disease and bleeding.[52, 61]

The most obvious use for lady's bedstraw, as the name suggests, was for stuffing matresses. An early version of vegetarian cheese was made using this plant as rennet to curdle milk, sometimes with the addition of nettle leaves.[75, 62]

This herb is common in dry grassland throughout Scotland, but while visiting Barra in the late eighteenth century, John Walker found the collection of lady's bedstraw for dyeing was causing erosion of the machair:

> There is a plant grows in this Island, of the Root of which the Natives make an exceeding fine Red Dye. It is the Galium verum, Linn. The yellow Ladies Bedstraw, or cheese rening, which, though a plant that grows universally over Scotland, is not anywhere known to be of use as a dye, excepting in some places in the Western Islands. It grows most luxuriantly and affords the largest Roots upon sandy Downs, so that it is found in Barra in the greatest perfection, but in these Places, the People are prohibited from digging it up, for as there is nothing but blowing sand under the Grass, when once the surface is broke a sand Drift commences, which will soon destroy a whole field.[136]

Lightfoot also found people using lady's bedstraw roots for dyeing red. The bark, which contains most of the dye stuff, was stripped from the roots, which were then boiled in water, to extract any remaining dye. The roots were removed and the bark added to be boiled with the yarn and alum to fix the colour. The flowering plant (without its roots) dyes yellow. The plant was used to dye wool for the Harris Tweed industry. It was replaced by imported madder (*Rubia tinctorum*, a related plant from Asia).[52, 75]

Salicaceae
WILLOW FAMILY

Aspen
Populus tremula

SCOTS NAME: quakin ash
LOCAL NAME: old wives' tongues (Rox)
GAELIC NAMES: *craobh chrithinn, a'chritheann*

The difficulties of folklore research are illustrated by the following: Alexander Carmichael describes the 'ever-tremulous, ever-quivering, ever-quaking motion of the guilty hateful aspen even in the stillest air' being due to the fact that it was the tree from which the cross of Jesus was made, the tree that

> *haughtily held up its head while all the other trees of creation bowed their heads lowly down as the King of all created things was being led to Calvary...Clods and stones and other missiles, as well as curses, are hurled at the aspen...No crofter in Uist would use aspen about his plough or about his harrows, or about his farming implements of any kind. Nor would a fisherman use aspen about his boat or about his creels or about any fishing-gear whatsoever.[23]*

although as Grigson comments wryly, if the timber had been more durable and more valuable, perhaps the legends would have been different. In contrast, according to Rorie, in the Highlands protective teething rings were made of aspen wood because the tree, as the wood of the Cross, was sacred. Of course both may be correct versions of localised traditions; but this is a salutary example of the need to be cautious.[62, 115]

Yellow and black leaves are obtained from the young leaves and brown from the bark.[52] Aspen is fairly widespread and is one of the few surviving trees on steep cliffs in Orkney and the Outer Isles.

Willows, Sallows
Salix species

GAELIC NAMES: *seileach, saileog, sal, suil*

> *The various species of willow were extensively used for tackle of every sort...In the Hebrides, where there is so great a scarcity of the tree kind, there is not a twig, even of the meanest willow, but what is turned by the inhabitants to some useful purpose.[18]*

Early colonisers of wet ground, willows were one of the first trees to appear in Scotland after the last Ice Age and no doubt this versatile species has been used since prehistoric times for a great variety of purposes.

In addition to the many practical uses of willow for basketry, rope, housebuilding, fencing, beehives, lobster pots and coracle frames, it was a magic tree. A willow wand symbolised the goddess, and was used for divination—the original magic wand. It was sometimes used for the peeled white wand carried by the corn sheaf made to represent Bride at a spring festival in the Highlands and Islands (see p. 142). Indeed (digressing to a more characteristically *English* use for a moment!) there is a belief that the three cricket stumps, traditionally made from willow, originally symbolised the triple goddess. Willow was one of the druids sacred woods, surely because it makes good fuel and charcoal. The word *wicca* (the craft and wisdom of witches) is said to be derived from the use of willow to make a wicker frame to build an effigy of the Celtic god Balder, king/consort to the queen/goddess, ceremonially sacrificed on Beltane (May 1) fires.[11, 18, 50, 76, 98]

Fear of the power of willow persisted long into Christian times: witches' broomsticks sometimes had a willow shaft, and persecuted witches from North Berwick were said to sail in willow winnowing riddles. In central Perthshire willow wands were reportedly used to work the evil eye. Black magic worked with willow could be counteracted by rowan.[117]

On the other hand, a branch of willow catkins in the home is still believed to bring good health; this may relate to its medicinal uses. The bark contains acetylsalicylic acid (the main constituent of aspirin) and has long been used as a pain killer. Drinking the sap of flowering willow was said to clear the vision. That willow is often associated with female moon-magic is surely connected with other medicinal uses: a large amount of sap from young shoots was described as a contraceptive and as being effective in smaller amounts to control bleeding in a medical text (*Lyber Graduum* by Nicolaus) used by fifteenth century Scottish physicians. Other medicinal uses of the bark were to treat liver pain, wounds and warts. [32, 50]

One of the oldest baskets found in Scotland, excavated by archaeologists from a bog in Shetland and carbon-dated to the sixth century, appears to have been made from willow, using exactly the same 'stake-and-strand' method of weaving that Scottish basketmakers use today. It was a large, strongly-made basket that could have been used for carrying heavy weights. The basket is being conserved in the Royal Museum of Scotland in Edinburgh.

Willow bark was also used as fodder for cattle and livestock, to tan leather and to obtain cinnamon-coloured dye.[52, 96]

Great sallow, goat willow
S. caprea

SCOTS NAMES: saugh, suagh tree, common sallow
GAELIC NAME: *suileag*

One of the few willows to grow away from water. Sallow wood and branches were considered the best for hurdle-making, hatchet and tool handles, and shoemakers' cutting boards. The bark was used to tan leather.[96]

Grey sallow
S. cinerea

Used mainly for agricultural creels and tanning leather. In spring, when the sap was rising and the bark could be easily peeled, boys made whistles from the smooth branches.[96]

Crack willow
S. fragilis

Crack willow, a much larger tree than the other willows that grow in Scotland, was used to build small boats when no other wood was available; it was said to be as good as pine or larch for the purpose.[125]

Common osier
S. viminalis

SCOTS NAME: cooper's willow
GAELIC NAMES: *bunsag, bun* (stump, stock), *fineamhain* (long twig), *gall sheilach* (foreign willow), *maothan* (smooth, tender)

This common lowland riverside plant may have been introduced for basketmaking. It was used in ancient times for making skin-covered shields and coracle frames, and for baskets said to be of such quality they were

Crack Willow

exported to Rome. Also presumably used for barrels, by the name Cameron uses.[18, 96, 125]

Scrophulariaceae
FIGWORT FAMILY

Foxglove
Digitalis purpurea

Foxglove

SCOTS NAMES: bloody fingers, deadmen's bells, foxter, witch's thimble
LOCAL NAMES: bloody bells, fairy's thimbles (Lan), deadmen's fingers (Inv), Scotch mercury, wild mercury (Berw)
GAELIC NAMES: *an lus mor* (the big plant) *ciochan nan cailleachan marblia* (dead old women's paps), *lus-nam-ban-sith* (fairy women's plant) *meuran nan caillich mharbha* (dead women's thimbles), *meuran nan daoine marbh* (dead men's thimbles)

❀Foxgloves have been used for medicinal and magic purposes for centuries and the many Gaelic and Scots names reflect this. The common name foxglove is said to derive from folksglove, i.e. glove of the fairy folk, because it grows in shady hollows and forest dells, their favourite haunts. There is also a story that fairies gave foxes the flowers to put on their toes so they could tread softly when hunting.[61]

The leaves and occasionally the roots were used medicinally. Martin recorded foxglove being used after fevers both to induce sleep and applied as a warm plaster to painful joints. The best known use was for heart complaints and dropsy but it was also used to treat scrofula (tuberculosis), epilepsy, delirium and mental disorders, diptheria, skin diseases and boils.[7,61,100]

In 1623 a Scottish woman called Isobel Haldane was tried for witchcraft and confessed to associating with fairy folk; she treated a changeling child with tea made from foxglove leaves and the child died. However, it is possible that the unfortunate Isobel was in fact a healer who knew the powerful medicinal effects of foxgloves but, ascribing it to magic powers she could not explain, used the plant unwisely to treat a fairly common and deeply worrying condition. Fear of fairies stealing children and leaving behind one of their own was widespread; many precautions were taken to protect newborn babies, and many children with unexplainable ill-health, odd behaviour or appearance, were believed to be changelings. Had the child not died but been restored to normality, no doubt the casewould never have come to the attention of the witch hunters.[62]

164

Although well-known and not specifically Scottish, it is worth referring to the medical history of foxglove as a remedy for heart disease
because it illustrates some essential points in the understanding of folk
medicine. In the eighteenth century dropsy (swelling of the arms, legs and
belly due to fluid retention when the kidneys malfunction because of long-
term heart disease) was a common ailment for which doctors had many
herbal remedies. Most accounts attribute the discovery of the effectiveness of foxglove in treating dropsy to William Withering, an English doctor
who obtained his M.D. from Edinburgh University in 1766; he is generally said to have got the herbal remedy from a woman who does not even
merit a name in some accounts. In fact Withering bought it from Mrs
Hutton, a botanist and pharmacist who had been systematically studying
the remedy to find the most effective dose and combination of herbs. She
knew the plant was most effective when picked at certain times and used
in combination with other herbs that moderated its effect.[15, 97]

Withering also made careful observations of the effects of plants on
insects, animals and people, and having obtained the remedy from Mrs
Hutton kept detailed records of 163 case histories in which foxglove was
used. He published his findings in 1785 as a monograph called *An Account
of the Foxglove and some of its Medical Uses: with Practical Remarks on
Dropsy and other Diseases*. This was the first published systematic empiri-
cal study of a drug and was unmatched until scientific clinical trials of
drugs began in the twentieth century.[97]

While Withering deserves full credit for his work, it should be noted
that he no more understood the way in which the drug operated (by
strengthening heart muscle) than did Mrs Hutton who had been using it
with equal effect and that after his work was published foxglove began to
be over-used by physicians for every illness they encountered, resulting in
decreased confidence in the plant because it did not cure everything![97]
(The plant is however a constituent of modern heart drugs.) Meanwhile,
all the anonymous wise women presumably went on curing people with
their herbal remedies, unrecorded, judged locally by their success or otherwise, and always in danger of persecution as witches.

Foxglove was included in a love charm collected by Carmichael in the
late nineteenth century; it had to be burned to ashes with butterbur, seaweed, royal fern and an old man's bones on a flat stone at the shore, then
the ashes sprinkled on the loved one's chest, ensuring he would never leave.[23]

In Scotland, the leaves were applied to skin rashes including eczema
and erysipelas, and chopped leaves mixed with butter and garlic or onion
were used to draw boils. Crushed foxglove roots, heated then wrapped in
a flannel, were used to relieve the pain of internal swelling.[6]

Eyebright
Euphrasia officinalis

GAELIC NAME: *lus-na-leac*

❀A tiny, exquisite plant of grassy places throughout Scotland. Juice from this plant has been widely used since the time of the ancient Greeks to treat eye disorders but during the eighteenth century it fell into disrepute, as Lightfoot describes, illustrating the uncertainties around when traditional remedies were scrutinised by medical men:

> *It has been reputed good for sore eyes, but the gentlemen of the faculty have declared it does more harm than good in applications of that kind, there having been instances of persons rendered almost blind by the use of it. The Highlanders do however still retain the practice of it, by making an infusion of it in milk, and annointing the patient's eyes with a feather dipped in it.*[75]

Toadflax
Linaria vulgaris

LOCAL NAME: doggies (Aber)

❀Toadflax has astringent, cleansing, purgative and diuretic properties, and was used to treat jaundice, sores, ulcers and skin disease, scrofula, dropsy, liver obstructions and piles.[61] It is a common wayside plant along the east coast and in the south of Scotland, but rare in the north-west and may not be native.

Red rattle, marsh lousewort
Pedicularis palustris

SCOTS NAMES: cock's comb, deadmen's bellows (i.e. penises)
GAELIC NAMES: *bainne ghabhar* (goat's milk), *lus na mial* (louse wort), *lus riabhach* (brindled plant), *modhalan dearg* (red modest one)

Occurs throughout Scotland in damp grassy areas and bogs. The plant contains an insecticide, glycoside aucubin, and the root was used externally against lice and internally to treat infestations of worms.[136]

According to Cameron, the Gaelic name *bainne ghabhar* derived from the belief that when goats ate the plant their milk yield increased. He interpreted the saying:

> *Rub thy face with violet and goat's milk,*
> *And there is no prince in the world*

Who will not follow thee[18]

meant the lovely pink flowers were used as a cosmetic, but Lightfoot understood 'goat's milk' literally (see p. 175).

Lousewort
Pedicularis sylvatica

SCOTS NAME: cock's comb
LOCAL NAMES: bee-sookies, honeysookies, sookies (Shet)
GAELIC NAMES: *lus riablach, modhalan dearg*

> *The Gaelic names...were derived from the honey secreted in the flowers, which children were in the habit of sucking.[96]*

Common throughout Scotland especially in heather moorland and bogs. This pretty little flower is rich in nectar and children used to suck it, hence the local names. *Pedicularis* means 'of lice', suggesting the plant has insect-repellent qualities, but no reference to this use in practice has been found. There was an unsubstantiated belief that the plant carried the liver fluke and could infect cattle and sheep that grazed on it.

Figwort
Scrophularia nodosa

LOCAL NAMES: rose-noble (Kirk,Wigt), stinking Roger (Ayr)
GAELIC NAMES. *dunn-lus* (brown plant), *farach dubh* (black mallet), *farach don* (brown mallet), *farum, forum* (probably forms of *farach*), *fothlus, fotlus* (crumbs, refuse, scrofulous), *lus nan clugan* (plant of the clusters), *lus-nan-cnapan* (knobbed plant), *lus an torranain* (plant of the thunderer), *tarrann, torrann, torranan, tarranan* (possibly variants of Taranis, thunder god of the Gauls, also herb of St Torranan/Ternan)[1]

❀Figwort, found in damp shady places in most parts of Scotland though more common in the south, was used to treat a great variety of skin problems, including scrofula[2] and piles ('the fig' being a name for piles, having a similar appearance to the plant's roots).[18, 61, 62]

Carmichael collected a great variety of Gaelic names for the plant, and wrote:

> *On the mainland the figwort is known for its medicinal properties, and in the islands for its magical powers. On the mainland the leaf of the*

1. According to Carmichael.[23]
2. Scrofula was a condition thought to be a form of tuberculosis that affected the lymphatic glands and bones.

plant is applied to cuts and bruises, and the tuber to sores and tumours. In the islands the plant was placed on the cow fetter, under the milk boyne,[1] and over the byre door, to ensure milk in the cows.[23]

He recorded several charms to be said while using the 'noble plant... of thousand blessings, of thousand virtues', including:

> *I will pluck the figwort,*
> *With the fruitage of sea and land,*
> *The plant of joy and gladness,*
> *The plant of rich milk.*

and:

> *I will pluck the figwort*
> *With the fulness of sea and land,*
> *At the flow, not the ebb of the tide,*
> *By thine hand, gentle Mary...*

His anonymous but eloquent informant continued:

> *The* torranan *is a blessed plant. It grows in sight of the sea. Its root is a cluster of four bulbs like the four teats of a cow. The stalk of the plant is as long as the arm, and the bloom is as large as the breast of a woman, and as white as the driven snow of the hill.[2] It is full of the milk of grace and goodness and of the gift of peace and power, and fills with the filling and ebbs with the ebbing tide. It is therefore meet to cull the plant with the flow and not with the ebb of the restless sea. If I had the* torranan *it would ensure to me abundant milk in my cow all year.*

St Torranan or Ternan was a sea-faring missionary and the plant named after him was supposed to grow only near the sea which the saint loved (it is in fact common throughout Scotland except in the north, in woods and hedgebanks). Carmichael tells the story that, having been driven out of Ireland by folk not yet ready to hear his Christian message, Torranan's coracle carried him to Benbecula, where, desperately thirsty after his voyage, he climbed the only hill, Ruaival, from where he saw the extraordinary landscape of:

> *fords and channels, islands, peninsulas and mainlands, seas and lakes, and of moors and machairs broken up and dotted over in the most marvellous manner with shallow pools, tarns, and lakes scattered broadcast*

---

1. Boyne—a broad, shallow container used to collect and skim milk.
2. Either poetic license or misidentification seems to have crept in here: although figwort grows to be around 80 cm tall, the flower is tiny, yellow and brown. Carmichael called *torranan* figwort having had a specimen identified by Professor Bayley Balfour, then Regius Keeper of the Royal Botanic Garden Edinburgh.

beyond count, beyond number.[23]

Despite this abundance, Torranan found it necessary to pray for water to drink, and miraculously the red rock at his feet split open and clear, cold water streamed out. He named the rill *Gamnach*, farrow cow,[1] prayed it would never run dry, and strengthened by God's gift managed to convert the people of the Uists. The rill became a place of pilgrimage, and each visitor was supposed to give a leaf of the plant *torranan* to feed the farrow cow, although by the late nineteenth century any kind of leaf or even grass was being given as an offering.

Mullein, Aaron's rod
Verbascum thapsus

SCOTS NAMES: aaron's rod, shepherd's club, white mullein
LOCAL NAME: cuddy-lugs (donkey's ears, Rox)

❀Used medicinally to treat piles, diarrhoea, coughs, tuberculosis, bleeding of the lungs and bowels.[61] Mullein is a plant of dry, sandy or chalky soils, with a localised distribution in Scotland.

Brooklime
Veronica beccabunga

SCOTS NAMES: horse wellcress, water purpie, water purple, wellink
LOCAL NAME: beccabung (Shet)
GAELIC NAMES: *lochal* (lake-weed), *lochal mothair, lothal* (*lo* = water)

❀Widespread in wet places in lowland and coastal parts of Scotland, brooklime was used to treat scurvy and as a spring salad vegetable, but, according to Lightfoot, it is bitter and less palatable than watercress.[75]

Germander speedwell
V. chamaedrys

SCOTS NAME: fluellen
GAELIC NAME: *nuallach*

❀Common throughout Scotland, speedwell was used as a blood purifier and to treat skin irritation, smallpox, measles, cancer, fever, coughs, asthma, catarrh and kidney complaints. The leaves can be made into tea. Speedwell seeds, either *V. chamaedrys* or the rarer alpine speedwell, *V. alpina*, were included in a charm given in 1815 to Colonel John Cameron of Fassfern,

Brooklime

---

1. That is, a cow in milk without a calf.

near Loch Eil, to protect him as he went into battle; sadly it proved ineffective—he was killed on the day before the Battle of Waterloo.[7, 61, 110]

Solanaceae
NIGHTSHADE FAMILY

Deadly nightshade, belladonna
Atropa belladonna

SCOTS NAME: dwale

The devil's plant, rare in Scotland and now thought not to be native. According to McNeill it was used by witches in the south, perhaps as a narcotic. Every part of the plant is extremely poisonous. Legend has it that Macbeth's soldiers, in the reign of King Duncan I, used the sedative properties of the plant to destroy an entire Danish army attempting to invade Scotland, by calling a truce, giving the unsuspecting enemy drink laced with deadly nightshade, then murdering them while they slept. It was grown in the Physic Garden at Holyrood Abbey, where Lightfoot found it about a hundred years after the Garden had moved to another site.[17, 61, 95]

Henbane
Hyoscyamus niger

SCOTS NAME: black henbane

✿Also a rare, poisonous plant used for magic as well as medicine in Scotland. It grows by the sea on sand and rough ground. At the medieval monastery at Soutra, a cache of 448 henbane and 31 hemlock (see p. 67) seeds has been found by archaeologists excavating the hospital site. Henbane was used for pain relief, as a sedative and mild diuretic and it is likely the seeds were kept ready for use in an anaesthetic drink, compress, poultice or douche before drastic surgery such as amputation. There is ample documentary and pictorial evidence from medieval times of people surviving such major operations.[61, 103]

In some places (not specifically recorded in Scotland) a necklace for teething children was made from henbane roots cut into small discs and threaded on string; the necklace was wrapped in fine cloth then hung around the child's neck, so the plant chemicals (alkaloids) would be absorbed through the skin. A Scottish traveller, Willie MacPhee, born in 1910, remembers his grandmother collecting henbane in full flower from

Henbane

170

fields of turnips, potatoes, lettuce, carrots or corn (oats). The flower heads were boiled and the decoction kept in a stone jam jar for at least 21 days (it became more effective the longer it was kept) for use internally to treat headaches and measles, or on a soaked rag applied to relieve earache and toothache.[103]

Bittersweet, woody nightshade
Solanum dulcamara

SCOTS NAME: poisonberry
LOCAL NAME: mad dog's berries (Mor)

✿Common throughout Scotland except in the west, where it is localised. Juice from the crushed twigs was used externally to treat bruises and skin diseases including scrofula and ulcers; internally for rheumatism, fever, catarrh, asthma, whooping cough and jaundice.[61]

Ulmaceae
ELM FAMILY

Wych elm
Ulmus glabra

LOCAL NAME: chewbark (Berw)

'Wych' means pliant, as in switch, not referring to witches, who in fact were believed to hate this tree, though it was said to have been sacred to druids.[61, 95]

An early kind of tie-dyeing used twine made from the inner bark of wych elm to tie the hank tightly and prevent dye reaching the wool.[116]

Urticaceae
NETTLE FAMILY

Pellitory of the wall
Parietaria judaica

✿Uncommon in Scotland and therefore probably mainly grown in physic gardens for medicinal use; it is sometimes found growing on old walls or

171

ruins. The plant has diuretic, laxative and cooling properties, used medicinally to treat bladder infections, kidney stones and gravel, other urinary disorders, dropsy, coughs, sore throat, toothache, skin complaints, piles and gout.[61]

Nettle
Urtica dioica

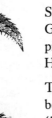

Nettle

SCOTS NAME: heg-beg
GAELIC NAMES: *feanntag, neandog, deanntag* (*feannta*, flayed, pierced, pinched, referring to blisters), *iontag, iuntag* (*ionga*, nails), *stradag* (spark, Hebrides)

Today the nettle is generally despised as an unpleasant weed, yet this has been one of Scotland's most useful plants. The poet Thomas Campbell (1777-1844) wrote a robust defence of the plant:

In Scotland, I have eaten nettles, I have slept in nettle sheets, and I have dined off a nettle tablecloth. The young and tender nettle is an excellent potherb. The stalks of the old nettle are as good as flax for making cloth. I have heard my mother say that she thought nettle cloth more durable than any other species of linen.[22]

Nettles are delicious, easily digested and highly nutritious, containing vitamins A and C and several useful minerals such as calcium, potassium, iron and manganese. Confronted with spring growth of nettles in the herbaceous border, most gardeners sigh, search out their thickest gloves and consign the offending plants to the compost heap. Indeed, they make excellent nitrogen-rich compost. Yet previous generations of Scots gardeners actually forced nettles under glass as 'early spring kale', a practice referred to by Sir Walter Scott in *Rob Roy*. The young tops are best when 15-25 cm high and repeated cutting keeps the plant in a juvenile state for much of the summer.[61]

Traditional Scottish dishes include nettle soup (thickened with oatmeal) and nettles as greens (prepared like spinach but best sieved or liquidised because of its fibrous nature). Nettle tea was widely drunk, especially in spring, as a beverage before what we now call simply 'tea' became fashionable and in times of scarcity.[18, 57] Cooking does of course de-activate the sting. A recipe for nettle soup, *cal-feanndag*, from Islay, written down in 1898, required 'a large apronful of nettles, Two handfuls of meal, Two gallons of water, a piece of salt beef or braxy'. One imagines this was to serve a large family.[65]

Mrs McLintock gives a recipe for nettle syrup and Martin Martin describes good nettle ale brewed for celebrations by the resourceful and generally sober St Kildans in the eighteenth century, using nettle roots fermented with barley meal dough, which 'when they drink plentifully of it...disposes them to dance merrily'.[93, 100]

An extract of nettles was used in the Highlands and Islands as a substitute for rennet in cheese making: one spoonful of the liquid was enough to coagulate a large bowl of milk; salt was added to the extract so it could be bottled and stored for use when required.[52]

❀Nettle tea was considered to be an excellent spring tonic. It is now possible to buy nettle tea bags, and as well as being a pleasant drink, it makes a stimulating tonic with astringent, laxative and diuretic properties. Medicinal herbalists also prescribe it to relieve asthma and other chest complaints, eczema and excessive bleeding and to lower blood sugar levels and blood pressure. Fife mining families used an infusion of nettles to treat dropsy. Nettle beer used to be brewed as a remedy for jaundice, gout and rheumatism.[115]

In Scotland it has also been used to relieve nose-bleeds and headaches. Long-suffering Roman soldiers exposed to the bitter north winds in inadequate clothing were said to have flayed themselves with nettles; nearly 2,000 years later David Rorie found people in Fife doing the same to relieve the pain of rheumatism. In Lewis the roots were fermented with yeast to make cough syrup, and the tops mixed with raw egg whites were spread on the forehead and temples to induce sleep in Skye. In homoeopathy *Urtica* is a useful remedy for various skin conditions (especially rashes and burns) and for cystitis. Nettles are still in commercial use in Scotland as a hair tonic.[57, 100, 115]

Shetlanders had a curious way of endearing themselves to each other, by gathering nettles on Halloween to place between the blankets of the desired one; this would procure their love. Nettles gathered on St John's eve (23 June) could be used to undo a spell cast on milk production, if the plants were picked on the suspected witch's land and put under the milk pails. In the Highlands and Islands, nettles were believed to grow from the bodies of dead men.[62, 101]

The use of nettle fibres to weave cloth persisted in Scotland until the late eighteenth century and may have begun in prehistoric times (Bronze Age nettle fibre cloth has been found in Denmark). Nitinaht Indians of Vancouver Island made nettle fibre until the 1970s, using a traditional method that may well have been the same in Scottish domestic production. The stems were harvested in autumn, dried and pounded to separate and soften the fibrous tissue. The fibres were then spun together on the bare thighs, sometimes with the addition of bark fibre for strength. They used the fibre for binding, sewing, fishing nets and lines.[62, 134]

Nettle fabric could be made as fine as linen and was very strong and durable, but was gradually replaced by flax, which produces longer, finer fibres on poorer soil than nettles, and the fibres are easier to extract. The fabric could even be self-dyed; young nettle tops produce both yellow and grey-green dyes, which have been used in the manufacture of Harris tweed.

Perhaps the great variety of uses to which nettles were put reflects the fact that they grew around every dwelling, thriving in the nitrogen-rich soil beside walls of houses with no internal sanitary facilities. Many ruined crofts still have a nettle patch beside the door.

Valerianaceae
VALERIAN FAMILY

Valerian
Valeriana officinalis

❀The dried root of valerian has sedative and antispasmodic properties known since ancient times—there is evidence the Romans were using it when they were in Scotland. It was used to treat childless women, epilepsy, plague and croup.[23, 32, 61]

The leaves can be made into tea, the tops added to wine and beer.[110] Valerian is a common plant of marshes and damp grassland.

Violaceae
VIOLET FAMILY

Violets
Viola species

SCOTS NAMES: love-idleness, quaich, cogie (drinking cup)
GAELIC NAME: *brog-na-cuthaig, fail cuach* (scented bowl)

❀Martin recorded that on Skye, whey in which violets had been boiled was given to feverish patients as a cool and refreshing drink. Heartsease (*V. tricolor*), also known in Scotland as love-idleness, was used to treat epilepsy, asthma, heart disease and eczema.[61]

Lightfoot wrote:

The flowers are esteemed to be anodyne, cooling and emollient. A syrup

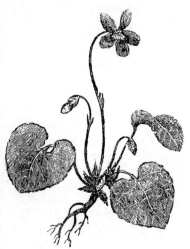

Violet

174

made of them proves an agreeable and useful laxative to children: the leaves are also emollient, and the seeds diuretic...

The Caledonian ladies formerly used them as a cosmetic, as appears from the advice given in the following Gaulic lines: 'Anoint thy face with goat's milk[1] in which violets have been infused, and there is not a young prince on earth who would not be charmed with thy beauty'.[75]

Violet flowers were made into syrup; Mrs McLintock gives a recipe. The petals soaked in white wine make a drink that used to be very popular called shrub.[93, 100, 110]

Bog violet (*V. palustris*) was said to be a sacred plant on Skye.[95]

Viscaceae
MISTLETOE FAMILY

Mistletoe
Viscum album

Mistletoe

SCOTS NAME: misle
GAELIC NAMES: *druidhe-lus* (druid's weed), *sugh dharaich* (sap/substance of oak), *uile-ice* (all-heal)

The druids' reverence for mistletoe, the evergreen plant that appears to grow magically in the boughs of oak and apple trees, is well known; they cut it for ceremonial purposes at the summer and winter solstices, using a special gold sickle-shaped knife. Mistletoe is a parasitic plant spread by birds that feed on the fruit, then excrete the seeds as they rest on branches. In fact it rarely grows on oak trees, its preferred hosts being lime and poplar trees and members of the rose family (Rosaceae) such as apple, pear, hawthorn and rose trees.[6, 95]

Belief in its magic powers may have derived from knowledge of mistletoe's medicinal properties: it was certainly in use by Roman times and throughout the Middle Ages to treat a variety of ailments, as indicated by the Gaelic name *uile-ice*, all-heal. One of the remedies from *Lyber Graduum* by Nicolaus, a text used by fifteenth century Scottish medical practitioners, recommends mistletoe and fenugreek boiled with sorrel for applying to abscesses. A woman living in Inverness in the nineteenth century was scorned by her neighbours for drinking mistletoe tea to steady heart palpitations, but it has in fact been recognised to act similarly to foxglove and used as a heart tonic, as well as to treat epilepsy.[7, 32, 61, 76]

1. See also p. 167.

Pennant, on his Scottish tour with Lightfoot, recorded people cutting stems of mistletoe and ivy, which they kept all year to cure fevers (he does not specify how they were used).[111] However, mistletoe is actually very rarely found growing wild in Scotland, suggesting either they were in fact collecting a completely different plant, or that mistletoe was traded northwards from parts of England where it grew more abundantly, as is still the case at Christmas time when lorry loads are marketed.[7]

Belief in the plant's supernatural qualities was sustained by the Hay family of Errol, who chose mistletoe as their badge. They placed a sprig of the plant in their babies' cradles to prevent them from being stolen by fairies and replaced with changelings; and they carried mistletoe as a charm against witchcraft and for protection in battle. It had to be cut on All Hallows Eve (the old Celtic New Year's Eve, *Samhain*, when the veil between the known and supernatural worlds was thin and spirits walked the earth), using a new dirk, after walking three times sun-wise around the tree, chanting a spell (which is not recorded).[95]

Frazer quotes a verse said to have been written by Thomas the Rhymer, the legendary fourteenth century poet who spent seven years in fairy land:

> *When the mistletoe bats on Errol's aik* [oak]
> *And that aik stands fast,*
> *The Hays sall flourish, and their good grey hawk*
> *Sall nocht flinch before the blast.*
>
> *But when the root of the aik decays,*
> *And the mistletoe dwines on its withered breast,*
> *The grass sall grow on Errol's hearthstone,*
> *And the corbie* [crow] *roup in the falcon's nest.*[53]

Zosteraceae
SEA GRASS FAMILY

Sweet sea-grass, grasswrack
Zostera marina

SCOTS NAME: marlie (Shet)
GAELIC NAME: *bilearach* (*bileag*—grass-blade)

Found locally on seashores in most parts of Scotland, sea-grass was dried and used for packing, stuffing matresses (which were flea-repellent) and thatching; it was said to be more durable than straw. It was used as green manure in Orkney.[18, 96, 135]

BIBLIOGRAPHY

1. Achterberg, Jeanne, *Woman as Healer* (London, Rider, 1990)
2. Anon, *Beyond the Plough* (Edinburgh, Scottish Agricultural Museum, undated)
3. Arvigo, Rosita and Nadine Epstein, *Sastun* (San Francisco, Harper Collins, 1995)
4. Atkinson, Robert, *Island Going* (first edition, 1949; Edinburgh, Birlinn, 1995)
5. Bannerman, J., *The Beatons* (Edinburgh, John Donald, 1986)
6. Beith, Mary, *'Gaelic Medical Tradition'*, *West Highland Free Press* (various articles, 1990-95)
7. Beith, Mary, *Healing Threads* (Edinburgh, Polygon, 1995)
8. Bell, Diane, *Daughters of the Dreaming* (Australia, Allen & Unwin, 1993)
9. Bennet, Margaret, 'Plant Lore in Gaelic Scotland' in R.J. Pankhurst & J.M. Mullin (eds.) *Flora of the Outer Hebrides* (Edinburgh, HMSO, 1991)
10. Black, Ronald, *West Highland Free Press* (various articles, 1990)
11. Bleakley, Robert, *Fruits of the Moon Tree* (Bath, Gateway, 1984)
12. Bliss, Anne, *Weeds: a Guide for Dyers and Herbalists* (Colorado, Juniper House, 1978)
13. Bord, J. and C. Bord, *Earth Rites* (London, Granada, 1982)
14. Dowden, Jean K., *John Lightfoot, His Work and Travels* (Royal Botanic Gardens Kew, 1989)
15. Brooke, Elisabeth, *Women Healers through History* (London, Women's Press, 1993)
16. Buchan, William, *Domestic Medicine* (1769)
17. Buchanan, George, *History of Scotland* (1582, 4 vols., trans. from Latin by James Aikman, Glasgow, 1827)
18. Cameron, John, *Gaelic Names of Plants* (Edinburgh, Blackwood, 1883)
19. Cammock, Ruth, 'Auchindrain's Loom', *J. Weavers, Spinners & Dyers* 142 (1987), 12-13
20. Campbell, John Francis, *Popular Tales of the West Highlands* (4 vols., Edinburgh, 1860-62)
21. Campbell, John Gregorson, *Witchcraft and Second Sight in the Highlands and Islands of Scotland* (Glasgow, MacLehose, 1902)
22. Campbell, Thomas, *Letters from the South* (first published in *New Monthly*, 1835; 2 vols., London, 1837)
23. Carmichael, Alexander, *Carmina Gadelica* (6 vols. in Gaelic and English, Edinburgh 1900-71; English only version Edinburgh, Floris, 1992)

24. Casselman, Karen Leigh, *Craft of the Dyer: colour from plant lichens of the Northeast* (University of Toronto Press, 1980)

25. Chambers, Robert, *Popular Rhymes of Scotland* (first edition, 1841; new edition, 1870)

26. Chambers, *Concise Scots Dictionary*, ed. Mairi Robinson (Aberdeen University Press, 1985)

27. Cheape, Hugh and Gavin Sprott, *Angus Country Life* (Edinburgh, National Trust for Scotland, 1980)

28. City of Edinburgh Museums, *The Burry Man of South Queensferry* (Pamphet No. 8, Edinburgh, undated)

29. Clarke, David L., 'Mesolithic Europe, the Economic Basis' in G. Sieveking et al, *Problems in Economic and Social Anthropology* (London, Duckworth, 1976)

30. Clarke, D.V., *The Neolithic Village at Skara Brae, Orkney* (Edinburgh, HMSO, 1976)

31. Clarke, J.G.D., *Prehistoric Europe* (London, Methuen, 1952)

32. Comrie J.D., *History of Scottish Medicine* (second edition, 2 vols., London, Wellcome, 1932)

33. Cooper, Derek, *Road to the Isles* (Edinburgh, Chambers, 1979)

34. Coppins, Brian J. and Roy Watling, 'Lichenised and non-lichenised fungi: folklore and fact', *Botanical J. of Scotland* 47:2 (1995) 249-62

35. Cramb, Auslan, '200 year old trees felled for castle roof', *The Scotsman*, 10 February 1995

36. Dall, Nan, 'Scots Herbal Lore', *Proc. Scott. Anthrop. and Folklore Soc.* III:1 (1938)

37. Daly, Mary, *Gyn/Ecology* (London, Women's Press, 1979)

38. Deering, C., *Catalogus Stirpium* (1738)

39. Dickson, James H., 'Bronze Age Mead', *Antiquity* LII (1978) 108-113

40. 'North American driftwood, especially Picea (spruce) from archaeological sites in the Hebrides and Northern Isles of Scotland 1992' *Review of Palaeobotany and Palynology*, 73 (1992) 49-56

41. Personal communication, lecture at the Royal Botanic Garden (1995)

42. Dods, Meg, *Edinburgh Cookery Book* (1826)

43. Eaton, S. Boyd, Marjory Shostak and Melvin Konner, *The Stone Age Health Programme* (London, Angus & Robertson, 1989)

44. Edwards, Kevin, 'Human impact on the prehistoric environment', in T.C. Smout (ed.), *Scotland Since Prehistory* (Aberdeen, Scottish Cultural Press, 1993)

45. Ehrenberg, Margaret, *Women in Prehistory* (London, British Museum Press, 1989)

46. Ehrenreich, Barbara and Deirdre English, *Witches, Midwives and Nurses:*

a history of women healers (New York, Feminist Press, 1973)

47. Ellis, Kim, *Eident Calanas* (unpublished thesis, Colorado State University, 1990)
48. Fairweather, Barbara, *Highland Heritage* (Glencoe Folk Museum, 1984)
49. Fenton, Alexander, *Scottish Country Life* (Edinburgh, John Donald, 1977)
50. Fife, Hugh, *The Lore of Highland Trees* (Gartocharn, Famedram, undated)
51. Fletcher, Harold and William Brown, *The Royal Botanic Garden Edinburgh 1670-1970* (Edinburgh, HMSO, 1970)
52. Fraser, Jean, *Traditional Scottish Dyes* (Edinburgh, Canongate, 1983)
53. Frazer, J.G., *Golden Bough* (13 vols., 1936; London, Macmillan, abridged edition, 1978)
54. Gillies, Hugh Cameron, *Regimen Sanitas* (trans. of Gaelic medicine ms, Glasgow, 1911)
55. Gould, Richard, 'Plants that map the path of pollution', *The Guardian*, 25 May 1989
56. Graham, Henry G., *The Social Life of Scotland in the Eighteenth Century* (London, Adam & Charles Black, 1899)
57. Grant, Isabel, *Highland Folk Ways* (London, Routledge & Kegan Paul, 1961)
58. Graves, Robert, *The White Goddess* (London, Faber & Faber, 1961)
59. Gregor, Walter, 'Some old farming customs and notions in Aberdeenshire', *Folklore J* 2: 11 (1884) 331
60. Grierson, Su, *The Colour Cauldron* (Perth, Mill Books, 1986)
61. Grieve, M., *A Modern Herbal* (first edition 1931; London, Penguin 1982)
62. Grigson, Geoffrey, *The Engishman's Flora* (first edition 1958; St. Albans, Paladin, 1975)
63. Hall, James, *Travels in Scotland* (1807)
64. Hamilton, David, *The Healers*: a history of medicine in Scotland (first edition, 1974; Edinburgh, Canongate 1981)
65. Henderson, Hamish, and others, *Tocher* 31(1979) 4-5, 26
66. Hoffman, David, *The Holistic Herbal* (second edition, Forres, Findhorn Press, 1986)
67. Hooker, J., *Flora Scotica* (1821)
68. Hope, Annette, *A Caledonian Feast* (London, Grafton, 1989)
69. Humphries, C.J. and E. Shaughnessy, *Gorse* (Buckinghamshire, Shire Nat. His. Series No. 9, 1987)
70. Hutton, Ronald, *The Pagan Religions of the Ancient British Isles* (Oxford, Blackwell, 1991)

71. Johnstone, Anne, *The Wild Frontier: exploring the Antonine Wall* (Edinburgh, Moubray House Publishing, 1986)
72. Jordan, Michael, *Gods of the Earth* (London, Bantam, 1992)
73. Kirkwood, James, *A Collection of Highland Rites and Customs 1650-1709*, ed. J.L. Campbell (Cambridge, 1975)
74. Lambie, David, *Introducing Heather* (Fort William, Firtree, 1994)
75. Lightfoot, John, *Flora Scotica* (London, 1777)
76. Logan, James, *The Scottish Gael* (first edition 1831; 2 vols., Inverness 1876)
77. Mabey, Richard, *Plants with a Purpose* (London, Collins, 1977)
78. MacDonald, Finlay J., *Crowdie and Cream* (London, Macdonald 1982)
79. MacDonald, Fiona, *Island Voices* (Irvine, Carrick Media, 1992)
80. MacDonald, Kate, 'Angus MacLellan telling stories', *Tocher* 31 (1979) 65
81. McGhee, James, 'Myrtle oil keeps bloodsucking midge at bay', *New Scientist* (1 July 1995)
82. MacKenzie, Donald A., *Scottish Folk Lore and Folk-life* (London & Glasgow, Blackie, 1935
83. MacKenzie, J.B., *Episodes in the Life of the Reverend Neil MacKenzie at St. Kilda from 1829-43* (Privately published, 1911)
84. MacKenzie, Osgood Hanbury, *A Hundred Years in the Highlands* (Edward Arnold, 1921)
85. MacKenzie, W.M., *The Book of Arran* (Vol. 2, Glasgow, 1914)
86. MacKinnon, Hugh, 'Playing shinty in Eigg', *Tocher* 36-37 (1982) 365-377
87. MacKinnon Nan, 'Milk in a Tangle', *Tocher* 38 (1983) 43
88. Maclagan, R.C., 'On Highland dyeing and colourings of native-made tartans', *Trans. Royal Scott. Soc. of Arts* XIV (1898)
89. MacLean, Malcolm and C. Carell (eds.), *As an Fhearann* (From the Land) (Edinburgh, Mainstream, 1986)
90. MacLellan, Kate, in Fiona McDonald, *Island Voices* (Irvine, Carrick Media 1992)
91. MacLennan, Malcolm, *Gaelic Dictionary* (Aberdeen, Acair and Aberdeen University Press, 1979)
92. McLintock, H.F., *Old Highland Dress and Tartans* (Dundalk, Dundalgan, 1949)
93. McLintock, Mrs, *Receipts for Cookery and Pastry Work* (first edition 1736, Aberdeen University, 1986)
94. McNeill, F. Marian, *The Scots Kitchen* (Blackie, 1929)
95. McNeill, F. Marian, *The Silver Bough* (First edition in 4 vols., Glasgow, 1957-68; vol. 1 Edinburgh, Canongate, 1989)

96. McNeill, Murdo, *Colonsay* (Edinburgh, 1910)

97. Mann, John, *Murder, Magic and Medicine* (Oxford University Press, 1992)

98. Manners, John, *Crafts of the Scottish Highlands and Islands* (Newton Abbot, David & Charles, 1978)

99. Marshall, Lorna, *The !Kung of Nyae Nyae* (Harvard University Press, 1976)

100. Martin, Martin, *A Description of the Western Isles of Scotland 1695* (first edition, 1703; facsimile of second (1716) edition, Edinburgh, Mercat, 1981)

101. Marwick, Ernest, *Folklore of Orkney and Shetland* (London, Batsford, 1975)

102. Miller, Hugh, *The Cruise of the Betsey* (1858)

103. Moffat, Brian, G. Euart and L. Euan, *Sharp Practice* (Edinburgh, several vols., 1986-9)

104. Morrison, Norman, 'Highland Plant Dyes', *Scottish Field* LIII:318 (1929) 233

105. Naddair, Kaledon, *Keltic Folk and Faerie Tales* (London, Rider, 1987)

106. Neill, Patrick, *A Tour through some of the Islands of Orkney and Shetland* (Edinburgh, A. Constable & John Murray, 1806)

107. Nickalls, Susan, 'Cashing in on dead wood', *The Scotsman*, 28 July 1995

108. O'Cathain, Seamas, *Festival of Brigit, Celtic Goddess and Holy Woman* (Dublin, DBA, 1995)

109. Page, Chris, *Ferns* (London, Collins, 1974)

110. Paterson, Wilma, *A Country Cup* (London, Pelham, 1980)

111. Pennant, Thomas, *A Tour in Scotland and a Voyage to the Hebrides* (2 vols., Chester, 1774)

112. Renfrew, Jane, *Palaeoethnobotany* (London, Methuen, 1973)

113. Renfrew, Jane, *Food and Cooking in Prehistoric Britain* (Historic Buildings and Monuments Commission for England, 1985)

114. Ritchie, Anna, et al, 'Excavation of a Neolithic farmstead at Knap Howe, Papa Westray, Orkney', *Proc. Soc. Antiq. Scot.* 113 (1983) 40-121

115. Rorie, David, *Folk Tradition and Folk Medicine in Scotland* ed. David Buchan (Edinburgh, Canongate, 1994)

116. Ross, Alexander, *Scottish Home Industries*: a reprint of an account written by Provost A.R. Ross in Inverness in 1895 (Glasgow, Molendinar, 1974)

117. Ross, Anne, *Folklore of the Scottish Highlands* (London, Batsford, 1976)

118. Scarlett, James, 'The Highland Cloth and Art Form' in John Butt and Kenneth Ponting (eds.), *Scottish Textile History* (Aberdeen University Press, 1987)

119. Seymour, John, *The Forgotten Arts* (London, Dorling Kindersley, 1984)

120. *Shetland Folk Book* (Vols. 1-5, Shetland Folk Society, 1947)

121. Simpson, Christine, Personal communication (1996)

122. Simpson, Evelyn Blantyre, *Folklore in Lowland Scotland* (London, Dent, 1908)

123. Sinclair, John (ed.), *An Analysis of the Statistical Account of Scotland* (2 vols., Edinburgh, 1825)

124. Smout, T. C. (ed.), *Scotland Since Prehistory: natural change and human impact* (Aberdeen, Scottish Cultural Press, 1993)

125. Sowerby, John and C. Pierpoint Johnson, *The Useful Plants of Great Britain* (London, Robert Hardwicke, undated)

126. Spindler, Konrad, *The Man in the Ice* (London, Phoenix, 1993)

127. Steven, Maisie, *The Good Scots Diet* (Aberdeen University Press, 1985)

128. Stevenson, R.L., *Poems* (London, Eveleigh, Nash & Grayson, undated)

129. Sutherland, James, *Hortus Medicus Edinburgensis: a catalogue of the plants in the Physical Garden at Edinburgh* (1683)

130. Sutton, Ann and Richard Carr, *Tartans: their art and history* (New York, Arco, 1984)

131. Thompson, Francis, *Crofting Years* (Ayrshire, Luath, 1984)

132. Thomson, Derek, *Introduction to Gaelic Poetry* (London, Gollancz, 1974)

133. Toulson, Shirley, *The Celtic Year* (Dorset, Element, 1993)

134. Turner, Nancy, *Ethnobotany of the Nitinaht Indians of Vancouver Island* (British Columbia Provincial Museum, 1983)

135. Vickery, Roy, *A Dictionary of Plant Lore* (Oxford University Press, 1995)

136. Walker, John, *Report on the Hebrides 1764 & 1771* ed. Margaret MacKay (Edinburgh, John Donald, 1980)

137. Whittington, Graeme, 'Pollen analysis as a tool in environmental history', in T.C.Smout (ed.), *Scotland Since Prehistory* (Aberdeen, Scottish Cultural Press, 1993)

138. Wickham-Jones, C.R., 'Rhum: Mesolithic and later sites at Kinloch, excavations 1984-1986', *Soc. Antiquaries of Scot.* (Monograph Series No. 7)

139. Wickham-Jones, C.R., *Scotlands First Settlers* (London, Batsford, 1994)

140. Williamson, Duncan, *Tocher* 33 (1979) 160-4, 186

Index of Plants

aar, 84
Aaron's beard, 135
Aaron's rod, 169
Acer, 25
Achillea, 11, **73-74**
achlasan Chaluimchille, 95
Adam and Eve, 135
adder's grass, 135
adder's tongue, **60**, 74
airne, 155
Ajuga, 16
Agrimonia, 147
Agrimony, 147
 hemp, 78
Agrostis, 7, 27, 30, 34, **199**
aiomlach, 52
aiteann, *aiten*, aitnach,
 aitin, *aittin*, 33, 62
Alaria, 52
Alchemilla, 148
alder, 1, 25, 29, 32, 39,
 41, **84**
alexanders, 70, **71**
Algae, 18 55
allas Mhuire, 95
aller, allertree, 84
allgood, 95
all-heal, 81, **126**
Allium 3, 5, 6, 7, **128-9**
Alnus glutinosa, 1, 29 32,
 39, 41, **84**
 viridis, 25
Alopecurus, 36, **120**
Althea, 131
altuinn, 90
amharag, 88
Ammophila, 30, 31, 35, 37,
 120
Anagallis, 16, **141-2**
Anemone, 144
Angelica, 21
angelica, wild, 21
Anthriscus, 37, **67**
Anthyllis, 21, **111**

Aphanes, 148
Apiaceae, **67-71**
Apium, 5
apple, 4, 41, **150-1**, 175
Aquifoliaceae, **71-2**
Araceae, **72**
Araliaceae, **73-3**
Arctium, 75-6
Arctostaphylos, 41, **104-5**
arn, 84
arnut, lousy/lucy, 68
aron, 72
Arrhenatherum, 120
arsemart/arsmart/arssmart,
 dead, 140
 hot, 139
 spotted, 140
Asteraceae, **73-83**
Artemesia, 76
Arum, 72
arva, arvi, 94
ash, 24, 25, 32, 41, **133-4**
 mountain, 158-9
aspen, 7, 41, 91, **161**
Asplenium, 59
athair thalmhainn, 73
Atriplex, 3
Atropa, 170
Avena, 6, **120**
averin, 156

back-cresses, 88
badan-measgain, 128
badminnie, 70
bairnwort, 76
baldeeri, 135
balg peitach bocan, balg
 smuid, 43
bainne ghabhar, 166
bardog, 75
barberry, barbrag, 41, 84
barley, 5
barr-braonan-nan-con, 152
bawdringie, 70
beac, beacan, 44
bealaidh, bealuidh, 112
beannaichte, 92
bearberry, 41, **104-5**

beard of the rock, 46
bearnan Bride/Brighde, 41,
 82
beatha, 41, 85
beaweed, 79
beccabung, 169
Bedstraw family, **159-61**
bedstraw, 5, 41, **160-1**
Beech family, **115**
beech, 24, 115
bee-sookies, 167
beilbheag, 137
beith, 85
beldairy, 135
belladonna, 170
Bellflower family, **89**
bell heather, 109
Bellis, 7, **76-7**
benner gowan, 76
bent grass, 7, 27, 30, 34,
 119
bentwood, 72
benweed, 79
berber, 84
Berberidaceae, **84**
Berberis, 41, **84**
berry-girse, 104
Beta, 94
betis, 94
betony, 81, **126**
Betulaceae, **84-85**
Betula, 25, 27, 28, 32, 35,
 37, 38, 41, 42, **85**
bhileach losgain, 157
biadh nan coinean, 136
bilberry, 110
bilearach, 176
Bindweed family, **97**
bindwood, 72
biolair, 41, 87, 88
 ghriagain, 87
 Moire, 88
bior nam bride, 82
biotas, 94
Birch family, **84-85**
birch, 25, 27, 28, 32, 35,
 37, 38, 41, 42, **85**
birch fungus, 11

bird's meat, 138
bird's nest, 68
birk, birken tree, 85
bistort, 3, 139
bitter aks, 82
bittercress, 3
bittersweet, 171
blackberry, 4, 7, 104, 108,
 122, **156-7**
black bindweed, 139
blackcurrant, 122
black henbane, 170
black spleenwort, 59
black tang, 53
blackthorn, 7, 11, 25, **155**
bladder campion, 93
bladder locks, 52
bladderwrack, 53
blaeberry, 4, 6, 7, 41, 108,
 110
blaewort, blaver, blawort,
 77, 89
blogda, 144
bloodspot, 47
bloodroot, 152
blood tongue, 159
bloody bells, 164
bloody fingers, 164
bludda, 144
bluebell, 89, **129**
blue blavers, 89
blue blawort 77
blue bonnet, 102
bluebottle, 77
bluegirse, 114
blue gommets, 77
blugga, 144
bodan coille, 71
bochan-bearrach, 43
Bogbean family, **131-2**
bogbean, 21, 114, **131-2**
bog cotton, 26
bog heather, 41, **110**
bog hyacinth, 135
bog myrtle, 41, **108**
bog nut, 131
bog *uisge*, 123
Bolboschoenus, 101

boldeeri, 135
Boletus, 44
boon tree, 90
Borage family, 86
Boraginaceae, 86
borral, 90
Botrychium, 59
boun/bour-tree, 90
Bovista, 43
bowel-hive grass, 148
bowlocks, 76, 79
bracken, brake 30, 38, 41, **61-2**
bramble, 4, 7, 41, 108, **156-7**
   stone, 157
braonan bachlag, 152
braonan bhuachail, 68
braonan fraoch, 152
Brassica, 3
Brassicaceae, 86-9
brawlins, 104
bread-and-cheese, 119
briar, briar-rose, 155
briosglan, brisgean, brislean, 151
brobh, 101
brog na cubhaig, 89, 129, 142
brog na cuthaig, 174
brooklime, 169
brook-weed, 143
broom, 30, 32, 42, **112**
Bryoria, 47
buadhlan, 41
buadhlan buidhe, 79
bualan, 80
buckbean, 131
buckie-faalie, 142
bugle, 16
bugloss, 14
buidheag, 145
buidhe-bealltain, 144
buidhe-mor, 41, 147
buidhghallan, 79
buine, 71
bulister, 155
bull-jumping, 147

bull-seg, 135
bull's bag, 135
bulrush, 101
bulwand, 76
bum-pipe, 82
bun, 163
bun an-ruadh, 41
bun na ruamh, 160
bundweed, 79
buneweed, 69
bunglas, 121
bunnen, bunnert, bunnle, 69
bunsag, 163
bunwort, 69
burdocken, 75
burdock, 75-6
burn-blade, 79
burnet,
   great, 157
   salad, 3
   saxifrage, 70
bur tistle, 78
butterbur, 79, 165
Buttercup family, 143-7
buttercup, 144, 145
butter plant, 128
butterplate, 145
Butterwort family, 128
butterwort, 5, 7, **128**

Cabbage family, 86-9
cabbage,
   wild, 3
   daisy, 147
Cain and Abel, 135
cairmeal, 41, 113
cairt-locha, -an-loch, 41, 133
caitlin, calldainn, callduin, 98
Calluna, 4, 27, 30, 31, 32, 35, 38, 42, **105-9**
Caltha, 144
Calystegia, 97
cambie-leaf, 133
Campanula 89
Campanulaceae, 89

cancer wort, 118
Cantharellus, 43
caod aslachan colum chille, 41
caora gad miann, 157
caorunn, 158
caperoiles, 113
Caprifoliaceae, 89-91
Capsella, 14, 86
Cardamine, 3, 21, 87
Carex arenaria, 101
Carex rostrata, 36
carl(e)-doddy, 78
carraceen, carrageen, 52
carran, 87
Carrot family, 67-71
carrot, 3, 6, **68-9**
carraway, 67
carsons, 87
Caryophyllaceae, 91-94
cas an uain, 111
cathair thalmainn, 73
cat-peas, 114
cean, cearban, 145
cearban feoir, 144, 145
celandine, 145
celery, 5
celery-leaved crowfoot, 146
Centaurea, 77
centaury, 117
Centaurium, 117
Cerastium, 16, **91**
Cetraria, 45
ceud bhileach, 117
chanterelle, 43
charlock, 3, **88**
cheeper, 123
Chenopodiaceae, 94-5
Chenopodium, 3, 95
cherry 154
chewbark, 171
chickenweed, chickenwir, chickweed 94
Chondrus, 52
Chorda, 52
Chrysanthemum, 77
chuillin, 71

ciob, ciob cheann dubh, 102
ciochan nan cailleachan marblia, 164
cinquefoil, 154
cipe, 102
Cirsium, 78
Cladonia, 47
Cladophera, 52
claver, 113
cleavers, 3, **159**
clois, 58
cloudberry, 156
clover 113
cluas liath, 83
cluaran deilgneach, 78
Clubmoss family, 56-7
clubmoss, 38, 56-7
clubrush 101
Clusiaceae, 95-7
cnapan dubh, 77
cockhead, 127
cock's comb, 166, 167
cock's kame, 135
Coclearia, 87
cogie, 174
coille, 158
coirc dubh, coirc fiadhain, 120
coll, colluinn, 98
coltsfoot, 15, **83**
comfrey, 86
conan, 121
conasg, 114
Confervae, 52
Conium, 67
Conopodium, 3, 6, 68
Convallaria, 129
Convolvulaceae, 97
copag, 141
copaig, 41
copan an druichd, 148
Coriolus, 44
corcur, 46
cormeille, 113
Cornaceae, 97
cornflower, 77
corn marigold, 77
corn spurrey, 94

Cornus, 25, 97
corrach-shod, 144
corra-meile, 113
Cortinarius, 44
Corylaceae, 98-9
Corylus, 4, 5, 6, 18, 29, 32, 33, 35, 35, **98-99**
cotton, 37
couch grass, 121
cowcloos, 113
cowcracker, 93
cowgrass, 113
cowheave, 83
cowkeep, -keeks, 69
cowmack, 93
cow parsley, 37, **67**
cow parsnip, 69
cowslip, 142
cranberry, 4, 7, 14, **110**
craneberry-wire, 104
craobh chaoran, 158
craobh crithinn, 161
craobh uinnseann, 133
Crassulaceae, 99-101
Crataegus, 4, 6, 25, **148-9,** 175
crawcroups, 104
crawtoes, 129, 135
creachlach dearg, 119
crested dog's tail grass, 121
Crithmum, 68
cromlus, 137
cross-leaved heath, 110
crosswort, 159
Crowberry family, 104
crowberry, 35, **104**
crowfoot, 144
celery-leaved, 146
cruach luachair, 102
Cruciata, 159
cuach Phadraig, 138
cuckoo flower, 87
cuckoo pint, 72
cuckoo-sorrel, 136
cuckoo's meat, 136
cudbear, 46
cudweed, 79
Cupressaceae, 62-3

cuilc, 101, 122
cuilleann, 71
curl-doddy, curlie-doddy, 76, 102, 135, 137
curluns, 68
curcais, 101
curran, curran-petris, 69
Currant family, 122-3
Cynoglossum, 86
Cynosurus, 121
Cyperaceae, 101-2
cypress, 62-3
Cytisus, 30, 32, 42, **112**

Dactylorhiza, 21, **135**
daa-nettle, 125
daire, 115
Daisy family, 73-83
daisy, 7, **76-7**
cabbage, 147
ewe, 152
ox-eye, 79
dandelion, 3, 7, 41, 42, 75, **82-3**
darach, 41
darag, 115
darnel, 121
darn-grass, 144
darroch, 115
Daucus, 3, 6, **68-9**
dead man's fingers/hand, 135
dead man's mittens, 118
dead men's bellows, 166
dead men's bells, 164
dead men's fingers, 164
dead men's ropes, 52
deadly nightshade, 170
deadnettle,
white, 3
red, 125
dealt ruidhe, 103
deanntag, 172
dearcan dearga, 122
dearcan feanaig, 104
dearcan fithich, 110
dee-nettle, 125
deer's hair, 102

deil-in-a-bush, 129
deil's foot, 135
deil's lingels, 140
deil's meal, 67
devil's bit scabious, 7, 102
devil's milk-plant, 82
dew cup, 148
Diaphasiastrum, 38, 57
Digitalis, 7, 129, **170-2,** 175
diogan, 78
Dipsaceae, 102-3
Dipsacus, 102
dishilago, 83
dithean-oir, 77
Dock family, 139-41
dock, docken, 30, 40, 41, **141**
dogberry, 104
dog heather, 109
dog lichen, 46
dog-tansy, 151
dogwood, 25
doggies, 166
dog's carvi, 67
dog's chamomile, 83
dog's mercury, 111
dog's paise, 111
Dogwood family, 97
doire, 53
donn-lus, 167
doon-head clock, 82
dove-dock, 83
dreas, 41
dris muine, 156
droman, dromanach, 90
dropwort, 149
Drosera, 41, **103**
Droseraceae, 103
dru, 115
druidhe-lus, 175
druman, 41
druise beannaichte, 156
dryad's saddle, 44
Dryopteris, 12, **59**
dubhan, dubhanuith, 126
dubh chasach, 59
duck's foot, 148

dug's lug, 123
duileag bhaite ban, 133
duiliasg, 41, 54
duilluir, 83
dulse, 6, 41, 48, **54**
dur, 115
durlus, 88
dwale, 170
dwarf cornel, 97
dyer's rocket, 147

eala bhuidhe, 95
earning grass, 128
eart-barth, 152
earthnut, 6, **68**
Echium, 14
eidheann, eidheantach, 72
ekel-girse, 128
eksis girse, 82
elder, 4, 41, 42, **90-1**
eldin-docken, 79
Eleocharis 101
elf-shot, 148
ell-shinders, 79
Elm family, 171
elm, 25, 32, 35, 39, 41, **171**
Eltrigia, 121
Empetraceae, *104*
Empetrum, 35, 101
Enteromorpha, 52
Epilobium, 57
Equisetaceae, 58
Equisetum, 11, 36, **58**
Ericaceae, 104-110
Erica cinerea, 41, 42, 105
Erica tetralis, 105, 110
Erodium, 118
Eupatorium, 78
Euphorbiaceae, 111
Euphrasia, 166
Evernia, 47
evron, 156
ewe-daisy, 152
ewe gollan, gowan, 76
eyebright, 166

Fabaceae, 111-114

faerie's thimbles, 164
Fagaceae, 115
Fagus, 24, 115
fail cuach, 174
fair-days, fair-grass, 151
fala, 73, 76, 96
Fallopia, 139
farach don/dubh, farum,
    167
fat hen, 3, 95
feanntag, 172
fearna, fearnaich, 41, 103
fechters, 137
feireag, 156
fenugreek, 140
fern, 12, 30, 35, **58-62**, 165
Festuca, 36, 53, 121
fetches, 114
feur chaorach, 121
feverfew, 82
feverfouillie, 117
fiacal leaohain, 82
fiasg nan creag, 46
field penny cress, 89
Figwort family, 164-70
figwort, 167-8
filaera, 78
Filicopsida, 58-62
Filipendula, 4, **149**
fineamhain, 163
fintock, 156
finzach, 140
fionag, 104
fitchacks, 114
fiteag, 120
five-leaved grass, 154
fizz-gig, 79
flag, 123-4
flapper-bags, 75
Flax family, 129-30
flax, 37, **129-30**
    fairy, purging, 21,
      129-30
flesh-and-blood, 152
fliodh, fliogh, 94
flowering fern, 60
fluellen, 169
foal's foot, foal-foot, 83,

    145
fochas, 131
foghnan, 78
foighreag, 156
fola, 73, 86, 96
Fomes, 25
fool's stones, 135
foose, 100
forum, 167
fothros, 137
fothlus, fotlus, 167
foxglove, 7, 129, **164-6**,
    175
foxter, 164
Fragaria, 4, 5, 75, 108, **150**
fraoch, 109
    an derrasain, 109
    an ruinnse, 110
    bhadhain, 109
    frangach, 110
fraochan, 110
Fraxinus, 24, 25, 32, 41,
    133-4
frost-blite, 95
Fucus, 49-51, **53**
fuinseag coille, 81
Fumariaceae, 117
Fumaria, 117
Fumitory family, 117
fumitory, 117
Fungi, 43-4
fungi, 3, 4, 9, 12, 25, 42,
    43, 44

gair, 114
gairgean-creagh, 93
gale, 132
Galium aparine, 3, **159**
    odoratum, 4, **160**
    verum, 5, 41, **160-1**
gallsheilach, 163
gallsheilisdear, 101
gall-wood, 76
Ganoderma, 44
garbhag an t-sleibhe, 56
garbh lus, 159
garlic, wild, 3, 5, 6, 7,
    128-9

garten-berry, gatter-berry,
    gatter-tree, 156
geald-rhuidhe, 103
gean, 154
gearr-dhearc, 110
Gentian family, 117-8
gentian, 12, **117-8**
Gentiana, 117
Gentianaceae, 117-8
Gentianella, 12, 118
Geraniaceae, 118-9
Geranium family, 118-9
Geranium, 118, 119
Geum, 3, **150**
ghobhal luachair, 101
gille guirmein, 102
gille mu leann, 52
giogan, 78
giolach sleibhe, 112
glas-leun, 145
glaucous leafy lichen, 47
Glechoma, 125
globe flower, 147
Gnaphalium, 79
gnashaks, 104
goatsbeard, 3
golden rod, 81, 97
gollan, horse, 79
    yellow, 144
golland, 77
    water, 144
good King Henry, 95
gooseberry, 123
Goosefoot family, 94-5
goose-grass, 151, **159**
goosetongue, 145
gorm liath, 83
gorse, 4, 32, 40, 109, **114**
gourlins, 68
gowan, gowlan, 77, 79, 145
    horse, 79, 82
    lapper, locker, lockin,
      luggie, 147
    Mary, may, 77
    milk, 82
    tushy-lucky, 83
    witch(es), 82, 147
    yellow, 77, 82

gowk's hose, 129
    meat, 136
    thimbles/thumles, 89
gowlins, 68
grafan nan clach, 99
grain-aigein, 145
grainnseag, 41, 104
Gramineae, 119-22
Grass family, 119-22
grass, 26, 30, 35, 36, **119-
22**
grasswrack, 176
green lava, 55
grey bulwand, 76
grian mhuine, 156
grob, grobach, 53
goinear, goin fheur, 121
groser, groset, 123
Grossulariaceae, 122-3
ground ivy, 125
groundsel, 11, **80-1**
grozzle, 123
gulsa-girse, 131
grundavy, 125
grunnasg, 80
gruzel, 123
guacagan-baite, 133
guiseag bhuidhe/cuiseag, 79
guibhas, guithas, 63
gunnachan sputachain, 69

hackberry, hagberry, 154
Haematomma, 47
hardhead, 74
harebell, 89
hart's tongue fern, 60
has tree, 148
hather, 109
haw, hawberry, hawbush,
    148
hawthorn, 4, 6, **148-9**, 175
Hazel family, 98-9
hazel, 1, 4, 5, 6, 18, 25,
    29, 32, 33, 34, 35, **98-
9**
headman, 137
healing blade, leaf, 100,
    138

heart o' the earth, 126
hearts-ease, 174
Heath family, 104-10
heath, 28, 41, 42
 clubrush, 102
 cross-leaved, 110
 -pea, pease, 113
heather, 4, 27, 28, 30, 31, 32, 35, 38, 42, **105-9**
 bell, 109
 bog, 110
 he-, she- 109
hech-how, 67
Hedera, **72-3**, 156
hedder, 109
heg-beg, 172
hellebore, 114
Helleborus, 114
Hemanthalia, 52
hemlock, **67**, 69, 170
hemp agrimony, 78
henbane, 67, **170-1**
hens, hen's kames, 135
hen-ware, 52
Heracleum, 69
herb bennet, 3, **150**
herb paris, 129
herb Robert, 118
hindberry, 157
hockery-topner, 100
hogweed, 69
Holcus, 35, 36, 53
holine, holing, hollin, 71
holly, 71-2
honeyblob, 123
honey sookies, 167
Honeysuckle family, 89-91
honeysuckle, 89
honey-ware, 52
Hordeum, 5
hornecks, 68
horse knot, 77
horse wellcress, 169
horsetail, 11, 36, **58**
hound's tongue, **86**, 127
houseleek, 100
humlock, humly rose, 67

hundred-leaved grass, 73
Huperzia, 56
hyacinth, wild, 129
Hyacinthoides, 129
Hydrophorus, 26
Hylocomium, 26
Hyoscyamus, 67, **171-1**
Hypericum, 41, 42, 81, **95-7**
Hypogymnia, 47

Iceland moss, 45
Ilex, 71-2
Inonotus, 44
iomleach, 52
iontag, 172
Iridaceae, 123-4
iris, *Iris* 12, 14, 30, 41, 42, **123-4**
Irish moss, 52
Isatis, 57
iteotha, 67
iuntag, 172
ivery, ivin 72
Ivy family, 72-3
ivy, **72-3**, 156

jack-in-the-bush, 100
jessamine, wild, 144
Johnsmas-flooer, 138
 flowers, pairs, 138
Juncaceae, 124-5
Juncus, 18, 26, 30, 31, 34, **124-5**
juniper, *Juniperus*, 3, 12, 14, 25, 33, **62-3**

kail, kale, 88
kaka, 67
keeslip, 160
keksi, 69
kemp, kempseed, 137
kidney vetch, 21
kidney wort, 100
kingcup, 144
klonger, klunger, 155
knapperts, 113
knapweed, 77

knauperts, 104
Knautia, 102
knotberry, 156
knotgrass, 140
knotweed, 139
knotty meal, 68
knoutberry, 156
kokkeluri, 79
koukeleri, 77
korkalett, korkir, 46
kraa-tae, 144

Labiate family, 125-7
Labiateae, 125-7
lady-of-the-meadow, 149
lady-whin, 113
ladywrack, 53
lady's bed, 160
lady's bedstraw, 5, 41, **160-1**
lady's clover, 136
lady's fingers, 89, 111
lady's mantle, 148
lady's thimble, 89
lady's purses, 86
lady's smock, 3, 21, **86**
Laetiporus, 44
Lamiaceae, 125-7
Laminaria, 6, 48, 49, 53
Lamium, 3, **125**
lammie sourocks, 140
Langermania, 44
larch, *Larix*, 25, 26
lasair-leana, 145
Lathyrus, 113
Laurencia, 54
laver, 54
laverock's lint, 129
Lecanora, 41, 46
leek, wild, 128
Lentibulariaceae, 128
leobadh ban sith, 160
leolaicheann, 147
Leucanthemum, 79
lianach, 52
Lichens, 45-7

lichen, 37, 40, 41, **45-47**
Ligusticum, 21, **70**
Liliaceae, 128-9
Lily family, 128-9
lily of the valley, 129
lime, 4, 25
Linaceae, 129-30
Linaria, 166
linarich, *linnearach*, 52
ling, 30, 109
linseed, 130
Linum, 21, **129-30**
lion, 129, 130
liquorice, wild, 113
Lobaria, 45, 47
lochal, 169
Lolium, 121
Loncera, 89
Loosestrife family, 130
loosestrife, 130
lords and ladies, 72
lothal, 169
lousewort, 166-7
lovage, Scots, 21, **70**
love-idleness, 174
lover's links, 100
luachair, 101
luachar, 124
luan lus, 59
lucky minny's lines, 52
luibh mhor, 131
luireach, 52
luis, 158
lungwort lichen, 45, 47
lus a chraois, 97
 a chridh, 126
 an callain, 118
 an fhogair, 139
 an leasaich, 160
 an righ, 127
 an rois, 118
 an sith chainnt, 130
 an talaidh, 135
 an torranain, 167
 an t'slanuchaidh, 137
 beannaichte, 92
 buidhe, bealltain, 144
 buidhe, mor, 41, 147

caolach, 129
chasgadh na fala/na
    fola, 73
chrann ceusaidh, 140
Chuchulainn, 149
deathach-thalmnainn,
    117
gharaigh, 100
Ghlinne Bhracadail,
    111
mhic righ Bhreatainn,
    127
Mhuire, 144
mor, 164
na fala/fola, 73, 86,
    96
na fearnaich, 41, 103
na leic, 166
na Maighdinn Muire,
    95
nam bansith, 164
nam cnamh, 68
na mial, 166
nan broileag/dhearc,
    110
nan cluas, 100
nan-clugan/cnapan, 167
nan dhearc, 41, 110
nan eighreag, 156
nan gran dubh, 71
nan laogh, 131
nan sgor, 127
nan tri-beann, 131
na seilg, 59
Phara liath, 80
riablach, 167
Lycopodiaceae, 56-7
Lycopodium, 38, 56
Lysmachia, 130
Lythraceae, 130
Lythrum, 130

madder, 38, 57, 161
mad dog's berries, 171
maid-in-the-mist, 100
male fern, 60
maidenhair spleenwort, 58
mallow, 14, **131**

Malus, 4, 41, **150-11**
Malvaceae, 131
Malva, 14, **131**
manelet, 77
maothan, 163
maple, Norway, 25
marag bhuidhe, 88
maraich, 87
marc raineach, 60
marigold, 7
    corn, 77
    marsh, 144
marjoram, wild, 126
marlie, 176
marram grass, 30, 31, 35,
    37, **120**
marsh lousewort, 166-7
marsh trefoil, 131
marsh woundwort, 127
Mary gowlan, 77
maskert, 127
matweed, 120
may flooer, 142
may gowan, 77
mayweed, 83
meacan dubh, 86
meacan a-cruidh, 69
meadow foxtail grass, 120
meadow grass, 35, 122
meadow queen, 149
meadow rue, 146
meadowsweet, 4, 149
meal-and-folie, 73
meduart, 149
meilbheag, 137
melancholy, 73
meldi, 92, 94
meldweed, 95
Mentha, 3, 14, 36, **125**
Menyanthaceae, 131-2
Menyanthes, 21, 114, **131-
    2**
meoir Mhuire, 111
Mercurialis, 111
mercury, English, 95
    Scotch, 164
merry-tree, 154
Meum, 70

meuran nan daoine marbh,
    164
*meuran nan cailleach
    mharbha*, 164
micken, 70
midden mylies, 95
Mignonette family, 147
milfoil, 73
milk-ort, 89
milkwort, 138
mimnhear, 67
mint, 3, 14, 36, **125**
mionach, miosach, 130
mircean, 52
misle, 175
Mistletoe family, 175-6
mistletoe, 12, 115, 140,
    175-6
modhalan dearg, 166, 167
moleery-tea, 73, 74
Molinia, 121
molus, 92
moogard, 76
moonwort, 59
moor-grass, 151
mor, 164
moss, 11, 26, 29, **55-56**
mosscrop, 151
moth urach, 135
mothan, 92
mother's heart, 86
mouse-ear, 16, **91**
mugger, muggert,
    muggons, 76
mugwort, 76
muilceann, muilcionn, 70
muirineach, 119, 120
muirirean, muiririn, 52
muisean, 142
muir-druidhean, 147
mullein, 169
muran, 69, 119, 120
Musci, 55-6
mushroom, 3, 4, 9, 12, 25,
    42, 43, 44
mustard, 88
myles, 95
Myricaceae, 132-3

Myrica, 41, 108, 132-2
myrtle, bog, 132
myrrh, 70
Myrrhis, 70
napple, 113
nashag, 104
navelwort, 100
neandog, 172
Neckera, 26
neoinean, 77
Nettle family, 171-4
nettle, 3, 5, 6, 8, 37, 42,
    130, **172-4**
**Nightshade family, 170-
    1**
nightshade, deadly, 170-1
    woody, 171
noops, 156
Norway maple, 25
    spruce, 25
nuallach, 169
nub, nub-berry, 156
Nymphaceae, 133
Nymphaea, 41, **133**

oak, 4, 7, 24, 29, 32, 34,
    35, 40, 41, 64, 98,
    115-7, 152, 175, 176
oak lung, 45
oak moss, 47
oats, 6
oat grass, 120
Ochrolechia, 41, 46
odharan, 69
Oenanthe, 69
oighreag, oireag, 156
okkerdu, 125
old man's beard, 45, 47
old wives' tongues, 161
Oleaceae, 133-4
Olive family, 133-4
Ononis, 113
Ophioglossum, 60
orache, 3
Orchidaceae, 135-6
Orchid family, 135-6
orchid, 7, 21, 135-6
Orchis, 7, 21, 135-6

Origanum, 126
orpine, orppies, orpy-leaf, 100
osier, 163
Osmunda, 60
osmund royal, 60
Oxalidaceae, 136
Oxalis, 3, 42, 114, **136-7**

paipean ruadh, 137
Papaveraceae, 137
Papaver, 137
Parieta, 171
Paris, 129
Parmelia, **41,** 47
parsley, breakstone, 148
    piert, 148
    scotch, sea, 79
parsnip, wild, 3
passper, 68
Pastinaca, 3
Paxillus, 42, 44
Pea family, 111-4
pear, 175
pearlwort, 92-3
Pedicularis, 166-7
pellitory of the wall, 171
Peltigera, 46
pepper dulse, 54
    girse, 74
    water, 139
    wild, 73
pesair nan luch, 114
persicaria, 140
Persicaria, 139-40
Petasites, **79,** 165
Phaeolus, 44
Phragmites, 122
Phyllitis, 60
Picea, 25, 27
pight aits, 120
pignut, 3, 6, 68
pilewort, 145
pimpernel, 16
    scarlet, 141-2
    water, 143
Pimpinella, 70
pimrose, 142

Pinaceae, 63-5
Pine family, 63-5
pine, 12, 25, 31, 33, 63-5
Pinguicula, 5, 7, **128**
Pink family, 91-4
Pinus, 12, 25, 31, 33, 63-5
Piptoporus, 11, 44
piss-a-bed, 82
Plantaginaceae, 137-8
Plantago, 7, **137-8**
Plantain family, 137-8
plantain, great, 138
    ribwort, 7, 137
Platismatia, 47
plyvens, 113
Poa, 36
poisonberry, 171
Polygalaceae, 138
Polygala, 138
Polygonaceae, 139-41
Polygonum, 3, **140**
polypore, 11, **44**
Polyporus, 11, **44**
Polystichum, 61
ponair chapull, 131
poor man's weather glass, 141
Poppy family, 137
poppy, 137
Populus, 7, 41, 91, **161**
Porphyria, 54
Potentilla anserina, 3, 6, **151-2**
Potentilla erecta, 14, 38, 41, 127, **152-4**
Poterium, 3
pounce, 135
prablach, 53
praiseach brathair, 95
praiseach fiadhain, 95
praiseach garbh, 88
preas deilgneach, 84
preas nan airnaig/airneag, 41, 45
preas nan gear dhearc, 84
preas nan sgeachag, 148
preas subh chraobh, 157
priest's pintel, 99

Primrose family, 141-3
primrose, 142-3
Primulaceae, 141-3
Primula, 142-3
prince's feather, 126
propach, 53
Prunella, 81, **126**
Prunus avium, 154
Prunus padus, 154
Prunus spinosa, 4, 6, 11, 25, 41, **155**
Pseudevernia, 47
Psilocybe, 43
Pteridium, 30, 38, 41, **61-2**
puddock's spindles, 135
puffball, 44
puffed shield lichen, 47
punglas, 121
puns, 35
purple loosestrife, 130
purple melic/moor grass, 121
purple restharrow, 113

quaich, 174
quakin ash, 161
queen-of-the-meadow, 149
Quercus, 4, 7, 24, 29, 32, 34, 35, 40, 41, 64, 98, 115-7, 152, 175, 176
quicken, 27, 158

ragweed, ragwort, 11, 34, 35, 41, 42, **79-80**
raineach, rainnich, roineach, 41, 58
Ramalina, 41, **46**
ramsons, ramps, 3, 5, 6, 7, **128-9**
Ranunculaceae, 143-7
Ranunculus, 55, 145
raosar dearc, 41
rapper-dandy, 104
rashes, 30
rasp, raspberry, 4, 5, 6, **157**
rat's tails, 138
red archangel, 125

red currant, 41, **122**
red deadnettle, 125
red fescue, 36, 53
red fog, 53
red rattle, 166
red rot, 103
redshank, 140
reed, 29, 37, **122**
reindeer moss, 47
Resedaceae, 147
Reseda, 38, 41, 57, **147**
restharrow, 113
Rhodymenia, 41, **54**
Ribes, 41, **122-3**
ribgrass, 137
ribwort plantain, 7, 137
rideag, 41, 132
ridin' girse, 118
righ, 127
righeal cuil, 118
rios Chuchulainn, 149
ripple-girs, 138
rizzles, 122
robin-run-in-the-hedge, 159
roddin, roddin tree, 158
roebuck, 157
rofle the lady's purses, 86
rota, 132
Rorippa, 41 88, 114
ros an t'solais, 103
Rosaceae, 147-59
Rosa, rose, 4, 6, 9, 12, **155-6,** 175
Rose family, 147-59
rose, noble, 167
    root, 99-100
rot grass, 128
rowan, 4, 7, 27, 38, 156, 158-9
royal fern, 60
ruamh, 160
ru beg, 146
Rubiaceae, 159-61
Rubia, 38, 57, 161
Rubus chamaemorus, 156
Rubus fruticosus, 4, 7, 41, 108, **156-7**

Rubus idaeus, 4, 5, 6, 108, **157**
Rubus saxatilis, 157
ruin, 160
ruis, 90
ruisg conasg, 41
Rumex, 3, 30, 36, 40, 41, **140-1**, 175
runch, runchie, runchik, runch balls, 88
Rush family, 124-5
rush, 18, 26, 30, 31, 34, **124-5**
russles, 122

sage, wild, wood, 127
saggon, 123
Sagina, 92-3
saimbhir, 68
St John's wort, 41, 42, 81, **95-7**
St Peter's wort, 95
Salicaceae, 161-4
Salix, 25, 26, 30, 32, 33, 34, 35, **162-4**
sallow, 162-4
Salsola, 95
saltwort, 95
Sambucus, 4, 41, 42, **90-1**
samh, 62, 136, 140
Samolus, 143
samphire, rock, 68
Sanguisorba, 157
sanicle, *Sanicula*, 16, 71
Saponaria, 93
Sargassum, 55
scabious, 102
scaldricks, 88
sceallan, 88
Schoenoplectus, 101
Scotch fir, 63
Scotch gale, 132
Scotch mercury, 164
Scotch parsley, 70
Scots lovage, 21, **70**
Scots pine, 12, **63-5**
scrab, 150
screeby, 87

scrogg, 150
Scrophularia, **167-8**
Scrophulariaceae, 164–70
scurvy grass, 87
sea beet, 94
sea bindweed, 97
sea clubrush, 101
sea girdles, 53
sea grapes, 55
sea grass, 176
sea ivory, 46
sea laces, 52
sea lettuce, 55
sea matgrass, 101
sea mayweed, 83
sea reed, 35
sea sedge, 101
sea ware, 53
seaweed, 3, 6, 8, 9, 15, 23, 35, 41, **48-55**
sea wormwood, 81
Seagrass family, 176
Seaweed family, 48-55
seachdamh aran, 151
sealbhag, sealbhag ruanaidh, 140
seamar chaphuill, 113
searraiche, 145
Sedge family, 101-2
sedge, 101
Sedum, 99-100
seggen, 123
seilisdear, seileasdear, 41, 123
seilsdear amh, 101
Selago, 56
self-heal, 126
Sempervivum, 100
Senecio jacobaea, 11, 34, 35, 41, 42, **79-80**
Senecio vulgaris, 11, **80-1**
sengreen, 100
Seriphydium, 81
sgealag, 88
sgiteach, sgithich, 148
sgor, 127

sguab, 112
sheep-root/rot, 128
sheep's fescue grass, 121
she-heather, 109
shepherd's club, 169
shepherd's knot, 152
shepherd's purse, 14, **86**
shield fern, 61
sholgirse, 74
Silene, 93
silverweed, 3, 6, **151-2**
Sinapis arvensis, 3, **88**
siolaster, 123
sirist, 154
Sisymbrium, 88
sitsticker, 144
sivven, 157
skellocks, 88
slan-lus, 126, 137, 138
slat-mhara, 53
sleepy dose, 79
sloe, 4, 6, 11, 41
slochdan, sloke, *sloucan*, 54
sluach, 155
small house-leek, 99
smear docken, 95
smear phreas, smeuran, 156
smiddy leaves, 95
Smyrmium, 71
snaithlus, 137
snakeweed, 139
sneezewort, 74-5
soapwort, 93
sobrag, sobrach, 142
Solanaceae, 170-1
Solanum, 171
soldiers, 137
Solidago, 81, 97
Sonchus, 3, 81
sookies, 167
soorik, 140
Sorbus, 4, 7, 27, 38, 156, **158-9**
sorrel, 3, 36, **140**, 175
wood, 42, **114**
soukies, soukie soo, 113
sour clover, 136
sourlick, sourock, 140

sow thistle, 3, **81**
spades, 139
spearwort, 55, **145**
speedwell, 97, 108, **169**
Spergula, 94
Sphagnum, 11, **55-6**
spignel, 70
spike-rush, 101
spinach, spinage, 6, 95
spleenwort, 59
spoon-wort, 87, **139**
spotted knotweed, 139
spruce, 25, 28
spuing, 83
Spurge family, 111
Stachys, 81, **126-7**
stamh, 53
stanch-girs, 73
Stellaria, 94
sticky willie, 159
stink davie, 82
stinking alisander, 79
stinking davies, 79
stinking Roger, 167
stinking weed, 79
stinking willie, 41
stolgirse, 74
Stonecrop family, 99-101
stonecrop, 99
storksbill, 118
stradag, 172
strawberry, 4, 5, 74, 108, **150**
subh, subhan laire, 150
Succissa, 7, **102-3**
suagh, 163
sugag, 113
sugh dharaich, 175
suibhean, 157
suileag, 163
suinas, 70
sundew, 41, **103**
suth thalhmain, 150
sweet cicely, 70
sweet gale, 132
sweet grass, 160
sweet humlick, 70

sweet sea grass, 176
swinen arnit, 127
swine's beads, 127
swine's grass, 140, 151
swine's maskert, 127
swine's murricks, 127, 151
Symphytum, 86

taegirse, 127
Tanacetum, 3, **82**
tangle, 6, 48, 49, **53**
tansy, 3
Taraxacum 3, 7, 41, 42,
    75, **82-3**
tare, 114
tarrann, tarranan, 167
tassel, 177
Taxaceae, 65-6
Taxus, 24, 25, 32, 37, 65-6
teantguidh, 117
Teasel family, 102-3
teasel, 102
Teucrium, 127
Thalictrum, 146
thimbles, 89
thistle, 26, 35, **78**
    melancholy, 7
    milk, 81
    sow, 3, **81**
Thlapsi, 89
thousand-leaf clover, 73
thrissel, 78
thyme, 4, 14, 108, **127**
    mother of, 127
Thymus, 4, 14, 108, **127**
Tilia, 4, 25
tinder fungus, 25
*tin gealch, tineas na
    gealaich*, 100
tistle, 78
tlachd subh, 150
toadflax, 166
tongue-bluiders, 159
torachas biadhain, 146
tormentil, 14, 38, 41, 127,
    152-4
*torrann, torranain,
    torranan*, 167

Tragopogon, 3
treacle mustard trefold,131
    trefoil, 114
*tribeann, tribhealeach, tri-
    bhileach*, 131
tri-bilean, 113
Trichophorum, 102
Trifolium, 113, 114
Tripleurospermum, 83
Triticum, 5
Trolius, 147
trow bura, 124
trows' cairds, 58
true-love, 129
truffle, 68
trusgar, 55
tufted scirpus, 102
turusgar, 55
Tussilago, 15, 83
Typha, 36

ubhal-fiadhaich, 50
ucas frangach, 131
uile-ice, 175
uinseag coille, 158
uinnseann, uinsinn, 133
Ulex, 4, 32, 40, 109, **114**
Ulmaceae, 171
Ulmus, 25, 32, 35, 39, 41,
    171
Ulva, 55
ura bhallach, 102
Urceolaria, 41
Urticaceae, 171-4
Urtica, 3, 5, 6, 8, 37, 42,
    130, **172-4**
useless, 140
Usnea, 45, 47

Vaccinium myrtillus, 4, 6,
    7, 41, 108, **110**
Vaccinium microcarpon, 4,
    7, 14
Valerian family, 174
valerian, *Valeriana*, 12, 21,
    174
Valerianaceae, 174
venus-basons, 102

Veronica, 97, 108, **169**
vetch, 41
    bitter, 113
    heath, 113
    kidney, 21, **111**
    tufted, 114
Viburnum, 24, 25
Vicia, 41, **114**
Violaceae, 174-5
Viola, 14, **174-5**
violet, 14, **174-5**
Viscaceae, 175-6
Viscum, 12, 115, 140, **175-
6**

waaverin-leaf, wabran-leaf,
    138
wake robin, 72
wall-penny wort,
    walpenny woort, 100
wall-pepper, 99
watercress, 6, 41, 88, 114
water lily, 41, **133**
water purpie/purple, 169
water skegg, 123
wattery drums, 80
wavy bittercress, 87
waybread, wayburn leaf,
    138
wayfaring tree, 24, 25
weebo, 79
weld, 38, 41, 57, **147**
well-girse,karse/kerse, 88
wellink, 169
wheat, 5
whin, 4, 32, 40, 109, **114**
white-blite, 95
whortleberry, 110
wildfire, 144
wilfire, 145
Willow family, 161-4
willow, 1, 25, 26, 30, 32,
    33, 34, 35, **162-4**
willowherb, 57
windflower, 144
wineberry, 122
witch bells, 89
witches' thimble(s), 89,164

witherips, 160
woad, 57
woodbind, woodbine, 89
woodrep, woodroof,
    woodruff, 4, **160**
wood anemone, 144
wood avens, 150
wood-pease, 113
wood-rasp, 157
wood sorrel, 3, 42, 114,
    136-7
wormwood, 76
    sea, 81
woundwort, 127
wych elm, 25, 32, 35, 39,
    41, **171**

Xanthoria, 45, **47**

yarr, 94
yarrow, 11, **73-4**
yellow prick madam, 99
yellow goatsbeard, 3
yellow gollan, 144
yellow gowan 77
yellow gowlan, 144
yellow loosestrife, 130
yellow rocket, 147
yellow wall lichen, 41
yellow weed, 88
yellowin girse, 140
yew, 24, 25, 32, 37, **65-6**
yirnin-girse, 128
Yorkshire fog, 35, 36, 53

Zosteraceae, 176
Zostera, 176

General Index

abscess *see* boils
Aberdeen, 21, 33, 62, 74
Aberdeen University, 85
Aberdeenshire, 4, 20, 24, 43, 48, 136
Aberlady, 38
Aborigines, 2
abortifacients, 56, 63, 130, 146
Achilles, 73
agriculture, 2, 4-5, 8
ague *see* fever, malaria
AIDS, 23
Alba, 80
alchemy, 10
ale, 68-9, 73, 76, 82-3, 97, 108, 109, 116, 120, 133, 172-3, 174
heather, 108, 109
Alps, 24
anaemia, 49, 144, 154
anaesthetic, 67, 170,
Andrew, St, 96
antibiotic, 11
Antonine Wall, 5
aphrodisiac, 70, 118
apothecary, 17
appetiser, 70, 76, 97, 136, 159
Archbishop of St Andrews, 15
Argyll, 30, 64, 65, 75, 85, 101, 108, 117, 133
Arran, 42, 136, 147, 158
arrow, 24, 25, 57, 122, *see* elf-shot
arthritis, 109, 134, *see* rheumatism
aspirin, 162
asthma, 67, 71, 79, 83, 90, 91, 125, 132
Austria, 24
axe, 24, 25, *see* tools

backpack, 24
badger, 3
Bailefuil Wood, 29
Bald, Balder, 162
Bald, Leech Book of, 14
Balder, 162
Balfour, Andrew, 16, 17
Balfour, Professor Bayley, 168
Banks, Joseph, 21
bannock, 7
bard, 98
bark containers, 25, 85
barley, 5
Barra, 19, 160
barrels, barrel making, 116, 117, 158, 164
baskets, basket making, 5, 27, 28, 32-35, 63, 85, 99, 101, 106, 119, 120, 125, 141, 162, 163
bast, 24-5, 39, 85, *see* bark, twine
Bearsden, 5
Beaton, John, 14
Beaton, Neil, 19
bed, bedding, 26, 28, 30, 61, 107, 109, 160, 176
bee, 42; bee hive, 162; beeswax, 64
beer *see* ale
Beith, Mary, 43, 44, 57, 70, 81, 73, 91, 107, 112, 123, 126, 149, 151, 155
Beltane, 66, 96, 115, 158, 162
belt pouch, 25
Belus, 112
Benbecula, 168
berries *see* fruit
besom *see* brush
bing, recolonisation, 56
birth *see* childbirth
bites, 82, 139 *see* snake bite
bladder, 14, 68, 69, 85,

86, 104, 112, 121, 124, 130, 148, 160, 172, 173
Blair Atholl, 106
Blair Castle, 112
blancmange, 52
blight, 8
blindness (livestock), 127
blisters *see* skin disorders
blood, 7, 59 *see* styptic
blood-letting, 14, 15, 18, 20
blood pressure, 149, 173
boats, boat building, 35, 64, 115, 116, 134, 158, 163, 165
bobbins, 37, 67
Boerhaave, 21
boils, 64, 81, 94, 102, 130, 132, 133, 145, 164, 166, 175 *see* skin disorders, sores, ulcers
Bonawe, 117
bonesetting, 18, 81, 86, 97, 155
Borneo, 21
bothy, 31 *see* shieling
bow, 24, 25, 65
bowel, 138, 139, 148, 159, 169 *see* constipation
brandy, flavouring, 154, 157
breasts, sore, swollen, 94, 131
breathlessness *see* asthma, chest, lungs
Bredalbane, 113
Brendan, St, 116
brewing *see* ale
Briannuil, 48
Bride, Brigit, St, 13, 32, 82, 85, 92, 112, 142-3, 156, 162
British Seaweed Company, 50
bronchitis, 67, 90, 129, 154, 156
Bronze Age, 4, 5, 11, 55, 139, 173

Brorera, 145
broth, 49, 54, 70, 71, 88, 172
bruise, 60, 73, 79, 80, 86, 91, 123, 125, 139, 140, 168, 171
brushes, 30, 32, 85, 108, 109, 110, 112, 119, 124, 140, 162, 168, 171
Buchan, 89
Buchan, George, 20
Buchanan, George, 107
bull, 92, 92 *see* cattle, cows
burial rites, 10-11, 24, 29, 65, 90, 149
burns, 49, 52, 73, 80, 86, 91, 100, 130, 132, 138, 156, 158 *see* scalds
Burns, Robert, 80
burr, Burry Man, 75
Bute, 19
butter, flavouring, 5, 36, 55, 79, 90

cairn, 113
Caithness, 54, 106
Caledonian pinewood, 64
caman, 35 *see* shinty
Cameron, John, 55, 59, 83, 86, 88, 95, 98, 100, 103, 131, 145, 164, 166
Cameron, Col. John, 170
Campbell, Archibald, 62
Campbell, Janet, 19
Campbell, Thomas, 172
Canada, 26, 58 *see* Nitinaht, Vancouver Is.
candle *see* lighting
Candlemas, 90, 142
cancer, 23, 67, 69, 80, 100, 118, 129, 168, 169
Cardano, Geronimo, 15
Carmichael, Alexander, 6, 7, 22, 27, 32, 33, 57, 60, 67, 73, 79, 80, 82,

88, 92, 96, 99, 114, 142, 151, 160, 165, 167, 168
carrot festival, 6
catarrh, 14, 78, 79, 91, 156, 169, 171, colds
Carmina Gadelica see Carmichael
cattle, 5, 69, 92, 93, 158, 167 *see* bulls, cows, livestock
champagne *see* wine
changeling, 128, 164, 176
charcoal, 1, 25, 32, 116, 162
charms, 13, 22, 53, 55, 58, 60, 62, 71, 74, 79, 88, 123, 135, 138, 165, 168, 176
cheese, 5, 53 *see* rennet substitutes
chest complaints, 45, 52, 83, 113, 126, 173 *see* lung disorders
chilblain, 91, 94, 101
childbirth, 54, 64, 92, 134, 157
childlessness *see* infertility
cholera, 130, 139, 153
chimney sweeping, 109
Christian, Christianity, 12, 13, 22, 43, 48, 65, 96, 98, 115, 150, 162
Christison, Robert, 65
cleansing, laundry, 137, 141 *see* soap
Clearances, Highland, 8, 36, 50
clogs, 84
Clontarf, Battle of, 56
cloth, nettle, 172, 173-4 *see* textiles
Clunie, 6
Clyde, 76
coffee substitutes, 83, 112, 115, 116, 124, 159
coffin, 158
colds, 73, 74-5, 83, 86, 91,

124, 125, 130, 149, 150, 157, 159, 160
colic, 82, 91, 117, 129, 132, 140, 155 *see* flatulence, indigestion
Col, 152, 153,
Colonsay, 91, 101, 118, 128, 148
Columba, St, 13, 55, 65, 92, 96-7, 115
Comrie, J.D., 15, 60, 123, 143
condiments, 54, 55
constipation, 14, 18, 49, 54, 73, 82, 91, 94, 124, 130, 171, 173, 175
consumption, 18, 20, 21, 58, 59, 70, 71, 73, 76, 88, 90, 108, 116, 125, 132, 155, 160, 169 *see* scrofula
contraceptive, 162
convulsion, 123, 144
Cook, Captain, 21
coppice, 1, 134
copperas, 39
coracle, 116, 162, 163 *see* boats
cord *see* twine
cordial, 122, 160
corns, 73, 103, 133, 145
cosmetic, 150, 166, 175
cough, 18, 59, 69, 73, 79, 82, 83, 86, 90, 94, 102, 103, 108, 122, 123, 125, 129, 130, 132, 140, 155, 169, 172, 173 *see* whooping cough
cows, 27, 70, 80, 90, 92, 93, 118, 121, 127, 128, 141, 143, 168
cradle cap, 73, 117
cramp, 67, 129, 151
crannog, 29, 84
creel, 34, 51, 99, 163
cricket, 162
crook, 33, 99, 134

crotal, crottle, 45
croup, 91, 174
Cuchulainn, 149, 150
Culpepper, 102
cystitis *see* bladder

dagger *see* dirk
Dalmuir, 50
dandruff, 59, 102, 103 *see* hair
Danes, Denmark, 170, 173
Dark Ages, 13
David I, 14
death *see* burial
delirium, 113, 164
depression, 82, 108
desserts, 49, 52, 156 *see* fruit
devil, 19, 67, 89, 170
diabetes, 139, 173
diarrhoea, 14, 18, 45, 86, 91, 100, 110, 116, 123, 125, 130, 133, 135, 139, 140, 148, 150, 153, 154, 155, 157, 169, dysentery
diet, 3, 6, 8, 61
digestion, 68 *see* indigestion
Dioscorides, 11
diphtheria, 164
dirk, 25, 33
diuretic, 14, 43, 58, 72, 75, 82, 91, 95, 97, 117, 124, 129, 134, 148, 166, 170, 171, 172, 175
divination, 20, 74, 98, 99, 134, 137, 150, 162 *see* prophecy
Doctrine of Signatures, 45, 145
Dods, Meg, 8, 122
Donald, Adam, 20
Dornoch, 85
drainage, 106-7
dream, prophetic, 135
driftwood, 28, 32
dropsy, 58, 69, 71, 75, 86,

91, 112, 123, 134, 148, 159, 164, 165, 166, 172, 173
druid, 12, 56, 65, 84, 98, 112, 115, 134, 136, 143, 162, 171, 175
Duchess of Portland, 153
Dumbartonshire, 20
Duncan I, 170
Dundee, 33, 112
dye plants, 37-47, 57, 61, 63, 64, 67, 74, 77, 78, 80, 83, 84, 85, 87, 91, 97, 101, 103, 104, 109, 110, 112, 114, 116, 118, 122, 123, 124, 127, 129, 132, 133, 140, 141, 144, 145, 147, 149, 151, 153, 154, 155, 157, 159, 160, 161, 163, 174
dyeing, 14, 26, 38-44, 45, 46, 171
dysentery, 16, 69, 86, 130, 133, 138, 139, 140, 150, 153, 155

ear-ache, 100, 171
earth cure, 22
East Lothian, 67
Easter, 114, 144
eczema, 73, 117, 165, 173, 174
Edinburgh, 21, 22, 67
Edinburgh College of Physicians, 16
Edinburgh College of Surgeons and Barbers, 14
Edinburgh University, 165
Efamol, 132
egg-baskets, 34; dyeing, 114, 144
Eigg, 33, 35, 99, 153
elf-shot, 148
Elgin, 119
emetic, 91, 111
enchantment *see* magic

Enlightenment, 21
epilepsy, 63, 67, 87, 91,
    101, 140, 160, 164, 175
ergot, 121
erysipelas, 155, 165
evil eye *see* protection,
    witchcraft
ewe *see* sheep
exorcism, 153
eye, disorders, 56, 58, 69,
    73, 77, 80, 91, 94,
    102, 123, 130, 137,
    153, 162, 166

face paint, 26
face wash, 148 *see* soap
fairy, 55, 67, 71, 72, 80,
    89, 90, 92, 109, 122,
    128, 133, 144, 150,
    164, 176,
famine, 8, 16, 151
farming *see* agriculture
feet, inflammation, 45, 55,
    84, 152
fencing, 134, 162
fertiliser, 30, 48, 53, 119
    see green manure
fertility rites, 48, 65, 150;
    symbols, 6, 64, 69; *see*
    infertility
Ferguson, Ferquhar, 147
festivals, 6-8, 67, 69, 112,
    142, 147
fever, 11, 16, 18, 21, 45,
    49, 53, 64, 71, 76, 77,
    87, 90, 91, 94, 96,
    100, 102, 103, 116,
    125, 130, 134, 136,
    137, 138, 139, 149,
    150, 151, 153, 154,
    155, 157, 160, 164,
    169, 171, 174, 175, 175
Fife, 4, 16, 22, 73, 75, 82,
    83, 103, 114, 156, 173
fire, 32, 115 *see* fuel
fishermen's clothes, 45
fishing tackle, 26, 49, 52,
    76, 121, 153, 173

Fladder, 87
flatulence, 69, 70, 73, 83,
    124, 134, 140
flooring, 106
Flora Scotica, 20-1 *see*
    Lightfoot
flour, 2, 92, 94, 101, 120
flummery, 159
fodder, 36, 45, 49, 53, 69,
    86, 102, 113, 114, 115,
    121, 122, 130, 138,
    141, 163
footpath, 106
Forfarshire, 136
Fortingall, 65
fracture *see* bonesetting
Franklin, John, 45
Fraser, Jean, 84, 97
freckles, 90, 103
fruit, 4, 5, 6, 9, 33, 62, 84,
    104, 110, 122, 123,
    150, 156, 157
fuel, 1, 25, 27, 31, 32, 51,
    61, 62, 65, 85, 109,
    115, 116, 159, 162
fumigation, 56, 62, 117
Furnace, 117
furniture, 30, 32, 91, 112,
    116, 134

Galloway, 5, 74
games, 80, 138, 159 *see*
    toys
gangrene, 73, 81, 102, 140
gin, 62, 154, 155
Girl Guides, 56, 156
glandular disease, 54, 130
Glasgow, 21, 46, 50, 62,
    108, 116
glass, 49, 61
Glen Bracadale, 107
Glencoe, 82
Glen Golly, 110
Glen Lyon, 65
Glenrea, 30
glue, 25, 27, 129
goat, 5, 166
goblin, 43

goddess, 6, 82, 149, 150,
    162 *see* Bride
goitre, 52
gonorrhoea *see* venereal
    disease
Gordon, Cuthbert and
    George, 46
gout, 71, 73, 75, 80, 101,
    121, 134, 140, 143,
    150, 172, 173
Gow, Duncan, 67
Grant, Isobel, 119
gravel *see* kidney
graves, graveyards *see*
    burial
green manure, 8, 35-6, 49,
    61, 176
Grierson, Su, 32, 41, 42,
    45
Grieve, Mrs, 75, 100, 102,
    126, 136, 139, 145
Grigson, Geoffrey, 93,
    100, 103, 104, 117,
    135, 139, 152, 160
grinding stones, 2
grove, sacred, 65, 115, 149
Guills of Scalpa, 21
gum disease *see* mouth

Haddington, 38
Hadrian's Wall, 5
haemorrhage *see* styptic
haemorrhoids *see* piles
hair treatment, 27, 45, 59,
    86, 173; dye, 103;
Haldane, Isobel, 164
Halloween, 48, 90, 98,
    150, 173, 176
hallucinogen, 12, 43
Hamilton, John, 15
Hamilton, Mary, 63
Harris, 68, 107, 127, 128
Harris tweed, 37, 40, 67,
    45, 91, 124, 133, 147,
    151, 161, 174
Hay family, 176
hay, 111, 120, 122
headache, 14, 49, 52, 54,

55, 73, 82, 91, 100,
    125, 126, 141, 143,
    145, 149, 150, 171, 173
head lice *see* lice
heart disorders, 23, 108,
    112, 129, 132, 138,
    164, 165, 174, 175 *see*
    dropsy
hearth, 32
Heather Centre, 106
Heather Gems, 106
Hebrides, 29, 34, 37, 39,
    46, 48, 49, 50, 80,
    101, 106, 110, 113,
    142, 153, 162, see also
    individual islands
hectic-fever *see* fever
hectic-stone *see* stones
henge, 28
Highland Birchwoods, 85
Hogmanay, New Year
Holland, 62
honey, 44, 108
Holyrood Abbey, 17, 170
horse, 3, 29, 35, 36, 59,
    80, 116, 127, 130;
    collar, 119
hospital, 13, 14, 22, 67,
    71, 170
housing, 27-31, 63, 64,
    105, 162
hunter-gatherer, 1-4, 26
hurdles, 99, 163
Hutton, Mrs, 165
Hutton, Ronald, 10, 13
hygrometer, 120
hysteria, 160

Ice Age, 1, 11, 85, 162
Iceland, 45
Iceman, 11, 24-6
indigestion, 58, 73, 76,
    117, 125, 152
industrialisation, 8, 22
infertility, 88, 100, 158,
    174 *see* fertility
inflammation *see* swelling
influenza, 78, 91, 125, 157

ink, 116, 124
insomnia, 49, 52, 94, 109, 141, 160, 173
insulation, 56, 106
Inverness, 33, 34, 62, 65, 85, 175
Inverugie Castle, 20
Iona, 55, 65, 115
Iraq, 10
Ireland, 12, 116
Iron Age, 5, 28, 29, 107
Islay, 95, 106, 172
Italy, 24
itch, 131

Jacobites, 156
jam, 156
James III, 78
James IV, 15, 78, 150
James VI, 107
jaundice, 45, 47, 59, 60, 69, 73, 84, 86, 88, 102, 117, 132, 134, 139, 148, 166, 171, 173
Jedburgh, Abbey, 14; monastery, 153
jelly, 54, 55, 122, 157, 159
jewellery, 106, 159
John, St, 13, 96, 137, 173; St John's nut, 97
Johnson, Samuel, 21
Josina, King, 12
Jura, 32, 34, 39, 53

kail, kale, 8
kelp, 23, 49-51
Kenmore, 29
Kentigern, St, 98
kidney disorders, 14, 18, 58, 59, 68, 69, 73, 75, 85, 100, 101, 104, 110, 112, 113, 121, 124, 125, 126, 128, 130, 134, 140, 148, 149, 155, 160, 169, 172
Kilchurn Castle, 64
Kilda, St, 18, 53, 87, 140, 141, 152, 173

Kirk Session, 19
Kirkwall, 21, 50, 114
Kirkwood, 155
Knapdale, 62
!Kung, 2

ladder, 33
Lambie, David, 106
Lammas, 90, 114
lamp *see* lighting
Lanarkshire, 128, 142
laxative *see* constipation
lazy beds, 49
leather *see* tanning
leech, 14
Leiden, 17, 21
Leith, 46
leprosy, 117, 134
Lerwick Museum, 141
Lesmahagow, 138
Lewis, 48, 81, 119, 122, 126, 173
lice, 68, 166, 167
Lighiche, Fearchar, 110
Lightfoot, John, 20, 22, 46, 57, 61, 78, 81, 94, 95, 97, 103, 107, 110, 111, 113, 120, 121, 122, 125, 134, 136, 146, 151-2, 153, 157, 160, 166, 169, 170, 174
lighting, 31, 64, 85, 124-5, 133
liqueur, 63, 115, 122, 149, 157
liver, 46, 68, 77, 101, 102, 117, 126, 130, 134, 135, 148, 160, 162, 166
livestock, 36, 61
lobster pots, 162
Lochaber, 73
Loch Eil, 170
Loch Lomond, 106
Lochmaddy, 51
Loch Rannoch, 157
Loch Tay, 29
lock, 30
Logan, James, 64, 104, 108

logwood, 39
longevity, 18
Lord of the Isles, 14
Lothian, 55
love, 18, 74, 77, 93, 135, 165, 173
lovers, 84, 85, 93, 99, 137
lumbago, 60
lung disorders, 45, 59, 73, 102, 130, 131, 149, 169 *see* chest complaints
lupin (cart), 34
Luss, 20
Lyber Graduum, 162, 175
MacDonald, Finlay J., 31, 37, 40, 120
Macbeth, 170
MacKenzie, Osgood, 107
McKenzie, Neil, 34
McKenzie, W. 158
MacLellan, Angus, 105
Maclellan, Kate Ann, 23, 49
MacLeod family, 14
McLintock, Mrs, 84, 112, 137, 156, 157, 172, 175
McNeill, Marian, 63, 71, 90, 170
McNeill, Murdo, 101, 103, 118, 159
McPhee, Willy, 170
magic, 10, 12, 13, 48, 58, 60, 65, 67, 71, 72, 73, 74, 82, 88, 89, 92, 98-9, 103, 112, 114, 115, 128, 132, 136, 137, 138, 144, 147-8, 149, 156, 158, 162, 164, 175
malaria, 16, 116, 149, 154 *see* fever
Manannan, 98
Margaret, Queen/St, 14
Margaret Tudor, 78
Marischal College, 21
Martin, Martin, 17-19, 20, 46, 53, 55, 69, 70, 80, 81, 84, 87, 94, 97,

107, 110, 111, 113, 116, 122, 123, 125, 126, 127, 128, 140, 145, 152, 164, 172
Martinmas, 90
Mary, Queen of Scots, 63
Mary, Virgin, 74, 96, 168
mat, 27, 101, 106
May Day, 89 *see* Beltane
Maundy Thursday, 48
mead, 4, 149, 157
meal *see* flour
mealtrach, 31, 120
measles, 91, 126, 139, 169, 171
Meldon Bridge, 28
meningitis, 121
menstruation, 82, 100, 123, 125, 150, 162
mermaid, 76
Mesolithic, 1, 28 *see* Stone Age
Michael, St, 6
Michaelmas, 69, 110
microlith, 2
midge repellent, 132
midsummer, 58, 96, 115, 137, 175
midwinter, 115 *see* New Year
migraine, 82 *see* headache
milk, 7, 36, 72, 90, 92-3, 96, 128, 138, 158, 166, 168, 173
Miller, Hugh, 153
missionaries, 13, 116
mites, 132
Mitchell, Willie, 30
monastery, 13, 14, 67, 71, 153, 170
Montpellier, 17
moon, influence of, 33, 46, 64, 74, 99, 162
Moray, Morayshire, 90, 114, 139
mordant, 38, 40, 57 *see* dyeing
mulch, 8 *see* fertiliser,

green manure
Mull, 61, 113, 115
Mull of Kintyre, 30
Mulvay, St, 48
Mungo, St, 98
murrain, 72, 159
mouse repellent, 80
mouth infections, 73, 77,
    116, 126, 136, 139,
    140, 152, 153

Napoleonic Wars, 47, 49
nappies, 27, 56
narcotics *see* sedatives
National Library of
    Scotland, 14
National Museum of
    Scotland, 163, 33
needles, 26
Neanderthal, 10-11
Neill, Patrick, 21, 35, 36,
    50, 73, 104, 110, 139,
    153
Neolithic, 28 *see* Stone
    Age
nerves, 82, 108, 126, 127,
    140, 142, 160 *see*
    sedatives
New Year, 48, 72, 98
Nicolaus, 162, 175
nightmare, 127
Nitinaht, 26, 58, 173
nomads, 1-5, 27
North America, 28 *see*
    Canada
North Berwick, 162
North Ronaldsay, 49
nosebleed, 52, 60, 86, 112,
    139, 140, 173 *see*
    styptics
nuts, 2, 4, 5, 98, 115

oats, 6
obesity, 94, 134, 141
Orkney, 2, 21, 28, 34, 35,
    36, 43, 49, 50, 52, 54,
    64, 73, 101, 104, 105,
    114, 120, 124, 139

141, 154, 161, 176
Outer Isles, 32, 80, 161 *see*
    Hebrides
ox, 3, 5, 36, 130

packing, packaging, 61,176
Pagan, 7, 12, 13, 19, 22,
    48, 65, 76, 96, 162
pain, 18, 82, 91, 102, 123,
    162, 162
paint, 49, 64
Palaeolithic, 1-4, 10-11 *see*
    Stone Age
palsy, 142
Papa Westray, 2
paper, 44, 85
paralysis, 141, 143
Paris, 16, 17
pasture *see* fodder
Paterson, Wilma, 148
Patrick, St, 13, 136
peat, 31, 32, 39
Peebles, 28
Peebles, Dick, 9
Pennant, Thomas, 20, 27,
    31, 66, 116, 134, 176
perspiration, to promote,
    54, 75 *see* fever
Perth, 38, 57
Perthshire, 6, 11, 29, 65,
    106, 112, 116, 153, 162
pest-repellent, 61, 132, 176
pharmacopoeia, 12, 16, 22,
    23
physic gardens, 13, 17, 20,
    21, 131, 139, 171
physician, 17, 22
pickle, 84, 112, 134, 148
Picts, 108
pierman, 64
pigs, 5, 69, 115, 154
Pilate, Pontius, 65
piles, 60, 86, 91, 94, 99,
    100, 101, 116, 139,
    140, 145, 152, 153,
    166, 167, 169, 172
pipe, 91, 157
plague, 15, 16, 77, 139,

174
plate, platter, 26, 33, 58
pleurisy, 91, 102, 130
Pliny, 143
plough, 134, 158
poison, 22, 67, 69, 77, 89,
    110, 123, 129
pollen analysis, 1, 4
potato, 6, 8, 9, 151
potherbs, 6, 58, 70, 71,
    88, 94, 95, 141, 172
Presbyterian, 19
prickly plants, 71, 149, 155
prophecy, 18, 85, 150 *see*
    divination
protection, 57, 58, 62, 71,
    72, 90, 92-3, 96-7, 98,
    114, 128, 132, 134,
    155, 158, 176
punch, 159, 160
purgatives, 46, 63, 70, 72,
    87, 88, 91, 97, 111,
    134, 145, 155, 166
purification, 62, 75, 78,
    103, 169 *see* fumigation

quarter days, 90 158
Queensferry, 75
quinsy, 79
quiver, 24, 25

rabies, 45, 46, 86
rantree, 158
rash *see* skin disorders
ratafia, 154
Regimen Sanitas, 14, 103,
    151
Renfrew, Jane, 3
rennet-substitutes, 5, 78,
    128, 145, 160, 173
resin, 64
rheumatism, 71 75, 80 85,
    86, 88, 91, 94, 109,
    117, 121, 126, 129,
    134, 142, 143, 146,
    159, 171, 173
Rum, 1, 4, 60
rickets, 59, 60

ringworm, 72
Robertson, Mr, 33
Romans, 5, 6, 12, 38, 63,
    65, 87, 118, 123, 173,
    174, 175
roofing, 29, 30, 56, 64, 99,
    105, 106
roots, edible, 6, 68, 69,
    113, 145, 151-2
rope, 27, 30, 34, 35, 49,
    52, 64-5, 85, 101, 104,
    105-6, 121
Rorie, David, 20, 22, 47,
    85, 90, 132, 161, 173
Ross, Alexander, 39, 41,
    50-1
Ross, Lynn, 42
Ross-shire, 113
Royal Botanic Garden
    Edinburgh, 17, 168
Royal College of Physicians,
    22
Royal Highland Show, 42
Royal Infirmary, 22
rupture, 139, 148, 159

St Andrews, 15, 16
salad, 67, 70, 71, 82, 88,
    99, 114, 126, 128, 136,
    141, 169
salep, 135
salt (from plant ash), 49,
    53
salmon, 98
Samhain see Halloween
sanitary towel, 27, 56
sauce, 52, 54, 110, 141
Saxon, 14
scald, 60, 86, 130, 138
Scandinavia, 45, 70
scarlet fever, 91
scent, 27
sciatica, 18, 73, 80, 91,
    101, 121
Scotia Pharmaceuticals,
    132
Scott, Walter, 67, 172
Scottish Agricultural

College, 132
Scottish Agricultural
    Museum, 119
Scottish Basketmakers
    Circle, 34
Scottish Seaweed Research
    Association, 51
scourers, 31, 58, 110, 124
scrofula, 99, 100, 136,
    164, 166, 167, 171
scurvy, 49, 54, 64, 70, 77,
    86, 87, 88, 99, 117,
    136, 169
Second World War, 11,
    55, 106
sedatives, 67, 79, 112, 121,
    137, 142, 143, 170, 174
Servanus, St, 150
sheep, 5, 49, 70, 88, 127,
    158, 167; sheep rot,
    103; scab, 73
shellfish, 3, 5, 8
Shetland, 21, 28, 33, 46,
    50, 53, 87, 92, 94,
    101, 106, 124, 137,
    141, 163, 173
shielings, 6, 27, 31, 50
shield, 163
shiitake mushroom, 85
shingles, 100
shinty, 35, 85, 99
shoes, shoemaking, 26,
    153, 163
Shony, 48
shrub, 122, 175
shuttle, 37
Sibbald, Robert, 17
simples, 19
Simpson, Chris, 44
Skara Brae, 28, 43 105
skin disorders, 45, 54, 75,
    79, 80-1, 88, 91, 93,
    94, 102, 103, 117, 118,
    144, 148, 159, 160,
    164, 166, 167, 169,
    171, 172, 173 see boils,
    sores, ulcers
skin lotion, powder, 57

Skye, 19, 33, 46, 55, 59,
    69, 73, 80, 81, 94, 97,
    107, 111, 116, 121,
    123, 125, 127, 128,
    132, 150, 153, 157,
    173, 174
slat-drhraoidheachd, 65
sleep, 55, 159 *see* insomnia
smallpox, 16, 21, 139, 169
Smith, Bessie, 138
smoking (curing), 63, 117
smoking *see* tobacco
    substitutes
snake bite, 63, 123, 125,
    134, 159
snigging, 29
snuff, 124, 125
soap substitutes, 27, 49,
    61, 93
soda, 49, 61
solstice, 175 *see* midsummer
Somerset, 102
sorcery, 10 *see* witchcraft
sores, 43, 52, 59, 64, 69,
    80, 102, 103, 104, 111,
    117, 129, 130, 137,
    138, 139, 140, 145,
    153, 166, 168 *see* boils,
    skin disorders, ulcers
soup *see* broth
Soutra, 14, 67, 71, 170
spasm, 67, 126
Spindler, Konrad, 24
Spinners, Weaver and
    Dyers Guild, 42, 44
spinning wheel, 158
spleen, 14, 59, 61, 101,
    124, 126, 134
Sponish Alginate Industries,
    51
sprain, 91, 151
Stanydale, 28
Stevenson, R.L., 108
stew, 49, 54
Stewart, Janet, 90
stimulant, 70, 72, 82
stings, 138, 139, 141
Stirling Castle, 29

stitch, 87, 102
stomach ailments, 63, 73,
    82, 102, 132, 135, 138,
    139, 150, 152, 153,
    159, 160
Stone Age, 1-4, 10-11, 24,
    27-28
stone circles, 28
stones, healing, 13, 18, 73
Strathdon, 47
Strathyre, 29
strain, 86, 126
straw, 34
strewing herbs, 149, 160
string *see* twine
Stronsay, 49
struan, 7-8
strychnine, 67
Stuart, John, 20
stye, 123
styptic, 43, 58, 60, 73, 86,
    100, 116, 125 126, 133,
    139, 140, 148, 150,
    160, 173
Sumatra, 21
sunburn, 73, 90, 103, 150,
    153
Surgeon Apothecaries, 17
Sutherland, 57, 62, 106
Sutherland, Dr, 21, 139
Sutherland, James, 17,
    121, 126
swelling, 18, 59, 60, 77,
    94, 99, 111, 123, 126,
    129, 130, 131, 136,
    137, 140, 148, 155,
    156, 158, 166
switch, 80, 158
syphilis *see* venereal
    disease
syrup, 91, 137, 156, 157,
    175

Taigh-Chearsabhagh
    Museum, 51
tanning, 14, 85, 104, 109,
    116, 133, 153, 163
tartan, 38

Taynuilt, 117
tea, 63, 73, 78, 85, 86, 90,
    103, 108, 110, 114,
    116, 125, 126, 127,
    132, 136, 143, 148,
    149, 150, 155, 156,
    157, 159, 160, 169,
    172-3, 174, 175
teeth, cleaning, 116, 151;
    teething, 62, 67, 137,
    160, 170; toothache,
    71, 75, 123, 126, 140,
    171, 172
tent, 27, 31
Ternan, St,168
tether, 35, 53, 101, 125
textiles, 37-42, 49, 57,
    172, 173-4
thatch, 27, 29, 30, 34, 61,
    101, 105, 109, 112,
    119, 120, 121, 122,
    124, 176
Thomas the Rhymer, 65,
    176
Thor, 98, 115
thread, 25
throat, 71, 73, 79, 80, 84,
    90, 91, 94, 116, 123,
    126, 130, 139, 149,
    150, 152, 153, 156, 172
Thunor *see* Thor
Tigharry, 23
tinder, 25-6, 27, 31, 43,
    83
tipi, 27
Tiree, 116, 152, 153
tobacco substitutes, 49, 54,
    55, 68, 76, 83
toilet paper, 26, 56
tonics, 49, 54, 70, 72, 75,
    76, 78, 81, 82 84, 104,
    108, 116, 117, 118,
    125, 126, 127, 129,
    132, 136, 150, 173, 175
tonsillitis 79
tools, 2, 25, 32, 72, 99,
    134, 149, 163
Torranan, St, 168

tourism, 21
toys, 27, 53, 69, 91, 124
    see games
tranquilliser see sedatives
travelling folk, 27, 33, 170
Tree of Life, 134
Trinity, Holy, 74, 93, 136,
    148
troll, trow, 101, 141
tuberculosis see consump-
    tion, scrofula
twine, 26, 171
typhus, 15, 16, 21

ulcer, 58, 59, 61, 71, 77,
    79, 80, 82, 94, 102,
    123, 126, 130, 132,
    133, 136, 139, 140,
    146, 152, 153, 166,
    171 see boils, skin
    disorders, sores
Uist, 7, 19, 23, 46, 50, 51,
    119, 137, 146, 149,
    152, 161, 169
urinary disorders see
    bladder, kidney
urine, uses of, 40, 45, 46,
    158

vaginal discharge, 116, 130
Vancouver Island, 26, 43,
    56, 58, 173
Vatersay, 53
vegetables, wild see
    potherbs
venereal disease, 15, 91,
    133
vomiting, 60, 125, 148

Walker, John, 106, 160
walking stick, 33, 98, 155
wand, 99, 156, 158, 162
warts, 54, 102, 103, 123,
    162
Waterloo, Battle of, 170
wattle, 29, 30, 63, 99
Waverley Station, 17
weapons, 155

weaving, 37-41, 67, 120
    see textiles
well, healing, 13
Western Isles see Hebrides
West Highland Brewery,
    108
West Lothian, 56
wheat, 5
wheel, 116, 134, 158
whisky, 14, 63, 97, 110,
    113, 154
whistle, 27, 163
whitlow, 140
Whitsun, 90
whooping cough, 16, 67,
    79, 83, 103, 151, 159,
    171
Wicca, 162 see witchcraft
wildfowl, 3, 5
William of Dunbar, 78
Williams, Bruce, 108
Williamson, Duncan, 27
wine, 63, 83, 85, 90, 91,
    104, 112, 114, 115,
    116, 122, 123, 142,
    143, 148, 149, 155,
    156, 157, 160, 174, 175
witch, 53, 58, 67, 71, 80,
    98, 112, 134, 164, 170,
    171, 173
witchcraft, 15, 18, 19-20,
    72, 90, 96, 138, 147,
    155, 158, 162, 176
witch hunting, 13, 19-20
Withering, William, 165
wolf, 3
woodlice, 16
wool see dyeing, textiles
World Tree, 134
worms, 14 18, 54, 60, 61,
    88, 97, 99, 127
    (horse), 132, 139, 140,
    143, 153, 166
wounds, 11, 14, 16, 18,
    43, 55, 58, 60, 71, 73,
    77, 79, 80, 86, 99, 100
    101, 111, 117, 118,
    125, 126, 129, 130,

136, 137, 138, 138,
    140, 141, 143, 148,
    150, 159, 160, 162, 168

Yggdrasil, 134
yoke, 158
Yule log, 134